More praise for this new e

"This book is an extension and improvement to the excellent first edition, which appeared in 1996. Each chapter has an introduction covering a specific statistical method and gives examples of where the method is used. The introduction is followed by a synopsis presenting the necessary and significant information for the reader to get a good understanding of the statistical method. Excellent examples are given, followed by the SAS code for the example. Detailed annotations make the SAS output easy to understand. The book also gives numerous extensions for the methods.

Dr. Walker has certainly used his many years of consulting experience, his teaching experience, and his understanding of SAS to produce an even better book that is equally understandable and helpful to the novice as well as the experienced statistician. Each will benefit from this insightful journey into statistics and the use of SAS, whether as a teaching tool or a refresher. I can recommend this book wholeheartedly."

Stephan Ogenstad, Ph.D.
Senior Director, Biometrics
Vertex Pharmaceuticals Incorporated

SAS Publishing

SECOND EDITION

Common Statistical Methods for Clinical Research

with SAS® Examples

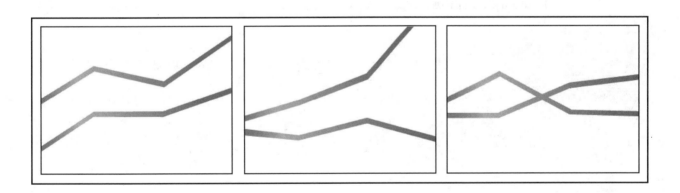

Glenn A. Walker

58086

The correct bibliographic citation for this manual is as follows: Walker, Glenn A. 2002. *Common Statistical Methods for Clinical Research with SAS® Examples, Second Edition*. Cary, NC: SAS Institute Inc.

Common Statistical Methods for Clinical Research with SAS® Examples, Second Edition

ISBN 1-59047-040-0

SAS Institute Inc., SAS Campus Drive, Cary, North Carolina 27513.

1st printing, July 2002

SAS Publishing provides a complete selection of books and electronic products to help customers use SAS software to its fullest potential. For more information about our e-books, e-learning products, CDs, and hardcopy books, visit the SAS Publishing Web site at **www.sas.com/pubs** or call 1-800-727-3228.

Table of Contents

Examples

Figures

Preface to the Second Edition

This second edition expands the first edition with the inclusion of new sections, examples, and extensions of statistical methods described in the first edition only in their most elementary forms. New methods sections include analysis of *crossover designs* (Chapter 9) and multiple comparison methods (Appendix D). Chapters that present *repeated measures analysis* (Chapter 8), *linear regression* (Chapter 10), *analysis of covariance* (Chapter 11), the *chi-square test* (Chapter 16), and *logistic regression* (Chapter 20) have been notably expanded, and 50% more examples have been added throughout the book. A new chapter of exercises has also been added to give the reader practice in applying the various methods presented. Also new in this edition is an introduction to α-adjustments for interim analyses (Chapter 2).

Although many of the new features will have wide appeal, some are targeted to the more experienced data analyst. These include discussion of the proportional odds model, the clustered binomial problem, collinearity in multiple regression, the use of time-dependent covariates with *Cox regression*, and the use of generalized estimating equations in *repeated measures analysis*. These methods, which are based on more advanced concepts than those found in most of the book, are routinely encountered in data analysis applications of clinical investigations and, as such, fit the description of 'common statistical methods for clinical research'. However, so as not to overwhelm the less experienced reader, these concepts are presented only briefly, usually by example, along with references for further reading.

First and foremost, this is a statistical methods book. It is designed to have particular appeal to those involved in clinical research, biometrics, epidemiology, and other health or medical related research applications. Unlike other books in the SAS Books by Users (BBU) library, SAS is not the primary focus of this book. Rather, SAS is presented as an indispensable tool that greatly simplifies the analyst's task. While consulting for dozens of companies over 25 years of statistical application to clinical investigation, I have never seen a successful clinical program that did not use SAS. Because of its widespread use within the pharmaceutical industry, I include SAS here as the 'tool' of choice to illustrate the statistical methods.

The examples have been updated to Version 8 of SAS, however, the programming statements used have been kept 'portable', meaning that most can be used in earlier versions of SAS as they appear in the examples, unless otherwise noted. This includes the use of portable variable and data set names, despite accommodation for use of long names beginning with Version 8. Because SAS is not the main focus of this book but is key to efficient data analysis, programming details are not included here, but they can be found in numerous references cited throughout the book. Many of these references are other books in the Books by Users program at SAS, which provide the details, including procedure options, use of ODS, and the naming standards that are new in Version 8. For statistical programming, my favorites include **Categorical Data Analysis Using the SAS System**, Second Edition, by Stokes, Davis, and Koch (2000) and **Survival Analysis Using the SAS System, A Practical Guide,** by Paul Allison (1995).

I welcome and appreciate reader comments and feedback through the SAS Publications Web site.

Glenn A. Walker
July 2002

Preface to the First Edition

This book was written for those involved in clinical research and who may, from time to time, need a guide to help demystify some of the most commonly used statistical methods encountered in our profession.

All too often, I have heard medical directors of clinical research departments express frustration at seemingly cryptic statistical methods sections of protocols which they are responsible for approving. Other nonstatisticians, including medical monitors, investigators, clinical project managers, medical writers and regulatory personnel, often voice similar sentiment when it comes to statistics, despite the profound reliance upon statistical methods in the success of the clinical program. For these people, I offer this book (sans technical details) as a reference guide to better understand statistical methods as applied to clinical investigation and the conditions and assumptions under which they are applied.

For the clinical data analyst and statistician new to clinical applications, the examples from a clinical trials setting may help in making the transition from other statistical fields to that of clinical trials. The discussions of 'Least-Squares' means, distinguishing features of the various SAS® types of sums-of-squares, and relationships among various tests (such as the *Chi-Square Test*, the *Cochran-Mantel-Haenszel Test* and the *Log-Rank Test*) may help crystalize the analyst's understanding of these methods. Analysts with no prior SAS experience should benefit by the simplifed SAS programming statements provided with each example as an introduction to SAS analyses.

This book may also aid the SAS programmer with limited statistical knowledge in better grasping an overall picture of the clinical trials process. Many times knowledge of the hypotheses being tested and appropriate interpretation of the SAS output relative to those hypotheses will help the programmer become more efficient in responding to the requests of other clinical project team members.

Finally, the medical student will find the focused presentation on the specific methods presented to be of value while proceeding through a first course in biostatistics.

For all readers, my goal was to provide a unique approach to the description of commonly used statistical methods by integrating both manual and computerized solutions to a wide variety of examples taken from clinical research. Those who learn best by example should find this approach rewarding. I have found no other book which demonstrates that the SAS output actually *does* have the same results as the manual solution of a problem using the calculating formulas. So ever reassuring this is for the student of clinical data analysis!

Each statistical test is presented in a separate chapter, and includes a brief, non-technical introduction, a synopsis of the test, one or two examples worked manually followed by an appropriate solution using the SAS statistical package, and finally, a discussion with details and relevant notes.

Chapters 1 and 2 are introductory in nature, and should be carefully read by all with no prior formal exposure to statistics. Chapter 1 provides an introduction to statistics and some of the basic concepts involved in inference-making. Chapter 2 goes into more detail with regard to the main aspects of hypothesis testing, including significance levels, power and sample size determination. For those who use analysis-of-variance, Appendix C provides a non-technical introduction to ANOVA methods. The remainder of the book may be used as a text or reference. As a reference, the reader should keep in mind that many of the tests discussed in later chapters rely on concepts presented earlier in the book, strongly suggesting prerequisite review.

This book focuses on statistical hypothesis testing as opposed to other inferential techniques. For each statistical method, the test summary is clearly provided, including the null hypothesis tested, the test statistic and the decision rule. Each statistical test is presented in one of its most elementary forms to provide the reader with a basic framework. Many of the tests discussed have extensions or variations which can be used with more complex data sets. The 18 statistical methods presented here (Chapters 3-20) represent a composite of those which, in my experience, are most commonly used in the analysis of clinical research data. I can't think of a single study I've analyzed in nearly 20 years which did not use at least one of these tests. Furthermore, many of the studies I've encountered have used exclusively the methods presented here, or variations or extensions thereof. Thus, the word 'common' in the title.

Understanding of many parts of this book requires some degree of statistical knowledge. The clinician without such a background may skip over many of the technical details and still come away with an overview of the test's applications, assumptions and limitations. Basic algebra is the only prerequisite, as derivations of test procedures are omitted, and matrix algebra is mentioned only in an appendix. My hope is that the statistical and SAS analysis aspects of the examples would provide a springboard for the motivated reader, both to go back to more elementary texts for additional background and to go forward to more advanced texts for further reading.

Many of the examples are based on actual clinical trials which I have analyzed. In all cases, the data are contrived, and in many cases fictitious names are used for different treatments or research facilities. Any resemblence of the data or the tests' results to actual cases is purely coincidental.

Glenn A. Walker
May 1996

Introduction & Basics

1.1   Statistics—the Field

In some ways, we are all born statisticians. Inferring general patterns from limited knowledge is nearly as automatic to the human consciousness as breathing. Yet, when inference is formalized through the science of mathematics to the field called **Statistics**, it often becomes clouded by preconceptions of abstruse theory. Let's see if we can provide some formalization to this natural process of rational inference without getting bogged down in theoretical details.

The purpose of the field of **Statistics** is to characterize a *population* based on the information contained in a *sample* taken from that population. The sample information is conveyed by functions of the observed data, which are called *statistics*. The field of **Statistics** is a discipline that endeavors to determine which functions are the most relevant in the characterization of various populations. (The concepts of 'populations', 'samples', and 'characterization' are discussed in this chapter.)

For example, the arithmetic mean might be the most appropriate statistic to help characterize certain populations, while the median might be more appropriate for others. Statisticians use statistical and probability theory to develop new methodology and apply the methods best suited for different types of data sets.

Applied Statistics can be viewed as a set of methodologies used to help carry out scientific experiments. In keeping with the *scientific method*, applied statistics consists of developing a hypothesis, determining the best experiment to test the hypothesis, conducting the experiment, observing the results, and making conclusions. The statistician's responsibilities include: study design, data collection, statistical analysis, and making appropriate inferences from the data. In doing so, the statistician seeks to limit bias, maximize objectivity, and obtain results that are scientifically valid.

▶ *Populations*

A *population* is a universe of entities to be characterized but is too vast to study in its entirety. The population in a clinical trial would be defined by its limiting conditions, usually specified via study inclusion and exclusion criteria.

Examples of populations include:

- patients with mild-to-moderate hypertension
- obese teenagers
- adult, insulin-dependent, diabetic patients.

The first example has only one limiting factor defining the population, that is, mild-to-moderate hypertension. This population could be defined more precisely as patients with diastolic blood pressure within a specific range of values as an inclusion criterion for the clinical protocol. Additional criteria would further limit the population to be studied.

The second example uses both age and weight as limiting conditions, and the third example uses age, diagnosis, and treatment as criteria for defining the population.

It is important to identify the population of interest in a clinical study at the time of protocol development, because the population is the 'universe' to which statistical inferences might apply. Severely restricting the population by using many specific criteria for admission might ultimately limit the clinical indication to a restricted subset of the intended market.

▶ *Samples*

You can describe a population by describing some representative entities in it. Measurements obtained from sample entities tend to characterize the entire population through inference.

The degree of representation of the entities in a sample that is taken from the population of interest depends on the sampling plan used. The simplest type of sampling plan is called a 'simple random sample'. It describes any method of selecting a sample of population entities such that each entity has the same chance of being selected as any other entity in the population. It's easy to see how random samples should represent the population, and the larger the sample, the greater the representation.

The method of obtaining a simple random sample from the population-of-interest is not always clear-cut. Simple random samples are rarely, if ever, used in clinical trials. Imagine the patients who comprise the populations in the three examples cited earlier, living all over the world. This would make the collection of a simple random sample an overwhelming task.

Although inferences can be biased if the sample is not random, adjustments can sometimes be used to control bias introduced by non-random sampling. An entire branch of **Statistics,** known as Sa*mpling Theory*, has been developed to provide alternative approaches to simple random sampling. Many of these approaches have the goal of minimizing bias. The techniques can become quite complex and are beyond the scope of this overview.

For logistical reasons, clinical studies are conducted at a convenient study center with the assumption that the patients enrolled at that center are typical of those that might be enrolled elsewhere. Multi-center studies are often used to blunt the effect of characteristics of the patient or of procedural anomalies that might be unique to any specific center.

Stratified sampling is another technique that is often used to obtain a better representation of patients. Stratified sampling uses random samples from each of several subgroups of a population, which are called 'strata'. Enrollment in a study is sometimes stratified by disease severity, age group, or some other characteristic of the patient.

Because inferences from non-random samples might not be as reliable as those made from random samples, the clinical statistician must specifically address the issue of selection bias in the analysis. Statistical methods can be applied to determine whether the treatment group assignment 'appears' random for certain response variables. For example, baseline values might be lower for Group A than Group B in a comparative clinical study. If Group A shows a greater response, part of that perceived response might be a regression-toward-the-mean effect, that is, a tendency to return to normal from an artificially low baseline level. Such effects should be investigated thoroughly to avoid making faulty conclusions due to selection bias.

Additional confirmatory studies in separate, independent samples from the same population can also be important in allaying concerns regarding possible sampling biases.

▶ *Characterization*

So how is the population characterized from a sample? Statistical methods used to characterize populations can be classified as descriptive or inferential.

Descriptive statistics are used to describe the distribution of population measurements by providing estimates of central tendency and measures of variability, or by using graphical techniques such as histograms. *Inferential* methods use probability to express the level of certainty about estimates and to test specific hypotheses.

Exploratory analyses represent a third type of statistical procedure used to characterize populations. Although exploratory methods use both descriptive and inferential techniques, conclusions cannot be drawn with the same level of certainty because hypotheses are not pre-planned. Given a large data set, it is very likely that at least one statistically significant result can be found by using exploratory analyses. Such results are 'hypothesis-generating' and often lead to new studies prospectively designed to test these new hypotheses.

Two main inferential methods are confidence interval estimation and hypothesis testing, which are discussed in detail later in this chapter.

1.2   Probability Distributions

An understanding of basic probability concepts is essential to grasp the fundamentals of statistical inference. Most introductory statistics texts discuss these basics, therefore, only some brief concepts of probability distributions are reviewed here.

Each outcome of a statistical experiment can be mapped to a numeric-valued function called a 'random variable'. Some values of the random variable might be more likely to occur than others. The probability distribution associated with the random variable X describes the likelihood of obtaining certain values or ranges of values of the random variable.

For example, consider two cancer patients, each having a 50-50 chance of surviving at least 3 months. Three months later, there are 4 possible outcomes, which are shown in Table 1.1.

TABLE 1.1. Probability Distribution of Number of Survivors (n=2)

Outcome	Patient 1	Patient 2	X	Probability
1	Died	Died	0	0.25
2	Died	Survived	1	0.25
3	Survived	Died	1	0.25
4	Survived	Survived	2	0.25

Each outcome can be mapped to the random variable X, which is defined as the number of patients surviving at least 3 months. X can take the values 0, 1, or 2 with probabilities 0.25, 0.50, and 0.25, respectively, because each outcome is equally likely.

The probability distribution for X is given by P_x as follows:

X	P_x
0	0.25
1	0.50
2	0.25

▶ Discrete Distributions

The preceding example is a *discrete probability* distribution because the random variable X can only take discrete values, in this case, integers from 0 to 2.

The *binomial* distribution is, perhaps, the most commonly used discrete distribution in clinical biostatistics. This distribution is used to model experiments involving n independent trials, each with 2 possible outcomes, say, '*event*' or '*non-event*', and the probability of '*event*', p, is the same for all n trials. The preceding example, which involves two cancer patients, is an example of a binomial distribution in which n = 2 (patients), p = 0.5, and '*event*' is survival of at least 3 months.

Other common discrete distributions include the *poisson* and the *hypergeometric* distributions.

▶ Continuous Distributions

If a random variable can take any value within an interval or continuum, it is called a *continuous* random variable. Height, weight, blood pressure, and cholesterol level are usually considered continuous random variables because they can take any value within certain intervals, even though the observed measurement is limited by the accuracy of the measuring device.

The probability distribution for a continuous random variable cannot be specified in a simple form as it is in the discrete example above. To do that would entail an infinite list of probabilities, one for each possible value within the interval. One way to specify the distribution for continuous random variables is to list the probabilities for ranges of X-values. However, such a specification can also be very cumbersome.

Continuous distributions are most conveniently approximated by functions of the random variable X, such as P_x. Examples of such functions are

$$P_x = 2x \quad \text{for } 0 < x < 1$$

or

$$P_x = ae^{-ax} \quad \text{for } 0 < x < \infty$$

The *normal* distribution is the most commonly used continuous distribution in clinical research statistics. Many naturally occurring phenomena follow the normal distribution, which can be explained by a powerful result from probability theory known as the *Central Limit Theorem*, discussed in the next section.

The normal probability distribution is given by the function

$$P_x = \frac{1}{\sqrt{2\pi}\sigma} \; e^{-\frac{(x-\mu)^2}{2\sigma^2}} \qquad \text{for} \; -\infty \; < \; x \; < \; \infty$$

where μ and σ are called 'parameters' of the distribution. For any values of μ and σ (>0), a plot of P_x versus x has a 'bell' shape (illustrated in Appendix B).

Other common continuous distributions are the *exponential* distribution, the *chi-square* distribution, the *F*-distribution and the Student *t*-distribution. Appendix B lists some analytic properties of common continuous distributions used in statistical inference (mentioned throughout this book). The *normal*, *chi-square*, *F*- and *t*-distributions are all interrelated, and some of these relationships are shown in Appendix B.

Whether discrete or continuous, every probability distribution has the property that the sum of the probabilities over all X-values equals 1.

▶ The Central Limit Theorem

The *Central Limit Theorem* states that, regardless of the distribution of measurements, sums and averages of a large number of like measurements tend to follow the normal distribution. Because many measurements related to growth, healing, or disease progression might be represented by a sum or an accumulation of incremental measurements over time, the normal distribution is often applicable to clinical data for large samples.

To illustrate the *Central Limit Theorem*, consider the following experiment. A placebo (inactive pill) is given to n patients, followed by an evaluation one hour later. Suppose that each patient's evaluation can result in 'improvement,' coded as +1, 'no change' (0), or 'deterioration' (−1), with each result equally probable. Let $X_1, X_2, ..., X_n$ represent the measurements for the n patients, and define Z to be a random variable that represents the sum of these evaluation scores for all n patients,

$$Z = X_1 + X_2 + ... + X_n$$

For n = 1, the probability distribution of Z is the same as X, which is constant for all possible values of X. This is called a 'uniform' distribution. See Fig. 1.1.

FIGURE 1.1. Probability Distribution for Z = X₁

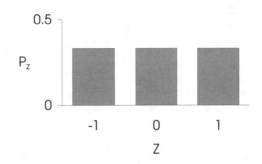

Z	P_z
-1	1/3
0	1/3
+1	1/3

For n = 2, there are 9 equally probable outcomes resulting in 5 possible, distinct values for Z, as shown in Table 1.2.

TABLE 1.2. All Possible Equally Probable Outcomes (n=2)

Patient 1	Patient 2	Z	Prob.
-1	-1	-2	1/9
-1	0	-1	1/9
0	-1	-1	1/9
-1	+1	0	1/9
0	0	0	1/9
+1	-1	0	1/9
0	+1	+1	1/9
+1	0	+1	1/9
+1	+1	+2	1/9

The resulting probability distribution for Z is shown in Figure 1.2.

FIGURE 1.2. Probability Distribution for Z = X₁+X₂

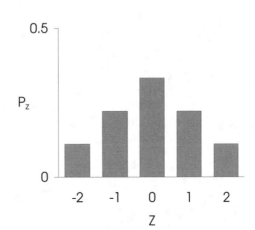

Z	P_z
-2	1/9
-1	2/9
0	3/9
+1	2/9
+2	1/9

For n = 3, Z can take values from -3 to +3. See Figure 1.3 for the distribution.

FIGURE 1.3. Probability Distribution for Z = $X_1+X_2+X_3$

Z	P_z
-3	1/27
-2	3/27
-1	6/27
0	7/27
+1	6/27
+2	3/27
+3	1/27

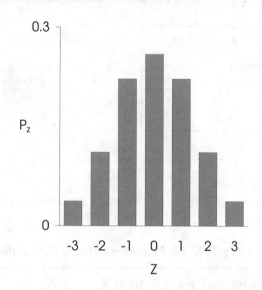

You can see from the histograms that, as n becomes larger, the distribution of Z takes on the bell-shaped characteristic of the normal distribution. The distribution of Z for 8 patients (n = 8) is shown in Figure 1.4.

While the probability distribution of the measurements (X) is 'uniform', the sum of these measurements (Z) is a random variable that tends toward a normal distribution as n increases. The *Central Limit Theorem* states that this will be the case regardless of the distribution of the X measurements. Because the sample mean, $\bar{x}$, is the sum of measurements (multiplied by a constant, 1/n), the *Central Limit Theorem* implies that $\bar{x}$ has an approximate normal distribution for large values of n regardless of the probability distribution of the measurements that comprise $\bar{x}$.

FIGURE 1.4. Probability Distribution for
$$Z = X_1+X_2+X_3+X_4+X_5+X_6+X_7+X_8$$

Z	P_z
-8	0.000
-7	0.001
-6	0.005
-5	0.017
-4	0.041
-3	0.077
-2	0.119
-1	0.155
0	0.169
+1	0.155
+2	0.119
+3	0.077
+4	0.041
+5	0.017
+6	0.005
+7	0.001
+8	0.000

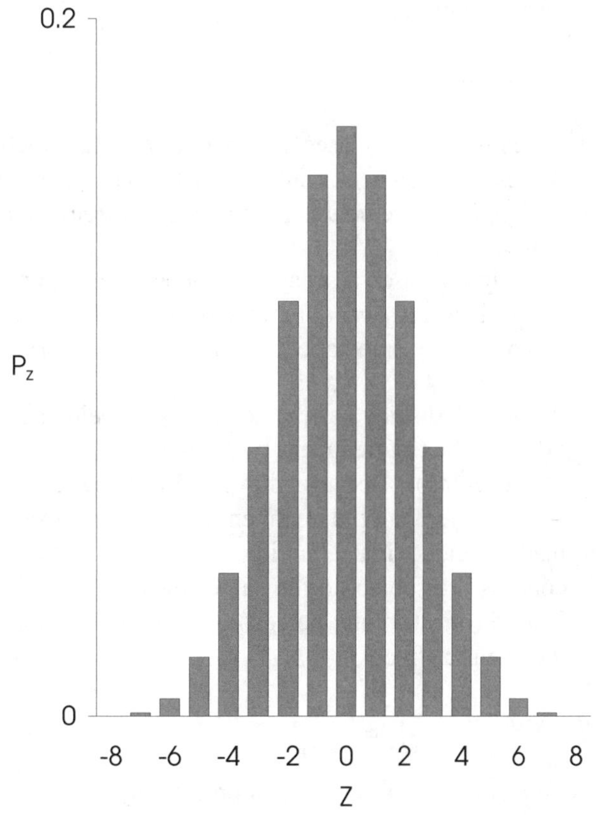

1.3 Study Design Features

Sound statistical results can be valid only if the study plan is well thought out and accompanied by appropriate data collection techniques. Even the most sophisticated statistical tests might not lead to valid inferences or appropriate characterizations of the population if the study itself is flawed. Therefore, it is imperative that statistical design considerations be addressed in clinical studies during protocol development.

There are many statistical design considerations that go into the planning stage of a new study. The probability distribution of the primary response variables will help predict how the measurements will vary. Because greater variability of the measurements requires a larger sample size, distributional assumptions enable the computation of sample-size requirements to distinguish a real trend from statistical variation. Determining the sample size is discussed in Chapter 2.

Methods to help reduce response variability can also be incorporated into the study design. Features of controlled clinical trials such as *randomization* and *blinding*, and statistical 'noise-reducing' techniques (such as the use of covariates, stratification or blocking factors, and the use of within-patient controls) are ways to help control extraneous variability and focus on the primary response measurements.

► Controlled Studies

A controlled study uses a known treatment, which is called a 'control', along with the test treatments. A control may be inactive, such as a placebo or sham, or it may be another active treatment, perhaps a currently marketed product.

A study that uses a separate, independent group of patients in a control group is called a *parallel-group* study. A study that gives both the test treatment and the control to the same patients is called a *within-patient control* study.

A controlled study has the advantage of being able to estimate the pure therapeutic effect of the test treatment by comparing its perceived benefit relative to the benefit of the control. Because the perceived benefit might be due to numerous study factors other than the treatment itself, a conclusion of therapeutic benefit cannot be made without first removing those other factors from consideration. Because the controls are subject to the same study factors, treatment effect *relative to* control, instead of absolute perceived benefit, is more relevant in estimating actual therapeutic effect.

► Randomization

Randomization is a means of objectively assigning experimental units or patients to treatment groups. In clinical trials, this is done by means of a randomization schedule generated prior to starting the enrollment of patients.

The randomization scheme should have the property that any randomly selected patient has the same chance as any other patient of being included in any treatment group. Randomization is used in controlled clinical trials to eliminate systematic treatment group assignment, which might lead to bias. In a non-randomized setting, patients with the most severe condition might be assigned to a group based on the treatment's anticipated benefit. Whether this assignment is intentional or not, this creates bias because the treatment groups would represent samples from different populations, some of whom might have more severe conditions than others. Randomization filters out such selection bias and helps establish baseline comparability among the treatment groups.

Randomization provides a basis for unbiased comparisons of the treatment groups. Omitting specific responses from the analysis is a form of tampering with this randomization and will probably bias the results if the exclusions are made in a non-randomized fashion. For this reason, the primary analysis of a clinical trial is often based on the 'intent-to-treat' principle, which includes all randomized patients in the analysis even though some might not comply with protocol requirements.

▶ *Blinded Randomization*

Blinded (or masked) randomization is one of the most important features of a controlled study. Single-blind, double-blind, and even triple-blind studies are common among clinical trials.

A *single-blind* study is one in which the patients are not aware of which treatment they receive. Many patients actually show a clinical response with medical care even if they are not treated. Some patients might respond when treated with a placebo but are unaware that their medication is inactive. These are examples of the well-known *placebo effect*, which might have a psychological component dependent on the patient's belief that he is receiving appropriate care. A 20% placebo response is not uncommon in many clinical indications.

Suppose that a response, Y, can be represented by a true therapeutic response component, TR, and a placebo effect, PE. Letting subscripts A and P denote 'active' and 'placebo' treatments, respectively, the estimated therapeutic benefit of the active compound might be measured by the difference

$$Y_A - Y_P = (TR_A + PE_A) - (TR_P + PE_P)$$

Because a placebo has no therapeutic benefit, $TR_P = 0$. With $PE_\Delta = PE_A - PE_P$, you obtain

$$Y_A - Y_P = TR_A + PE_\Delta$$

When patients are unaware of their treatment, the placebo effect (PE) should be the same for both groups, making $PE_\Delta = 0$. Therefore, the difference in response values estimates the true therapeutic benefit of the active compound.

However, if patients know which treatment they have been assigned, the placebo effect in the active group might differ from that of the control group, perhaps due to better compliance or expectation of benefit. In this case, the estimate of therapeutic benefit is contaminated by a non-zero PE_Δ.

In addition, bias, whether conscious or not, might arise if the investigator does not evaluate all patients uniformly. Evaluation of study measurements (such as global assessments and decisions regarding dosing changes, visit timing, use of concomitant medications, and degree of follow-up relating to adverse events or abnormal labs) might be affected by the investigator's knowledge of the patient's treatment. Such bias can be controlled by *double-blinding* the study, which means that information regarding treatment group assignment is withheld from the investigator as well as the patient.

Double-blinding is a common and important feature of a controlled clinical trial, especially when evaluations are open to some degree of subjectivity. However, double-blinding is not always possible or practical. For example, test and control treatments might not be available in the same formulation. In such cases, treatment can sometimes be administered by one investigator and the evaluations performed by a co-investigator at the same center in an attempt to maintain some sort of masking of the investigator.

Studies can also be *triple-blind*, wherein the patient, investigator, and clinical project team (including the statistician) are unaware of the treatment administered until the statistical analysis is complete. This reduces a third level of potential bias -- that of the interpretation of the results.

Selection of appropriate statistical methods for data analysis in confirmatory studies should be done in a blinded manner whenever possible. Usually, this is accomplished through the development of a statistical analysis plan prior to completing data collection. Such a plan helps remove the potential for biases associated with data-driven methodology. It also eliminates the ability to select a method for the purpose of producing a result closest to the outcome that is being sought.

▶ *Selection of Statistical Methods*

Features of controlled clinical trials, such as randomization and blinding, help to limit bias when making statistical inferences. The statistical methods themselves might also introduce bias if they are 'data-driven', that is the method is selected based on the study outcomes. In most cases, the study design and objectives will point to the most appropriate statistical methods for the primary analysis. These methods are usually detailed in a formal analysis plan prepared prior to data collection and, therefore, represent the best 'theoretical' methodology not influenced by the data.

Often, sufficient knowledge of the variability and distribution of the response in Phase 3 or in pivotal trials is obtained from previous studies. If necessary, there are ways to confirm distributional assumptions based on preliminary blinded data in order to fully pre-specify the methodology. Because different statistical methods might lead to different conclusions, failure to pre-specify the methods might lead to the appearance of selecting a method that results in the most desirable conclusion.

Methodology bias is one concern addressed by an analysis plan. More importantly, pre-specifying methodology helps to ensure that the study objectives are appropriately addressed. The statistical method selected will depend very strongly on the actual objective of the study. Consider a trial that includes three doses of an active compound and an inactive placebo. Possible study objectives include determining if

- there is any difference among the four groups being studied.
- any of the active doses is better than the placebo.
- the highest dose is superior to the lower doses.
- there is a dose-response.

A different statistical method might be required for each of these objectives. The study objective must be clear before the statistical method can be selected.

1.4   Descriptive Statistics

Descriptive statistics describe the probability distribution of the population. This is done by using histograms to depict the shape of the distribution, by estimating distributional parameters, and by computing various measures of central tendency and dispersion.

A *histogram* is a plot of the measured values of a random variable by their frequency. For example, height measurements for 16-year-old male students can be described by a sample histogram based on 25 students. See Figure 1.5.

Figure 1.5. Histogram of Height Measurements (n=25)

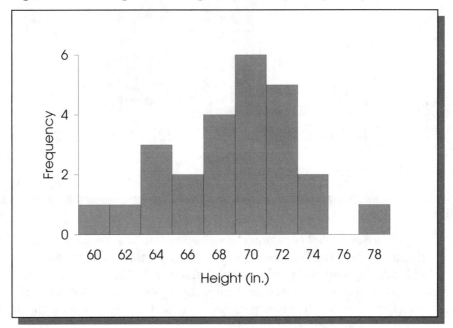

If more-and-more measurements are taken, the histogram might begin looking like a 'bell-shaped' curve, which is characteristic of a normal distribution. See Figure 1.6.

Figure 1.6. Histogram of Height Measurements (n=300)

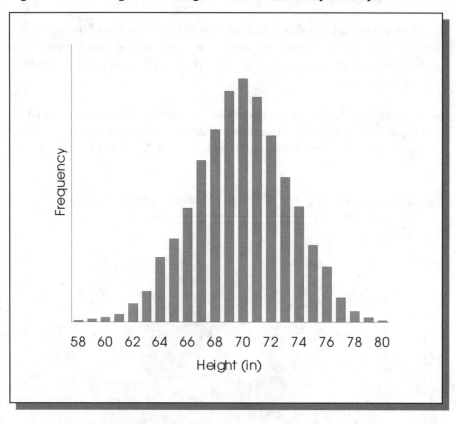

If you assume the population distribution can be modeled with a known distribution (such as the normal), you need only estimate the parameters associated with that distribution in order to fully describe it. The binomial distribution has only one parameter, p, which can be directly estimated from the observed data. The normal distribution has two parameters, μ and σ^2, representing the mean and variance, respectively.

Suppose a sample of n measurements, denoted by x_1, x_2, ..., x_n is obtained. Various descriptive statistics can be computed from these measurements to help describe the population. These include measures of *central tendency*, which describe the center of the distribution, and measures of *dispersion,* which describe the variation of the data. Common examples of each are shown in Table 1.3.

In addition to distributional parameters, you sometimes want to estimate parameters associated with a statistical model. If an unknown response can be modeled as a function of known or controlled variables, you can often obtain valuable information regarding the response by estimating the weights or coefficients of each of these known variables. These coefficients are called *model parameters*. They are estimated in a way that results in the greatest consistency between the model and the observed data.

TABLE 1.3. Common Descriptive Statistics

Measures of 'Central Tendency'	
Arithmetic Mean	$\bar{x} = (\sum x_i) / n = (x_1 + x_2 + ... + x_n) / n$
Median	the middle value, if n is odd; the average of the two middle values if n is even (50th percentile)
Mode	the most frequently occurring value
Geometric Mean	$(\prod x_i)^{1/n} = (x_1 \cdot x_2 \cdot ... \cdot x_n)^{1/n}$
Harmonic Mean	$n / \sum(x_i)^{-1} = n\{(1/x_1) + (1/x_2) + ... + (1/x_n)\}^{-1}$
Weighted Mean	$\bar{x}_w = (\sum w_i x_i) / W$, where $W = \sum w_i$
Trimmed Mean	Arithmetic mean omitting the largest and smallest observations
Winsorized Mean	Arithmetic mean after replacing outliers with the closest non-outlier values

Measures of 'Dispersion'	
Variance	$s^2 = \sum(x_i - \bar{x})^2 / (n - 1)$
Standard Deviation	s = square root of the variance
Standard Error (of the mean)	$(s^2 / n)^{1/2} = $ Standard deviation of $\bar{x}$
Range	Largest value - Smallest value
Mean Absolute Deviation	$(\sum |x_i - \bar{x}|) / n$
Inter-Quartile Range	75th percentile $- 25^{th}$ percentile
Coefficient of Variation	$s / \bar{x}$

Descriptive statistical methods are often the only approach that can be used for analyzing the results of pilot studies or Phase I clinical trials. Due to small sample sizes, the lack of blinding, or the omission of other features of a controlled trial, statistical inference might not be possible. However, trends or patterns observed in the data by using descriptive or exploratory methods will often help in building hypotheses and identifying important cofactors. These new hypotheses can then be tested in a more controlled manner in subsequent studies, wherein inferential statistical methods would be more appropriate.

1.5   Inferential Statistics

The two primary statistical methods for making inferences are confidence interval estimation and hypothesis testing.

▶ *Confidence Intervals*

Population parameters, such as the mean (μ) or the standard deviation (σ), can be estimated by using a point estimate, such as the sample mean ($\overline{x}$) or the sample standard deviation (s). A *confidence interval* is an interval around the point estimate that contains the parameter with a specific high probability or confidence level. A 95% confidence interval for the mean (μ) can be constructed from the sample data with the following interpretation: If the same experiment were conducted a large number of times and confidence intervals were constructed for each, approximately 95% of those intervals would contain the population mean (μ).

The general form of a confidence interval is [$\theta_L - \theta_U$], where θ_L represents the lower limit and θ_U is the upper limit of the interval. If the probability distribution of the point estimate is symmetric (such as the normal distribution), the interval can be found by

$$\hat{\theta} \pm C \cdot \sigma_{\hat{\theta}}$$

where $\hat{\theta}$ is the point estimate of the population parameter θ, $\sigma_{\hat{\theta}}$ is the standard error of the estimate, and C represents a value determined by the probability distribution of the estimate and the significance level that you want. When $\sigma_{\hat{\theta}}$ is unknown, the estimate $\hat{\sigma}_{\hat{\theta}}$ may be used.

For example, for α between 0 and 1, a $100(1-\alpha)$% confidence interval for a normal population mean (μ) is

$$\overline{x} \pm Z_{\alpha/2} \cdot \sigma / \sqrt{n}$$

where the point estimate of μ is $\overline{x}$, the standard error of $\overline{x}$ is $\sigma/\sqrt{n}$, and the value of $Z_{\alpha/2}$ is found in the normal probability tables (See Appendix A.1). Some commonly used values of α and the corresponding critical Z-values are

α	$Z_{\alpha/2}$
0.10	1.645
0.05	1.96
0.02	2.33
0.01	2.575

In most cases, the standard deviation (σ) will not be known. If it can be estimated using the sample standard deviation (s), a $100(1-\alpha)\%$ confidence interval for the mean (μ) can be formed as

$$\overline{x} \pm t_{\alpha/2} \cdot s / \sqrt{n}$$

where $t_{\alpha/2}$ is found from the Student-t probability tables (see Appendix A.2) based on the number of degrees of freedom, in this case, $n-1$. For example, a value of $t_{\alpha/2} = 2.093$ would be used for a 95% confidence interval when $n = 20$.

Many SAS procedures will print point estimates of parameters with their standard errors. These point estimates can be used to form confidence intervals using the general form for $\hat{\theta}$ that is given above. Some of the most commonly used confidence intervals are for population means (μ), differences in means between two populations ($\mu_1-\mu_2$), population proportions (p), and differences in proportions between two populations ($p_1 - p_2$). For each of these, the form for $\hat{\theta}$ and its standard error are shown in Table 1.4.

TABLE 1.4. Confidence Interval Components Associated with Means and Proportions

θ	$\hat{\theta}$	$\sigma_{\hat{\theta}}^2$	$\hat{\sigma}_{\hat{\theta}}^2$	C
μ	$\overline{x}$	σ^2 / n	s^2 / n	$Z_{\alpha/2}$ if σ is known; $t_{\alpha/2}$ if σ is unknown
$\mu_1 - \mu_2$	$\overline{x}_1 - \overline{x}_2$	$\sigma_1^2/n_1 + \sigma_2^2 / n_2$	$s^2 (1/n_1 + 1/n_2)$	$Z_{\alpha/2}$ if σ_1 and σ_2 are known; $t_{\alpha/2}$ if σ_1 or σ_2 is unknown. If unknown, assume equal variances and use $s^2 = (n_1-1)s_1^2 + (n_2-1)s_1^2 / (n_1 + n_2 - 2)$
p	$\hat{p} = x/n$	$p(1-p)/n$	$\hat{p}(1-\hat{p})/n$	$Z_{\alpha/2}$ (x 'events' in n binomial trials)*
$p_1 - p_2$	$\hat{p}_1 - \hat{p}_2$	$p_1(1-p_1)/n_1 + p_2(1-p_2)/n_2$	$\hat{p}_1(1-\hat{p}_1)/n_1 + \hat{p}_2(1-\hat{p}_2)/n_2$	$Z_{\alpha/2}$ ($\hat{p}_i = x_i/n_i$ for i = 1,2)*

* applies to large samples

▶ *Hypothesis Testing*

Hypothesis testing is a means of formalizing the inferential process for decision-making purposes. It is a statistical approach for testing hypothesized statements about population parameters based on logical argument.

To understand the concept behind the hypothesis test, let's examine a form of deductive argument from logic, using the following example:

If you have an apple, you do not have an orange. You have an orange. Therefore, you do not have an apple.

The first two statements of the argument are premises and the third is the conclusion. The conclusion is logically deduced from the two premises, and its truth depends on the truth of the premises.

If **P** represents the first premise and **Q** represents the second premise, the argument may be formulated as

if **P** then not **Q**	(conditional premise)
Q	(premise)
————————	
therefore, not **P**	(conclusion)

This is a deductively valid argument of logic that applies to any two statements, **P** and **Q**, whether true or false. Note that if you have both an apple and an orange, the conditional premise would be false, which makes the conclusion false because the argument is still valid.

Statistical arguments take the same form as this logical argument, but statistical arguments must account for random variations in statements that might not be known to be completely true. A statistical argument might be paraphrased from the logical argument above as

if **P** then *probably* not **Q**	(conditional premise)
Q	(premise)
————————	
therefore, *probably* not **P**	(conclusion)

The following examples illustrate such 'statistical arguments'.

Example 1

Statements:
    P = the coin is fair
    Q = you observe 10 tails in a row

Argument:
If the coin is fair, you would probably not observe 10 tails in a row. You observe 10 tails in a row. Therefore, the coin is probably not fair.

Example 2

Statements:
    P = Drug A has no effect on arthritis
    Q = from a sample of 25 patients, 23 showed
            improvement in their arthritis after taking Drug A

Argument:
If Drug A has no effect on arthritis, you would probably not see improvement in 23 or more of the sample of 25 arthritic patients treated with Drug A. You observe improvement in 23 of the sample of 25 arthritic patients treated with Drug A. Therefore, Drug A is probably effective for arthritis.

In the first example, you might initially suspect the coin of being biased in favor of tails. To test this hypothesis, assume the null case, which is that the coin is fair. Then, design an experiment that consists of tossing the coin 10 times and recording the outcome of each toss. You decide to reject the hypothesis concluding that the coin is biased in favor of tails if the experiment results in 10 consecutive tails.

Formally, the study is set out by identifying the hypothesis, developing a test criterion, and formulating a decision rule. For Example 1,

▶ **Null hypothesis**: the coin is fair

▶ **Alternative**: the coin is biased in favor of tails

▶ **Test criterion**: the number of tails in 10 consecutive tosses of the coin

▶ **Decision rule**: reject the null hypothesis if all 10 tosses result in 'tails'

First, establish the hypothesis **P**. The hypothesis is tested by observing the results of the study outcome **Q**. If you can determine that the probability of observing **Q** is very small when **P** is true and you do observe **Q**, you can conclude that **P** is probably not true. The degree of certainty of the conclusion is related to the probability associated with **Q**, assuming **P** is true.

Hypothesis testing can be set forth in an algorithm with 5 parts:

- . the null hypothesis (abbreviated H_0)
- the alternative hypothesis (abbreviated H_A)
- the test criterion
- the decision rule
- the conclusion.

The null hypothesis is the statement **P** translated into terms involving the population parameters. In Example 1, 'the coin is fair' is equivalent to 'the probability of tails on any toss is ½'. Parametrically, this is stated in terms of the binomial parameter p, which represents the probability of tails.

$$H_0: \ p \leq 0.5$$

The alternative hypothesis is 'not **P**', or

$$H_A: \ p > 0.5$$

Usually, you take 'not **P**' as the hypothesis to be demonstrated based on an acceptable risk for defining '*probably*' as used in Examples 1 and 2.

The test criterion or 'test statistic' is some function of the observed data. This is statement **Q** of the statistical argument. Statement **Q** might be the number of tails in 10 tosses of a coin or the number of improved arthritic patients, as used in Examples 1 and 2, or you might use a more complex function of the data. Often the test statistic is a function of the sample mean and variance or some other summary statistics.

The decision rule results in the rejection of the null hypothesis if unlikely values of the test statistic are observed when assuming the test statistic is true. To determine a decision rule, the degree of such 'unlikeliness' needs to be specified. This is referred to as the *significance level* of the test (denoted α) and, in clinical trials, is often (but not always) set to 0.05. By knowing the probability distribution of the test statistic when the null hypothesis is true, you can identify the most extreme $100\alpha\%$ of the values as a rejection region. The decision rule is simply, reject H_0 when the test statistic falls in the rejection region.

See Chapter 2 for more information about significance levels.

1.6   Summary

This introductory chapter provides some of the basic concepts of statistics, gives an overview of statistics as a scientific discipline, and shows that the results of a statistical analysis can be no better than the data collected. You've seen that the researcher must be vigilant about biases that can enter into a data set from a multitude of sources. With this in mind, it is important to emphasize the correct application of statistical techniques in study design and data collection as well as at the analysis stage.

Statistical methods used to characterize populations from sample data can be classified as descriptive or inferential, most notably, parameter estimates by confidence intervals and hypothesis testing. These techniques are the focus of the methods presented in this book, Chapters 4 through 22.

CHAPTER 2

Topics in Hypothesis Testing

2.1   Significance Levels

When conducting hypothesis testing, an erroneous conclusion is made if the null hypothesis is rejected when it is really true. This error is called a Type I error, and its probability is denoted by α, which is known as the 'significance level' of the test.

When setting up the hypothesis test, the rejection region is selected based on a predetermined value for α, usually a small value such as 0.05. This means that there is only a 5% chance of rejecting a true null hypothesis.

For example, suppose that administration of a drug was suspected to cause increased alkaline phosphatase levels in adult males, a population known to have an alkaline phosphatase mean of 60 U/l in a certain laboratory. To test this, the null and alternative hypotheses are set as

H_0: $\mu = 60$

versus

H_A: $\mu > 60$

where μ represents the population mean alkaline phosphatase in all men who might qualify to receive the drug and be tested at this testing facility.

A sample of n men treated with the drug is observed, and their alkaline phosphatase levels are measured. The *Z-test* which is based on the standard normal distribution and computed from the sample mean $\bar{x}$ is chosen as the test statistic. According to the *Central Limit Theorem* (Chapter 1), $\bar{x}$ has a normal distribution with mean μ and standard error $\sigma/\sqrt{n}$ for large n, so that

$$Z = \frac{\bar{x} - \mu}{\sigma / \sqrt{n}}$$

has a 'standard normal' distribution (see Appendix B).

The null hypothesis would be contradicted if the sample mean $\bar{x}$ is much greater than the known mean, 60. The decision rule is to reject H_0 in favor of H_A when the test statistic is too large, computed under the assumption that H_0 is true,

$$Z_0 = \frac{\bar{x} - 60}{\sigma / \sqrt{n}}$$

The rejection region is $Z_0 > c$, where c is selected according to the chosen significance level α. That is,

$$\alpha = \Pr(\text{reject } H_0 \text{ when } H_0 \text{ is true}) = \Pr(Z_0 > c)$$

The critical value, c, can be denoted by Z_α, which is found from widely available tables of the probabilities for the standard normal distribution, including Appendix A.1 of this book. For the commonly used value of $\alpha = 0.05$, $Z_\alpha = 1.645$.

Suppose that previous laboratory testing at the study laboratory established a mean alkaline phosphatase level of 60 U/l with a standard deviation of $\sigma = 15$. A current sample of 100 treated men resulted in a sample mean of 62 U/l. The *Z-test* summary is

null hypothesis:	H_0: $\mu = 60$
alt. hypothesis:	H_A: $\mu > 60$
test statistic:	$Z_0 = \dfrac{\bar{x} - 60}{\sigma/\sqrt{n}} = \dfrac{62 - 60}{15/\sqrt{100}} = 1.33$
rejection region:	Reject H_0 if $Z_0 > 1.645$ at significance level $\alpha = 0.05$
conclusion:	Because $1.33 < 1.645$, do not reject H_0. Insufficient evidence exists to indicate an increase in mean alkaline phosphatase levels.

2.2 Power

Accepting the null hypothesis when it is not true is a second type of error that can occur when testing a hypothesis. This is known as a Type II error and has the probability β.

For a given test, β is partly determined by the choice for α. Ideally, both α and β would be small. However, in general, there is an inverse relationship between α and β for a fixed sample size, n. Decreasing α (the probability of a Type I error) increases β (the probability of a Type II error) and, if taken too far, tends to render the test *powerless* in its ability to detect real deviations from the null hypothesis.

A test's *power* is defined by $1 - β$, the probability of rejecting the null hypothesis when it is not true. For the fixed significance level α, the sample size will determine β and, therefore, the power of the test.

In the example discussed in Section 2.1, if you accept H_0 and conclude that there is no increase in mean alkaline phosphatase levels with treatment, you would be guilty of a Type II error if a true increase goes undetected by the statistical test. Until the test's power can be investigated, you must conclude that there is 'insufficient evidence to indicate a change' rather than 'there is no change'.

Note that β is not only a function of the significance level and the sample size, but also of the value of the alternative hypothesis. The Type II error probability for this alkaline phosphatase example is given by

$$β = \Pr(\text{accept } H_0 \text{ when } H_A \text{ is true})$$

$$= \Pr(Z_0 \le 1.645 \text{ when } μ > 60)$$

which will differ for each alternative value of μ (> 60).

For example , the probability of a Type II error when $μ = 64$ is

$$β = \Pr(Z_0 \le 1.645 \ when \ μ = 64)$$

$$= \Pr\left(\frac{\overline{x} - 60}{σ/\sqrt{n}} \le 1.645 \ when \ μ = 64\right)$$

$$= \Pr\left(\frac{\overline{x} - 64}{σ/\sqrt{n}} \le 1.645 - \frac{4}{σ/\sqrt{n}}\right)$$

$$= \Pr(Z \le -1.022)$$

because σ = 15 and n = 100. From the normal probability tables (Appendix A.1), you obtain β = 0.153 and a power of 1–β = 0.847. Similar calculations when μ = 62 result in β = 0.623, which gives a power of 0.377.

The power function of the test can be described by a plot of alternative values of μ vs. the power, computed as demonstrated in the preceding equations. Figure 2.1 shows the power curve of the *Z-test* for our example.

Figure 2.1. Power Curve for the Z-Test

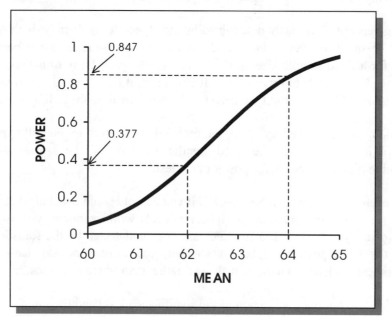

Power curves are important for determining the best test statistic to use. When more than one statistical test is a logical candidate for testing the same hypothesis, the statistician uses the test's power function to determine the more powerful test for a range of likely alternative values. Power curves are also important in sample size determination during study design. Sample size calculations are discussed in Section 2.5.

2.3   *One-Tailed* and *Two-Tailed* Tests

The form of the alternative hypothesis determines whether the test is a *one-* or *two-tailed* test. The alkaline phosphatase example is a *one-tailed test* because the alternative hypothesis $H_A: \mu > 60$ is only concerned with alternative mean values in one direction, that is, greater than 60. The *two-tailed* alternative for this example would be specified as $H_A: \mu \neq 60$, which indicates an interest in alternative values of the mean either greater or less than 60.

The rejection region for the *two-tailed Z-test* would include both very large *and* very small values of the test statistic. For a significance level of α, you reject H_0 in favor of the two-tailed alternative if $Z_0 > Z_{\alpha/2}$ or $Z_0 < -Z_{\alpha/2}$. For $\alpha = 0.05$, $\alpha/2 = 0.025$ in each 'tail' of the normal distribution, obtaining $Z_{0.025} = 1.96$ as the critical value for rejection from the normal probability tables (Appendix A.1). The rejection region for the *two-tailed Z-test* when $\alpha = 0.05$ is $|Z_0| > 1.96$ (that is, $Z_0 > 1.96$ or $Z_0 < -1.96$) due to the symmetry of the normal distribution. When the distribution of the test statistic is not symmetric, the relationship between *one-* and *two-tailed tests* is more complex and beyond the scope of this book.

2.4   p-Values

Formally, the conclusion of a statistical hypothesis test is to 'reject' or to 'not reject' the null hypothesis at a pre-set significance level. Another way to convey a test's level of significance is with its p-values. The p-value is the actual probability of obtaining the calculated test statistic or a value in a more extreme part of the rejection region, when H_0 is true.

In the alkaline phosphatase example discussed previously, the test statistic of $Z_0 = 1.33$ is obtained. The p-value is computed as

$$p = \Pr(Z_0 \geq 1.33, \text{ assuming } H_0 \text{ is true}) = 0.0918$$

based on the normal probability tables (Appendix A.1). Calculated p-values less than the pre-set significance level, such as 0.05, would be considered statistically significant.

If the probability distribution of the test statistic is symmetric, the p-value that corresponds to a *two-tailed test* can be halved to obtain the *p-value* corresponding to the *one-tailed-test*. This is true for the *Z-test* (Section 2.1), which has the standard normal distribution (Chapter 1), and for the *t-test* (Chapters 4, 5), which has the Student t-distribution, both of which are symmetrically distributed about 0.

The results of a statistical test are often described as 'highly significant' when very small p-values (such as $p < 0.01$, $p < 0.001$, etc.) are obtained.

2.5   Sample Size Determination

Sample size requirements are determined from the desired power of the test, the significance level, the measurement variability, and the stated alternative to the null hypothesis. In designing comparative clinical studies, $\alpha = 0.05$ is often used and a power of at least 80% is sought. Variability is estimated from previous studies or known data sets, and the alternative value of the hypothesis is determined by that which is clinically important.

Many excellent sources are available that show methods for computing sample sizes, including Lachin (1981), and these are not repeated here. Instead, three examples used quite frequently in determining sample sizes for clinical studies are presented here. These are approximate formulas based on the commonly used significance level of $\alpha = 0.05$.

▶ *One-Sample Test of a Mean*

For the *one-sample Z-test* about a population mean (presented earlier in Section 2.1) or the *one sample t-test* (Chapter 4), the sample size needed is given by

$$n = \frac{C}{(\Delta/\sigma)^2}$$

where σ is the standard deviation, Δ represents the difference between the hypothesized value and the alternative value, and C is obtained from Table 2.1 based on the power and type of test. If σ is unknown, the sample standard deviation (s) estimated from previous studies may be substituted.

In the alkaline phosphatase example discussed previously, the sample size required to detect an increase in mean alkaline phosphatase from 60 to 63 U/l, based on a standard deviation of 15, is

$$n = 6.2 / (3/15)^2 = 155 \text{ patients}$$

This sample size results in a power of 80% based on a one-tailed significance level of 0.05.

▶ *Two-Sample Comparison of Means*

The comparison of two means using a *two-sample Z-test* or the *two-sample t-test* (Chapter 5) typically tests whether the difference in means between two independent groups is 0. The alternative is that the difference is a non-zero value, such as, Δ. If patients will be equally divided between two groups based on a standard deviation in each group of σ, the sample size for each group is found by

$$n = \frac{2 \cdot C}{(\Delta/\sigma)^2}$$

where C is obtained from Table 2.1. Again, the sample standard deviation, s, may be substituted when σ is unknown.

For example, based on a *two-tailed test* at 90% power and a standard deviation of 10, a difference in means of at least 5 can be detected with a sample size of

$$n = 2(10.5) / (5/10)^2 = 84 \text{ patients per group}$$

▶ *Two-Sample Comparison of Proportions*

The comparison of two, independent, binomial proportions using a normal approximation (*Z-test*) or *chi-square test* (Chapter 16) tests for a 0 difference in proportions

$$H_0: \ p_1 - p_2 = 0$$

The alternative is that the difference is a non-zero value, say, Δ. The sample size (per group) that is required to detect a difference when the true difference is Δ is given by

$$n = \frac{2 \cdot C \cdot \overline{p} \cdot (1 - \overline{p})}{\Delta^2}$$

where $\overline{p} = (p_1 + p_2) / 2$, and C is obtained from Table 2.1. As in the two-sample means comparison, this formula can be used when the study calls for two groups that have the same number of patients in each.

For example, the sample size needed to detect a difference in true response rates of 25% vs. 35% with at least 80% power, is found as

$$n = 2(7.85)(0.3)(0.7) / (.1^2) = 330 \text{ patients per group}$$

This is based on a *two-tailed test* at a significance level of 0.05.

TABLE 2.1. C Values for $\alpha = 0.05$

POWER	β	C One-Tailed	C Two-Tailed
70%	0.30	4.7	6.2
75%	0.25	5.4	6.9
80%	0.20	6.2	7.85
85%	0.15	7.2	9.0
90%	0.10	8.6	10.5
95%	0.05	10.8	13.0

2.6   Multiple Testing

Consider the alkaline phosphatase example discussed at the beginning of this chapter and suppose that two such studies are conducted, one in each of two independent centers. The significance level, α, is the probability of an erroneously significant finding, i.e., the probability of a significant result in Center 1 or in Center 2 when H_0 is true. Using the law of probability that states: For any event A,

$$Pr(A) = 1 - Pr(\text{not } A)$$

you have, $\alpha = 1 - Pr(\text{a non-significant result in Centers 1 and 2, when } H_0 \text{ is true})$. If α_1 and α_2 represent the significance levels of the tests for Centers 1 and 2, respectively, you have,

$$Pr(\text{a non-significant result in Center i when } H_0 \text{ is true}) = 1 - \alpha_i \ (\text{for } i = 1, 2)$$

Applying a law of probability which states that for any two independent events A and B,

$$Pr(A \text{ and } B) = Pr(A) \cdot Pr(B)$$

you obtain $\alpha = 1 - (1 - \alpha_1)(1 - \alpha_2)$. If $\alpha_1 = \alpha_2 = 0.05$, you have

$$\alpha = 1 - (1 - 0.05)^2 = 0.0975$$

In general, if there are k centers or k independent tests, each conducted at a significance level of 0.05, the overall signficance level, α, is

$$\alpha = 1 - (1 - 0.05)^k$$

which is seen to increase markedly even for small values of k, as shown here.

k	α
1	0.050
2	0.098
3	0.143
4	0.185
5	0.226
10	0.401
15	0.537
20	0.642

This illustrates a problem encountered with simultaneously conducting many hypothesis tests. Although the tests usually will not be independent, the fact is that the overall significance level will differ from the significance level at which the individual tests are performed.

Multiple hypothesis testing arises in a number of ways in the analysis of clinical trials data, and the researcher must be aware of any effects on the overall conclusions resulting from these situations.

▶ *Multiple Comparisons of Treatment Response*

One type of multiple testing situation arises in the comparison of a single response variable among more than two randomized treatment groups. With three groups, for example, a low-active-dose group, a high-active-dose group, and a placebo group, you might want to compare the response of each active group to that of the placebo group, and compare the responses of the low-dose and the high-dose groups.

Multiple comparisons can be designed to answer specific questions, such as,

- Which, if any, treatments are better than a control group?
- Does response improve with increasing doses of a treatment?
- Which of several doses is the most effective?
- What is the smallest effective dose?
- Which treatments are statistically inferior to the 'best'?
- Is there a reversal of dose response at a higher dose?

In some cases, a statistical test designed to detect very specific alternative hypotheses can be applied to help answer such questions. The *Joncheere-Terpstra test* for monotonic dose response and the *Cochran-Armitage test* for linear trend are two examples (see SAS OnlineDoc for PROC FREQ). Often, contrasts (linear functions) of group means can be used to help answer specific questions about the relationships of responses among groups. Sets of contrasts can be simultaneously tested by using multiple comparison methods to adjust the p-values in order to maintain control of the overall significance levels.

Most commonly, the goals of multiple comparisons of treatment effects are (i) to perform all pairwise comparisons among the treatment groups, and (ii) to test each active treatment group against a single control group.

With K ($K \geq 3$) groups, there are $K \cdot (K-1)/2$ possible pairwise comparisons. However, when comparing each treated group with a control, there are only $K-1$ comparisons, a substantial reduction from the case of all pairwise comparisons, as shown in Table 2.2.

TABLE 2.2. Number of Group Comparisons for K=3 to 8

Number of Groups	Number of Pairwise Comparisons	Number of Comparisons with 'Control'
K	K(K–1)/2	K–1
3	3	2
4	6	3
5	10	4
6	15	5
7	21	6
8	28	7

In a study with 5 dose groups, for example, there would be 10 possible pairwise comparisons. If each of these is conducted at a significance level of 0.05, the overall significance level is affected so that the likelihood of obtaining at least one erroneous finding might increase substantially. Fortunately, this problem is easily overcome by using one or more of the many approaches to multiple comparisons that will control overall significance levels.

A vast array of multiple testing methods is available in SAS. Multiple comparison procedures can be carried out by using appropriate options in the MEANS statement in PROC ANOVA or in PROC GLM, or by using the LSMEANS statement with the ADJUST= option in PROC GLM or PROC MIXED. Certain multiple testing methods can also be conducted by using PROC MULTTEST or the PROBMC function in a DATA step. See Appendix E for further details.

▶ *Multiple Response Variables*

Another instance in which multiple testing arises is when conducting individual tests on many response variables. For example, testing for significant pre- to post-study changes in laboratory values by conducting individual Z- or t-tests on a large number of laboratory parameters might result in chance significance. With 20 independent t-tests each at a significance level of 0.05, you would expect one test result to be significant due to chance variation when there is no real deviation from the null hypothesis. If 30 or 50 or 100 tests are conducted on the laboratory data, although not independent, one might expect a number of these to be falsely significant.

Multiple testing situations might also arise when a study has more than one primary endpoint associated with establishing treatment efficacy. The overall significance level for efficacy depends on whether at least one, some, or all of the endpoints must individually attain a certain level of significance. Considerations must be given as to which combinations of primary response variables must show significance before treatment efficacy can be declared. Certain combinations might require use of a multivariate statistical method or an adjustment of the individual significance levels used to test each variable. Some of the many p-value adjustment methods available to address this multiplicity problem are discussed in Appendix E in the context of multiple comparisons.

While very conservative, a simple Bonferroni adjustment is often used in these situations. For example, when efficacy may be claimed if just one of k co-primary response variables is significant, the *Bonferroni* method calls for testing each of the k response variables at a significance level of α/k to maintain an overall significance level of α. A less conservative method can be used by taking into account the correlations among the response variables. Pocock, et al. (1987) have shown that with k normally distributed response variables and a correlation of ρ between any pair, the tests can be conducted at a significance level that is slightly higher than the Bonferroni value. This is illustrated in Table 2.3 for a *two-tailed test* with an overall significance level of 0.05.

TABLE 2.3. Adjusted Significance Levels Needed to Maintain an Overall 0.05 Level When Testing k Co-Primary Endpoints with Correlation ρ

k	Bonferroni	$\rho = 0.3$	$\rho = 0.5$	$\rho = 0.7$	$\rho = 0.9$
2	0.025	0.026	0.027	0.029	0.035
3	0.017	0.018	0.019	0.022	0.029
4	0.012	0.013	0.015	0.017	0.025

▶ *Interim Analyses*

Interim analyses of ongoing studies represents another situation involving multiple testing. Use of interim analyses has become highly accepted in large or lengthy clinical research studies. In some situations, it is looked upon as unethical to continue a study when there is overwhelming evidence of the efficacy of a new therapy. By continuing such a study, patients might receive a placebo or another less effective treatment that deprives them of the more effective treatment. Assuming there are no safety issues, it is generally preferable to make the new therapy available to patients as soon as possible.

When a decision is made to stop or to continue the study or to change the study in some fundamental way based on an interim look at the data, the final significance levels will be altered. *Group sequential methods* are special statistical approaches that can be applied to handle such problems, and in most cases, offer adjustments in order to maintain an overall significance level at a pre-determined value. The group sequential methods most commonly used in clinical trials include those described by Pocock (1977), O'Brien and Fleming (1979), and Lan and DeMets (1983). These are discussed in the sections that follow.

Because the issue of interim analyses can affect the overall significance level, careful planning at the design stage is very important in studies with anticipated interim analyses in order to protect the overall α. The study protocol and statistical analysis plans should specifically lay out the details, including

- the number of interim analyses that will be done
- when they will be conducted
- their purpose
- which variables will be analyzed
- how the analyses will be handled
- any adjustments to be made to the significance levels
- who will remain blinded.

When interim analyses occur without pre-planning, careful documentation must be kept to avoid compromising the study integrity.

To maintain an overall significance level, such as $\alpha = 0.05$, the interim analyses must be conducted at significance levels somewhat less than 0.05. One method is to conduct each interim analysis at a very small α-level, such as 0.001 or less, so that the final analysis can be conducted near the 0.05 level. This is a very conservative approach because it is extremely difficult to find a difference between treatment groups at interim testing at such a reduced α-level. However, it might accomplish the purpose of identifying overwhelming treatment differences early in the analysis while permitting almost a full α-level test at the final analysis.

Pocock's Approach

Pocock (1977) proposed a group sequential method whereby the analysis at each stage of testing, including the final analysis, is conducted at the same reduced significance level, α_P, in order to maintain an overall α of 0.05. Values of α_P are shown in Table 2.4 for 1 to 4 planned interim analyses.

TABLE 2.4. Pocock's α_P for $\alpha = 0.05$

Number of Analyses	Number of Interims	α_P
2	1	0.029
3	2	0.022
4	3	0.018
5	4	0.016

O'Brien-Fleming Approach

A drawback of Pocock's method is that the final analysis is conducted at a level much smaller than the 0.05 level. The O'Brien-Fleming approach (1979), probably the most widely used method in handling interim analyses of clinical trials, overcomes this objection, but at the expense of requiring even greater conservatism at the early interims. This method uses progressively increasing α levels at each interim analysis (such as, α_{OF}), so that the final analysis is conducted close to the 0.05 level while maintaining an overall α of 0.05. As shown in Table 2.5, the final analysis is conducted at an α_{OF} level between 0.04 and 0.05 when there are 4 or less planned interim analyses.

TABLE 2.5. O'Brien-Fleming's α_{OF} for $\alpha = 0.05$

Number of Analyses	Number of Interims	------------- Interim Analysis -------------				Final
		1	2	3	4	
2	1	0.005				0.048
3	2	0.0005	0.014			0.045
4	3	0.00005	0.0042	0.019		0.043
5	4	0.00001	0.0013	0.008	0.023	0.041

For example, in a two-stage design that uses the O'Brien-Fleming approach with one scheduled interim analysis, hypothesis testing would be conducted at an interim significance level of $\alpha_{OF} = 0.005$. If significance is found in favor of the test treatment, the study may be stopped with sufficient statistical evidence of efficacy. If the 0.005 level of significance is not reached at the interim, the study continues to normal completion, at which time the hypothesis testing is conducted at a significance level of $\alpha_{OF} = 0.048$. This stagewise procedure will have an overall significance of $\alpha = 0.05$.

When a study is designed to include one or more interim analyses, sample sizes can be pre-determined to achieve the power you want in a way that is similar to that discussed previously in this chapter. Because the final analysis of a group sequential design is conducted at an alpha level smaller than the nominal $\alpha = 0.05$, sample size requirements for studies involving interim analyses are generally larger than for similar fixed sample size studies (i.e., those with no planned interim analyses). One of the features of the O'Brien-Fleming approach is that sample size requirements are very close to those of the fixed sample size study, usually no more than 2% to 3% higher, in order to achieve the same power.

Lan-DeMets α-Spending Function

The O'Brien-Fleming approach was developed with the assumption that a pre-specified number of interim analyses will be performed at approximately, equally spaced intervals during the study, based on patient accrual. Simulation studies have shown that the procedure is not greatly affected under non-extreme deviations from this assumption. In many cases, the number or timing of interim analyses cannot be pre-specified. Lengthy trials, for example, might simply request an interim every 6 months, and patient accrual might not be uniform through each of those 6-month periods.

Lan and DeMets (1983) introduced a method for handling the multiplicity problem when the number of interim analyses is not known at the planning stage. This method is based on an 'α-spending function' that allocates a portion of the overall significance level, α, for testing at each interim analysis, based on the amount of information available at that analysis ('information fraction').

> The information fraction is usually based on the ratio of the number of patients available for interim analysis to the total anticipated sample size if the study were to go to completion. In some cases, the information fraction can be the fraction of elapsed time or, in the case of survival analysis, the number of deaths observed relative to the number of deaths expected.

A number of spending functions have been proposed for use with the Lan-DeMets method, including the spending function that is based on the O'Brien-Fleming approach. The rejection boundaries and interim testing levels can be obtained by using a computer program capable of evaluating multivariate normal probabilities. (While not available in SAS, many good software programs are available for computing these boundaries, including the interactive LANDEM program (available on the Internet), EaSt2000, and PASS.)

Table 2.6 shows the portion of α available for all interim analyses up-to and including a specified information fraction. This cumulative α uses the O'Brien-Fleming spending function and assumes a *two-tailed symmetric test* with overall α = 0.05. In Table 2.6, you see that only 0.00305 of the overall α (0.05) is allocated for all interim analyses conducted by the midpoint of the study (information fraction = 0.5).

TABLE 2.6. Cumulative Lan-DeMets α-Spending Function for the O'Brien-Fleming Spending Function, Two-Tailed Test at Overall $\alpha = 0.05$

Information Fraction	Cumulative α
0.1	0.00000
0.2	0.00000
0.25	0.00001
0.3	0.00009
0.333	0.00021
0.4	0.00079
0.5	0.00305
0.6	0.00762
0.667	0.01210
0.7	0.01477
0.75	0.01930
0.8	0.02442
0.9	0.03629
1.0	0.05000

Interim analysis testing levels (α_{LD}) for the O'Brien-Fleming spending function under the Lan-DeMets method are shown in Table 2.7. These assume equally spaced interim analyses during the study and are based on a *two-tailed test* with an overall significance level of 0.05.

For example, a study involving three, equally spaced interim analyses would entail testing at the 0.044 level at the final analysis, in order to maintain an overall two-tailed α of 0.05 (assuming the study goes to planned completion). As seen in Table 2.7, stopping the study at any interim stage would require overwhelming evidence of efficacy, namely, significance at <0.0001 at the first stage, <0.003 at the second stage, or <0.018 at the third stage of testing.

TABLE 2.7. Lan-DeMets α_{LD} for Overall $\alpha = 0.05$ Using the O'Brien-Fleming Spending Function, Equally Spaced Interims

Number of Interims	Number of Analyses	------------- Interim Analysis -------------				Final
		1	2	3	4	
1	2	0.003				0.049
2	3	<0.001	0.012			0.046
3	4	<0.0001	0.003	0.018		0.044
4	5	<0.00001	<0.001	0.007	0.022	0.042

2.7   Summary

This chapter presents a discussion of some of the most fundamental elements of hypothesis testing, including significance levels, power, p-values, illustration of the difference between *one-* and *two-tailed tests*, the idea behind sample size computations, and the effect of multiple testing on significance levels including interim analyses. Many of the statistical terms used in this chapter are frequently used by clinical researchers, both statisticians and non-statisticians, from protocol development through regulatory submission. The concepts presented here form a basis for a general overview of hypothesis testing, the primary inferential tool used in presenting the statistical methods in Chapters 4 through 22.

The Data Set TRIAL

3.1   Introduction

This chapter presents data from a very simple, hypothetical clinical trial that will be used to illustrate many of the methods discussed throughout this book. First, through the use of very rudimentary case report forms (CRF's), you'll see how response data can be collected in various formats: dichotomous, categorical, or numeric. Then, one of several methods available in SAS for creating a data set from these CRF's is illustrated. The data set TRIAL is used to demonstrate some elementary data summarization methods using SAS.

Finally, the data set TRIAL is used in the exercises presented in Chapter 23. The exercises are designed to give the reader practice in applying the statistical techniques discussed in this book.

3.2   Data Collection

Consider a very simple trial used to study a clinical response from each of 100 patients. The design is a multi-center, randomized, double-blind, parallel study conducted at three study centers. Patients are randomized in equal numbers to one of two treatment groups. The objective is to compare the efficacy of experimental drug (A) with that of reference drug (B) in reducing or eliminating the symptoms of an unspecified disease. The primary response variable that measures the severity of the symptoms is obtained by using a patient-rated global assessment at the end of the trial. Three types of responses are considered:

- presence or absence of symptoms (a dichotomous response)
- discrete severity rating (an ordered categorical response)
- percentile rating using a visual analog scale (VAS) (a continuous numeric response).

Sample data collection forms (CRF's), which illustrate how these responses might be obtained, are shown in Figures 3.1 to 3.3. The forms include basic patient information (patient identification, age, and gender), site number, and visit date in addition to the response measure.

FIGURE 3.1. Sample Data Collection Form 1 (Dichotomous Response)

PROTOCOL NO. _____   SITE NO. _____

PATIENT INFORMATION

PATIENT NO.   PATIENT INITIALS   VISIT DATE

_____   [ ] [ ] [ ]   [ ][ ] [ ][ ] [ ][ ]

                                                mm   dd   yy

AGE (years)   GENDER: [ ]   [ ]

_____   Male   Female

    GLOBAL ASSESSMENT

        [To be completed at study termination]

            Are symptoms present now?

                YES   NO

            [   ]   [   ]

FIGURE 3.2. Sample Data Collection Form 2 (Categorical Response)

PROTOCOL NO. _____   SITE NO. _____

PATIENT INFORMATION

PATIENT NO.   PATIENT INITIALS   VISIT DATE

_____   [ ] [ ] [ ]   [ ][ ] [ ][ ] [ ][ ]
                                        mm   dd   yy

AGE (years)   GENDER: [   ]   [   ]
_____   Male   Female

GLOBAL ASSESSMENT

[To be completed at study termination]

Check box corresponding to how your symptoms are now

No Symptoms   Mild   Moderate   Severe
[   ]   [   ]   [   ]   [   ]

FIGURE 3.3. Sample Data Collection Form 3 (Continuous Numeric Response)

PROTOCOL NO. _____   SITE NO. _____

PATIENT INFORMATION

PATIENT NO.   PATIENT INITIALS   VISIT DATE

_____   [ ] [ ] [ ]   [ ][ ] [ ][ ] [ ][ ]
                                        mm   dd   yy

AGE (years)   GENDER: [   ]   [   ]
_____   Male   Female

GLOBAL ASSESSMENT

[To be completed at study termination]

Place an 'X' on the line corresponding to how you feel now

|——————————————————————————|
0   100
(No symptoms)   (Most severe)

3.3   Creating the Data Set TRIAL

Create and store the data set TRIAL in the directory `bookfiles\examples\sas` on Drive C. The SAS code for creating this data set is shown below.

All three response types are input as follows:

- The dichotomous response variable is named RESP. It has coded values of 0 (if symptoms are absent) and 1 (if symptoms are present);
- The categorical response variable is named SEV. It is coded as 0, 1, 2, or 3 for 'none', 'mild', 'moderate', and 'severe';
- The continuous numeric response variable is named SCORE. Its values can range between 0 and 100. These values represent the percentage of the greatest possible severity perceived by the patient.

Because these data are used for illustrative purposes only, the values of the SCORE variable ❶ are entered and, for ease in constructing the data set, the other response variables (RESP and SEV) are computed rather than entered manually. RESP is set to 0 or 1, based on whether SCORE is 0 or >0, respectively ❷. The severity category (SEV) field is created as follows: SCORE values of 1 to 30 are defined as 'Mild'; 31 to 69, 'Moderate'; and 70 to 100, 'Severe' ❸.

SAS Code for Creating the Data Set TRIAL

```
LIBNAME EXAMP 'c:\bookfiles\examples\sas';

DATA EXAMP.TRIAL;
   INPUT TRT $ CENTER PAT SEX $ AGE SCORE @@;         ❶
   RESP = (SCORE GT 0);
   /* RESP=0 (symptoms are absent), =1 (symptoms are present)  */  ❷
   IF (SCORE = 0) THEN SEV = 0; /* "No Symptoms"              */
   IF ( 1 LE SCORE LE 30) THEN SEV = 1; /* "Mild Symptoms"      */
   IF (31 LE SCORE LE 69) THEN SEV = 2; /* "Moderate Symptoms" */  ❸
   IF (SCORE GE 70) THEN SEV = 3; /* "Severe Symptoms"          */
   DATALINES;
A 1 101 M 55  5     A 1 104 F 27  0     A 1 106 M 31 35
A 1 107 F 44 21     A 1 109 M 47 15     A 1 111 F 69 70
A 1 112 F 31 10     A 1 114 F 50  0     A 1 116 M 32 20
A 1 118 F 39 25     A 1 119 F 54  0     A 1 121 M 70 38
A 1 123 F 57 55     A 1 124 M 37 18     A 1 126 F 41  0
A 1 128 F 48  8     A 1 131 F 35  0     A 1 134 F 28  0
A 1 135 M 27 40     A 1 138 F 42 12     A 2 202 M 58 68
A 2 203 M 42 22     A 2 206 M 26 30     A 2 207 F 36  0
A 2 210 F 35 25     A 2 211 M 51  0     A 2 214 M 51 60
A 2 216 F 42 15     A 2 217 F 50 50     A 2 219 F 41 35
A 2 222 F 59  0     A 2 223 F 38 10     A 2 225 F 32  0
A 2 226 F 28 16     A 2 229 M 42 48     A 2 231 F 51 45
A 2 234 F 26 90     A 2 235 M 42  0     A 3 301 M 38 28
A 3 302 M 41 20     A 3 304 M 65 75     A 3 306 F 64  0
A 3 307 F 30 30     A 3 309 F 64  5     A 3 311 M 39 80
```

```
A 3 314 F 57 85      A 3 315 M 61 12      A 3 318 F 45 95
A 3 319 F 34 26      A 3 321 M 39 10      A 3 324 M 27  0
A 3 325 F 56 35      B 1 102 M 19 68      B 1 103 F 51 10
B 1 105 M 45 20      B 1 108 F 44 65      B 1 110 M 32 25
B 1 113 M 61 75      B 1 115 M 45 83      B 1 117 F 21  0
B 1 120 F 19 55      B 1 122 F 38  0      B 1 125 M 37 72
B 1 127 F 53 40      B 1 129 M 48  0      B 1 130 F 36 80
B 1 132 M 49 20      B 1 133 F 28  0      B 1 136 F 34 45
B 1 137 F 57 95      B 1 139 F 47 40      B 1 140 M 29  0
B 2 201 F 63 10      B 2 204 M 36 49      B 2 205 M 36 16
B 2 208 F 48 12      B 2 209 F 42 40      B 2 212 F 32  0
B 2 213 M 24 88      B 2 215 M 40 59      B 2 218 M 31 24
B 2 220 F 45 72      B 2 221 F 27 55      B 2 224 M 56 70
B 2 227 F 41  0      B 2 228 F 24 65      B 2 230 M 44 30
B 2 232 M 37 32      B 2 233 F 33  0      B 3 303 M 40 26
B 3 305 M 46 15      B 3 308 M 59 82      B 3 310 F 62 38
B 3 312 M 52 40      B 3 313 F 33 40      B 3 316 M 62 87
B 3 317 M 52 60      B 3 320 F 32  2      B 3 322 F 43  0
B 3 323 F 51 35
;
```

First, sort the data set by patient number, then obtain a printout (see **OUTPUT 3.1**) by using the following SAS statements:

```
PROC SORT DATA = EXAMP.TRIAL;
    BY PAT;
PROC PRINT DATA = EXAMP.TRIAL;
    VAR PAT TRT CENTER SEX AGE RESP SEV SCORE;
    TITLE 'Printout of Data Set TRIAL, Sorted by PAT';
RUN;
```

OUTPUT 3.1. Results from PROC PRINT: The Data Set TRIAL

```
                Printout of Data Set TRIAL, Sorted by PAT

   Obs    PAT    TRT    CENTER    SEX    AGE    RESP    SEV    SCORE

    1     101     A        1       M     55      1       1       5
    2     102     B        1       M     19      1       2      68
    3     103     B        1       F     51      1       1      10
    4     104     A        1       F     27      0       0       0
    5     105     B        1       M     45      1       1      20
    6     106     A        1       M     31      1       2      35
    7     107     A        1       F     44      1       1      21
    8     108     B        1       F     44      1       2      65
    9     109     A        1       M     47      1       1      15
   10     110     B        1       M     32      1       1      25
   11     111     A        1       F     69      1       3      70
   12     112     A        1       F     31      1       1      10
   13     113     B        1       M     61      1       3      75
   14     114     A        1       F     50      0       0       0
   15     115     B        1       M     45      1       3      83
   16     116     A        1       M     32      1       1      20
   17     117     B        1       F     21      0       0       0
   18     118     A        1       F     39      1       1      25
   19     119     A        1       F     54      0       0       0
   20     120     B        1       F     19      1       2      55
   21     121     A        1       M     70      1       2      38
   22     122     B        1       F     38      0       0       0
```

OUTPUT 3.1. Results from PROC PRINT: The Data Set TRIAL (*continued*)

23	123	A	1	F	57	1	2	55
24	124	A	1	M	37	1	1	18
25	125	B	1	M	37	1	3	72
26	126	A	1	F	41	0	0	0
27	127	B	1	F	53	1	2	40
28	128	A	1	F	48	1	1	8
29	129	B	1	M	48	0	0	0
30	130	B	1	F	36	1	3	80
31	131	A	1	F	35	0	0	0
32	132	B	1	M	49	1	1	20
33	133	B	1	F	28	0	0	0
34	134	A	1	F	28	0	0	0
35	135	A	1	M	27	1	2	40
36	136	B	1	F	34	1	2	45
37	137	B	1	F	57	1	3	95
38	138	A	1	F	42	1	1	12
39	139	B	1	F	47	1	2	40
40	140	B	1	M	29	0	0	0
41	201	B	2	F	63	1	1	10
42	202	A	2	M	58	1	2	68
43	203	A	2	M	42	1	1	22
44	204	B	2	M	36	1	2	49
45	205	B	2	M	36	1	1	16
46	206	A	2	M	26	1	1	30
47	207	A	2	F	36	0	0	0
48	208	B	2	F	48	1	1	12
49	209	B	2	F	42	1	2	40
50	210	A	2	F	35	1	1	25
51	211	A	2	M	51	0	0	0
52	212	B	2	F	32	0	0	0
53	213	B	2	M	24	1	3	88
54	214	A	2	M	51	1	2	60
55	215	B	2	M	40	1	2	59
56	216	A	2	F	42	1	1	15
57	217	A	2	F	50	1	2	50
58	218	B	2	M	31	1	1	24
59	219	A	2	F	41	1	2	35
60	220	B	2	F	45	1	3	72
61	221	B	2	F	27	1	2	55
62	222	A	2	F	59	0	0	0
63	223	A	2	F	38	1	1	10
64	224	B	2	M	56	1	3	70
65	225	A	2	F	32	0	0	0
66	226	A	2	F	28	1	1	16
67	227	B	2	F	41	0	0	0
68	228	B	2	F	24	1	2	65
69	229	A	2	M	42	1	2	48
70	230	B	2	M	44	1	1	30
71	231	A	2	F	51	1	2	45
72	232	B	2	M	37	1	2	32
73	233	B	2	F	33	0	0	0
74	234	A	2	F	26	1	3	90
75	235	A	2	M	42	0	0	0
76	301	A	3	M	38	1	1	28
77	302	A	3	M	41	1	1	20
78	303	B	3	M	40	1	1	26
79	304	A	3	M	65	1	3	75
80	305	B	3	M	46	1	1	15

OUTPUT 3.1. Results from PROC PRINT: The Data Set TRIAL (*continued*)

```
 81   306    A     3     F     64    0    0     0
 82   307    A     3     F     30    1    1    30
 83   308    B     3     M     59    1    3    82
 84   309    A     3     F     64    1    1     5
 86   311    A     3     M     39    1    3    80
 87   312    B     3     M     52    1    2    40
 88   313    B     3     F     33    1    2    40
 89   314    A     3     F     57    1    3    85
 90   315    A     3     M     61    1    1    12
 91   316    B     3     M     62    1    3    87
 92   317    B     3     M     52    1    2    60
 93   318    A     3     F     45    1    3    95
 94   319    A     3     F     34    1    1    26
 95   320    B     3     F     32    1    1     2
 96   321    A     3     M     39    1    1    10
 97   322    B     3     F     43    0    0     0
 98   323    B     3     F     51    1    2    35
 99   324    A     3     M     27    0    0     0
100   325    A     3     F     56    1    2    35
```

3.4 Statistical Summarization

▶ Let's begin with some elementary SAS procedures to obtain some simple data summaries, starting with the summary statistics for the variable SCORE for each treatment group.

> This book assumes some elementary knowledge of the SAS DATA step and basic procedures (e.g., PROC PRINT and PROC SORT). For more information about how to read data into SAS and working with variables, the new user is referred to "The Little SAS® Book: A Primer" by Delwiche and Slaughter, which is written under the SAS Books by Users program.

First use PROC MEANS (see **OUTPUT 3.2**).

```
PROC SORT DATA = EXAMP.TRIAL;
    BY TRT;
PROC MEANS MEAN STD N MIN MAX DATA = EXAMP.TRIAL;
    BY TRT;
    VAR SCORE AGE;
    TITLE "Summary Statistics for 'SCORE' and 'AGE' Variables";
RUN;
```

Now, use PROC UNIVARIATE (see **OUTPUT 3.3**)

```
PROC UNIVARIATE DATA = EXAMP.TRIAL;
    BY TRT;
    VAR SCORE;
    TITLE "Expanded Summary Statistics for 'SCORE'" ;
RUN;
```

▶ Next, write the mean and median values for SCORE for each treatment group and study center combination to an output data set, then print the results (see **OUTPUT 3.4**).

```
PROC SORT DATA = EXAMP.TRIAL;
    BY TRT CENTER;
PROC UNIVARIATE NOPRINT DATA = EXAMP.TRIAL;
    BY TRT CENTER;
    VAR SCORE;
    OUTPUT OUT = SUMMRY
        N      = NUM
        MEAN   = AVESCORE
        MEDIAN = MEDSCORE;
RUN;

PROC PRINT DATA = SUMMRY;
    TITLE "Summary Statistics for 'SCORE' by Treatment
    Group & Study Center";
RUN;
```

▶ Visualize the distribution of scores using a rough histogram (see **OUTPUT 3.5**).

```
PROC CHART DATA = EXAMP.TRIAL;
    VBAR SCORE / MIDPOINTS = 10 30 50 70 90  GROUP = TRT;
    TITLE "Distribution of 'SCORE' by Treatment Group";
RUN;
```

▶ Obtain response rates by treatment group using PROC FREQ (see **OUTPUT 3.6**).

```
PROC FORMAT;
    VALUE RSPFMT   0 = '0=Abs.'  1 = '1=Pres';
RUN;

PROC FREQ DATA = EXAMP.TRIAL;
    TABLES TRT*RESP / NOCOL NOPCT;
    FORMAT RESP RSPFMT.;
    TITLE 'Summary of Response Rates by Treatment Group';
RUN;
```

▶ Obtain the frequency tables for the severity categories using PROC FREQ (see **OUTPUT 3.7**).

```
PROC FORMAT;
    VALUE SEVFMT   0 = '0=None'
                   1 = '1=Mild'
                   2 = '2=Mod.'
                   3 = '3=Sev.'  ;
RUN;

PROC FREQ DATA = EXAMP.TRIAL;
    TABLES TRT*SEV / NOCOL NOPCT;
    FORMAT SEV SEVFMT.;
    TITLE 'Severity Distribution by Treatment Group';
RUN;
```

▶ Obtain the frequency distribution of severity category by treatment group stratified by SEX (see **OUTPUT 3.8**).

```
PROC FREQ DATA = EXAMP.TRIAL;
    TABLES SEX*TRT*SEV / NOCOL NOPCT;
    FORMAT SEV SEVFMT.;
    TITLE 'Severity Distribution by Treatment Group and Sex';
RUN;
```

▶ Obtain a histogram of severity for each treatment group   (see **OUTPUT 3.9**).

```
PROC CHART DATA = EXAMP.TRIAL;
    VBAR SEV / MIDPOINTS = 0 1 2 3   GROUP = TRT;
    TITLE "Distribution of 'SEV' by Treatment Group";
RUN;
```

The SORT, PRINT, FORMAT, MEANS, UNIVARIATE, FREQ, and CHART procedures represent some of the basic SAS procedures. More information about these and other SAS procedures, including syntax and available options, can be found in numerous SAS books (e.g., Delwiche and Slaughter (1998), Elliott (2000), the *SAS Procedures Guide,* or *SAS OnlineDoc).* The output generated from the preceding code provides a small sampling of the types of summaries available from the vast wealth of summarization possibilities using the various SAS procedures and options.

OUTPUT 3.2. Results from PROC MEANS

```
            Summary Statistics for 'SCORE' and 'AGE' Variables

--------------------------- TRT=A ---------------------------------
                        The MEANS Procedure

Variable        Mean      Std Dev      N      Minimum      Maximum
-----------------------------------------------------------------
SCORE      26.6730769  26.9507329    52           0    95.0000000
AGE        43.7307692  12.2187824    52   26.0000000    70.0000000
-----------------------------------------------------------------


--------------------------- TRT=B ---------------------------------

Variable        Mean      Std Dev      N      Minimum      Maximum
-----------------------------------------------------------------
SCORE      38.333333   29.6937083    48           0    95.0000000
AGE        41.3333333  11.7949382    48   19.0000000    63.0000000
-----------------------------------------------------------------
```

OUTPUT 3.3. Results from PROC UNIVARIATE

```
              Expanded Summary Statistics for 'SCORE'

-------------------------- TRT=A ----------------------------------

                    The UNIVARIATE Procedure
                        Variable:  SCORE

                            Moments

   N                      52      Sum Weights                   52
   Mean            26.6730769     Sum Observations            1387
   Std Deviation   26.9507329     Variance              726.342006
   Skewness         1.02297616    Kurtosis              0.13964333
   Uncorrected SS       74039     Corrected SS          37043.4423
   Coeff Variation  101.04096     Std Error Mean        3.73739421

                    Basic Statistical Measures
           Location                       Variability

      Mean      26.67308     Std Deviation        26.95073
      Median    20.00000     Variance            726.34201
      Mode       0.00000     Range                95.00000
                             Interquartile Range  36.50000

                    Tests for Location: Mu0=0
         Test            -Statistic-     -----p Value------

      Student's t     t  7.136811     Pr > |t|     <.0001
      Sign            M     19.5       Pr >= |M|    <.0001
      Signed Rank     S      390       Pr >= |S|    <.0001


                    Quantiles (Definition 5)
                      Quantile      Estimate

                      100% Max        95.0
                      99%             95.0
                      95%             85.0
                      90%             70.0
                      75% Q3          39.0
                      50% Median      20.0
                      25% Q1           2.5
                      10%              0.0
                      5%               0.0
                      1%               0.0
                      0% Min           0.0

                       Extreme Observations
              ----Lowest----          ----Highest---

              Value     Obs           Value     Obs

                  0      51              75       41
                  0      42              80       45
                  0      38              85       46
                  0      33              90       37
                  0      31              95       48
```

OUTPUT 3.3. Results from PROC UNIVARIATE (*continued*)

```
                Expanded Summary Statistics for 'SCORE'

---------------------------- TRT=B ------------------------------

                            Moments

N                         48    Sum Weights                   48
Mean              38.3333333    Sum Observations            1840
Std Deviation     29.6937083    Variance              881.716312
Skewness          0.21433323    Kurtosis              -1.2051435
Uncorrected SS        111974    Corrected SS          41440.6667
Coeff Variation   77.4618477    Std Error Mean        4.28591762


                    Basic Statistical Measures
         Location                        Variability

    Mean      38.33333     Std Deviation          29.69371
    Median    39.00000     Variance              881.71631
    Mode       0.00000     Range                  95.00000
                           Interquartile Range    54.00000




                  Tests for Location: Mu0=0

       Test              -Statistic-      -----p Value------

       Student's t    t   8.94402     Pr > |t|     <.0001
       Sign           M     19.5      Pr >= |M|    <.0001
       Signed Rank    S      390      Pr >= |S|    <.0001


                   Quantiles (Definition 5)
                   Quantile      Estimate

                   100% Max         95
                   99%             95
                   95%             87
                   90%             82
                   75% Q3          65
                   50% Median      39
                   25% Q1          11
                   10%              0
                   5%               0
                   1%               0
                   0% Min           0


                   Extreme Observations
            ----Lowest----          ----Highest---

            Value      Obs          Value      Obs

                0       47             82       40
                0       37             83        7
                0       33             87       44
                0       26             88       27
                0       20             95       18
```

OUTPUT 3.4. Summary Statistics in an Output Data Set

```
Summary Statistics for 'SCORE' by Treatment Group & Study Center

     Obs     TRT     CENTER     NUM     AVESCORE     MEDSCORE

      1       A        1        20      18.6000       13.5
      2       A        2        18      28.5556       23.5
      3       A        3        14      35.7857       27.0
      4       B        1        20      39.6500       40.0
      5       B        2        17      36.5882       32.0
      6       B        3        11      38.6364       38.0
```

OUTPUT 3.5. Results from PROC CHART

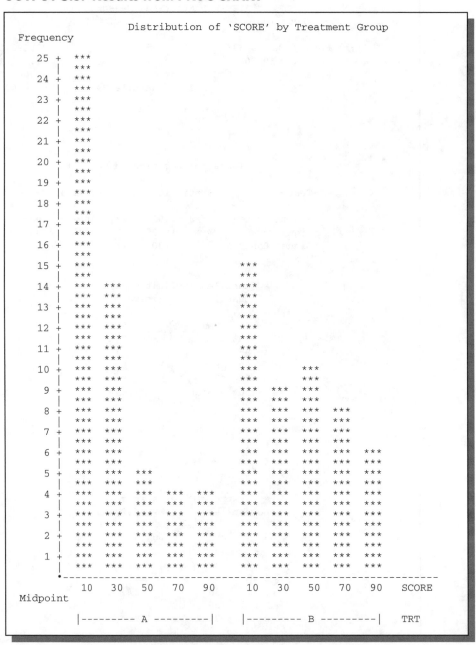

OUTPUT 3.6. Results from PROC FREQ: Dichotomous Response Frequencies

```
          Summary of Response Rates by Treatment Group

                      The FREQ Procedure
                     Table of TRT by RESP

          TRT          RESP

          Frequency|
          Row Pct  |0=Abs.  |1=Pres  |  Total
          ---------+--------+--------+
          A        |     13 |     39 |     52
                   |  25.00 |  75.00 |
          ---------+--------+--------+
          B        |      9 |     39 |     48
                   |  18.75 |  81.25 |
          ---------+--------+--------+
          Total          22       78      100
```

OUTPUT 3.7. Results from PROC FREQ: Severity Frequencies by Treatment Group

```
          Severity Distribution by Treatment Group

                      The FREQ Procedure
                     Table of TRT by SEV

     TRT          SEV

     Frequency|
     Row Pct  |0=None  |1=Mild  |2=Mod.  |3=Sev.  |  Total
     ---------+--------+--------+--------+--------+
     A        |     13 |     22 |     11 |      6 |     52
              |  25.00 |  42.31 |  21.15 |  11.54 |
     ---------+--------+--------+--------+--------+
     B        |      9 |     12 |     17 |     10 |     48
              |  18.75 |  25.00 |  35.42 |  20.83 |
     ---------+--------+--------+--------+--------+
     Total          22       34       28       16      100
```

OUTPUT 3.8. Results from PROC FREQ: Severity Frequencies by Gender and Treatment Group

```
                Severity Distribution by Treatment Group and Sex

                            The FREQ Procedure

                          Table 1 of TRT by SEV
                          Controlling for SEX=F

        TRT          SEV

        Frequency|
        Row Pct  |0=None  |1=Mild  |2=Mod.  |3=Sev.  |  Total
        ---------+--------+--------+--------+--------+
        A        |    10  |    12  |     5  |     4  |    31
                 | 32.26  | 38.71  | 16.13  | 12.90  |
        ---------+--------+--------+--------+--------+
        B        |     7  |     4  |    11  |     3  |    25
                 | 28.00  | 16.00  | 44.00  | 12.00  |
        ---------+--------+--------+--------+--------+
        Total         17       16       16        7       56

                          Table 2 of TRT by SEV
                          Controlling for SEX=M

        TRT          SEV

        Frequency|
        Row Pct  |0=None  |1=Mild  |2=Mod.  |3=Sev.  |  Total
        ---------+--------+--------+--------+--------+
        A        |     3  |    10  |     6  |     2  |    21
                 | 14.29  | 47.62  | 28.57  |  9.52  |
        ---------+--------+--------+--------+--------+
        B        |     2  |     8  |     6  |     7  |    23
                 |  8.70  | 34.78  | 26.09  | 30.43  |
        ---------+--------+--------+--------+--------+
        Total          5       18       12        9       44
```

OUTPUT 3.9. Results from PROC CHART: SEV by Gender and Treatment Group

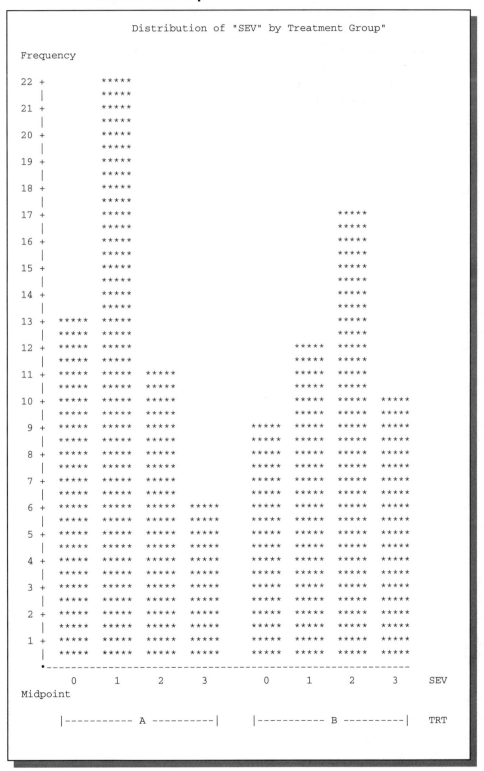

3.5   Summary

This chapter illustrates how data from a simplified hypothetical clinical trial can be collected and entered into a SAS data set, and how simple statistical summaries can be obtained for the key data. Three types of response variables are presented: a dichotomous binary variable (RESP), an ordered categorical variable (SEV), and a continuous numeric variable (SCORE). These types of responses are representative of those most often encountered in clinical studies. The data set TRIAL is used in the exercises in Chapter 23.

CHAPTER 4

The *One-Sample t-Test*

4.1   Introduction

The *one-sample t-test* is used to infer whether an unknown population mean differs from a hypothesized value. The test is based on a single sample of 'n' measurements from the population.

A special case of the *one-sample t-test* is often used to determine if a mean response changes under different experimental conditions by using paired observations. Paired measurements most often arise from repeated observations for the same patient, either at two different time points (e.g., pre- and post-study) or from two different treatments given to the same patient. Because the analyst uses the changes (differences) in the paired measurements, this test is often referred to as the 'paired-difference' *t*-test. A hypothesized mean difference of 0 might be interpreted as 'no clinical response'.

The *one-sample t-test*, along with its two-sample counterpart presented in the next chapter, must surely be the most frequently cited inferential tests used in statistics.

4.2   Synopsis

A sample of n data points, y_1, y_2, ..., y_n, is randomly selected from a normally distributed population with unknown mean, μ. This mean is estimated by the sample mean, $\overline{y}$. You hypothesize the mean to be some value, μ_0. The greater the deviation between $\overline{y}$ and μ_0, the greater the evidence that the hypothesis is untrue.

The test statistic t is a function of this deviation, standardized by the standard error of $\overline{y}$, namely, $s/\sqrt{n}$. Large values of t will lead to rejection of the null hypothesis. When H_0 is true, t has the Student-t probability distribution with n–1 degrees of freedom.

The *one-sample t-test* is summarized as follows:

---

null hypothesis: H_0: $\mu = \mu_0$

alt. hypothesis: H_A: $\mu \neq \mu_0$

test statistic: $$t = \frac{\overline{y} - \mu_0}{s / \sqrt{n}}$$

decision rule: reject H_0 if $|t| > t_{\alpha/2,n-1}$

The value $t_{\alpha/2,n-1}$ represents the 'critical t-value' of the Student t-distribution at a two-tailed significance level, α, and $n-1$ degrees of freedom. This value can be obtained from Appendix A.2 or from SAS, as described later (see 4.4.3).

The *one-sample t-test* is often used in matched-pairs situations, such as testing for pre- to post-study changes. The goal is to determine whether a difference exists between two time points or between two treatments based on data values from the same patients for both measures. The 'paired-difference' t-test is conducted using the procedures outlined for the *one-sample t-test* with μ=the mean difference (sometimes denoted μ_d), $\mu_0 = 0$, and the y_i's = the paired-differences. Examples 4.1 and 4.2 demonstrate application of the *one-sample t-test* in non-matched and matched situations, respectively.

4.3   Examples

✎ Example 4.1 –Body-Mass Index

In a number of previous Phase I and II studies of male, non-insulin-dependent diabetic (NIDDM) patients conducted by Mylitech Biosystems, Inc., the mean body mass index (BMI) was found to be 28.4. An investigator has 17 male NIDDM patients enrolled in a new study and wants to know if the BMI from this sample is consistent with previous findings. BMI is computed as the ratio of weight in kilograms to the square of the height in meters. What conclusion can the investigator make based on the following height and weight data from his 17 patients?

TABLE 4.1. Raw Data for Example 4.1

Patient Number	Height (cm)	Weight (kg)
1	178	101.7
2	170	97.1
3	191	114.2
4	179	101.9
5	182	93.1
6	177	108.1
7	184	85.0
8	182	89.1
9	179	95.8

Patient Number	Height (cm)	Weight (Kg)
10	183	97.8
11	n/a	78.7
12	172	77.5
13	183	102.8
14	169	81.1
15	177	102.1
16	180	112.1
17	184	89.7

Solution

First, calculate BMI as follows: convert height in centimeters to meters by dividing by 100, square this quantity, then divide it into the weight. BMI data (y_i) are shown below, along with the squares and summations. Because no height measurement is available for Patient No. 11, BMI cannot be computed and is considered a missing value.

TABLE 4.2. Computation of Sum of Squares / Example 4.1

Patient Number	BMI (y)	BMI^2 (y^2)
1	32.1	1030.30
2	33.6	1128.87
3	31.3	979.94
4	31.8	1011.43
5	28.1	789.98
6	34.5	1190.58
7	25.1	630.33
8	26.9	723.55
9	29.9	893.96

Patient Number	BMI (y)	BMI^2 (y^2)
10	29.2	852.85
11	.	.
12	26.2	686.26
13	30.7	942.28
14	28.4	806.30
15	32.6	1062.08
16	34.6	1197.07
17	26.5	701.96

$$\text{TOTALS} \quad \Sigma y_i = 481.5$$
$$\Sigma(y_i)^2 = 14627.74$$

The sample mean BMI, $\bar{y}$, and standard deviation, s, are computed from the n=16 patients with non-missing data as follows. The formula shown for s is equivalent to that given in Chapter 1, but it's in a more convenient format for manual computations.

$$\bar{y} = \frac{\sum y_i}{n} = \frac{481.5}{16} = 30.093$$

and

$$s = \sqrt{\frac{\sum y_i^2 - n(\bar{y})^2}{(n-1)}} = \sqrt{\frac{14627.74 - 16(30.093)^2}{15}} = 3.037$$

With a 0.05 significance level, the test summary becomes

null hypothesis: H_0: $\mu = 28.4$

alt. hypothesis: H_A: $\mu \neq 28.4$

test statistic: $t = \dfrac{\bar{y} - \mu_0}{s/\sqrt{n}} = \dfrac{30.093 - 28.4}{3.037/\sqrt{16}} = 2.23$

decision rule: reject H_0 if $|t| > t_{0.025,15} = 2.131$

conclusion: Because $2.23 > 2.131$, you reject H_0 and conclude that the BMI of the new patients differs from that of the patients studied previously.

SAS Analysis of Example 4.1

The SAS code and output for analyzing this data set are shown on the next two pages. The data are read into the data set DIAB ❶ using the INPUT statement ❷. (The INFILE statement can be used if the data are already in an external file.) The response variable BMI (body mass index) is computed ❸ as each record is read in.

The program prints a listing of the data by using PROC PRINT ❹. The *t-test* is conducted with the TTEST procedure, specifying the null value of 28.4 for H_0 ❺. The output shows a t-statistic of 2.23 ❻, which corroborates the manual calculations performed. The test is significant if the p-value ❼ is less than the significance level of the test. In this case, you reject the null hypothesis at a two-tailed significance level of 0.05 because the p-value of 0.041 is less than 0.05.

The output automatically shows the BMI summary statistics, namely, the mean ❽ and the standard deviation ❾. The standard error and the upper and lower confidence limits associated with a 95% confidence interval are also shown for both the mean and standard deviation.

In SAS Releases 6.12 and earlier, PROC TTEST cannot be used to conduct the *one-sample t-test*. Instead, you first transform the response variable in the DATA step by subtracting the null value (e.g., BMI0 = BMI-28.4), then use PROC MEANS with the T and PRT options on this new variable. The SAS statements for this example would be:

```
PROC MEANS T PRT DATA = DIAB;
    VAR BMI0;
RUN;
```

SAS Code for Example 4.1

```
DATA DIAB;                              ❶
    INPUT PATNO WT_KG HT_CM @@;         ❷
    BMI  = WT_KG / ((HT_CM/100)**2);    ❸
    DATALINES;
 1 101.7 178      2  97.1 170
 3 114.2 191      4 101.9 179
 5  93.1 182      6 108.1 177
 7  85.0 184      8  89.1 182
 9  95.8 179     10  97.8 183
11  78.7  .      12  77.5 172
13 102.8 183     14  81.1 169
15 102.1 177     16 112.1 180
17  89.7 184
;

PROC PRINT DATA = DIAB;                 ❹
    VAR PATNO HT_CM WT_KG BMI;
    FORMAT BMI 5.1;
    TITLE1 'One-Sample t-Test';
    TITLE2 'EXAMPLE 4.1: Body-Mass Index Data';
RUN;

PROC TTEST H0=28.4 DATA=DIAB;           ❺
    VAR BMI;
RUN;
```

Output 4.1. SAS Output for Example 4.1

```
                          One-Sample t-Test
                  EXAMPLE 4.1: Body-Mass Index Data

           Obs    PATNO      HT_CM     WT_KG      BMI

             1       1        178      101.7      32.1
             2       2        170       97.1      33.6
             3       3        191      114.2      31.3
             4       4        179      101.9      31.8
             5       5        182       93.1      28.1
             6       6        177      108.1      34.5
             7       7        184       85.0      25.1          ❹
             8       8        182       89.1      26.9
             9       9        179       95.8      29.9
            10      10        183       97.8      29.2
            11      11          .       78.7        .
            12      12        172       77.5      26.2
            13      13        183      102.8      30.7
            14      14        169       81.1      28.4
            15      15        177      102.1      32.6
            16      16        180      112.1      34.6
            17      17        184       89.7      26.5


                        The TTEST Procedure

                            Statistics
          Lower CL              Upper CL Lower CL              Upper CL
Variable  N    Mean     Mean      Mean   Std Dev   Std Dev    Std Dev
                         ❽                          ❾

BMI       16  28.478  30.093    31.709    2.24     3.0323     4.693

                            Statistics
            Variable    Std Err    Minimum    Maximum

            BMI          0.7581     25.106     34.599

                            T-Tests
            Variable     DF       t Value    Pr > |t|

            BMI          15          2.23      0.0411
                                      ❻          ❼
```

✍ **Example 4.2** -- Paired-Difference in Weight Loss

Mylitech is developing a new appetite suppressing compound for use in weight reduction. A preliminary study of 35 obese patients provided the following data on patients' body weights (in pounds) before and after 10 weeks of treatment with the new compound. Does the new treatment look at all promising?

TABLE 4.3. Raw Data for Example 4.2

Subject Number	Weight In Pounds Pre-	Weight In Pounds Post-	Subject Number	Weight In Pounds Pre-	Weight In Pounds Post-
1	165	160	19	177	171
2	202	200	20	181	170
3	256	259	21	148	154
4	155	156	22	167	170
5	135	134	23	190	180
6	175	162	24	165	154
7	180	187	25	155	150
8	174	172	26	153	145
9	136	138	27	205	206
10	168	162	28	186	184
11	207	197	29	178	166
12	155	155	30	129	132
13	220	205	31	125	127
14	163	153	32	165	169
15	159	150	33	156	158
16	253	255	34	170	161
17	138	128	35	145	152
18	287	280			

Solution

First, calculate the weight loss for each patient (y_i) by subtracting the 'post'- weight from the 'pre-' weight (see Output 4.2). The mean and standard deviation of these differences are $\bar{y}_d = 3.457$ and $s = 6.340$ based on $n = 35$ patients. A test for significant mean weight loss is equivalent to testing whether the mean loss, μ_d, is greater than 0. You use a one-tailed test because the interest is in weight loss (not weight 'change'). The hypothesis test is summarized as follows:

null hypothesis: $\quad H_0: \mu_d = 0$

alt. hypothesis: $\quad H_A: \mu_d > 0$

test statistic: $\quad t = \dfrac{\bar{y}_d}{s_d / \sqrt{n}} = \dfrac{3.457}{6.340 / \sqrt{35}} = 3.226$

decision rule: $\quad$ reject H_0 if $t > t_{0.05,34} = 1.691$

conclusion: $\quad$ Because $3.226 > 1.691$, you reject H_0 at a significance level of 0.05 and conclude that a significant mean weight loss occurs following treatment.

SAS Analysis of Example 4.2

The SAS code and output for analyzing this data set are shown below. The program computes the paired differences (variable=WTLOSS) ❿ as the data are read into the data set OBESE. The program prints a listing of the data by using PROC PRINT. A part of the listing is shown in Output 4.2 ⓫.

As in Example 4.1, PROC TTEST without a CLASS statement can be used to conduct the paired t-test. In this case, you tell SAS to compute the differences, WTLOSS, so you can simply include the VAR WTLOSS statement with PROC TTEST. Alternatively, you may omit the VAR statement and include the PAIRED statement followed by the pair of variables being compared, separated by an asterisk (*). This eliminates the need to compute the differences in a separate DATA step.

This example illustrates the PAIRED statement by including the two variables, WTPRE and WTPST ⓬. SAS will automatically compute the paired differences (WTPRE–WTPST), then conduct the t-test. The output shows a t-statistic of 3.23 ⓭, which corroborates the manual computations. Because SAS prints the two-tailed p-value ⓮, this value must be halved to obtain the one-tailed result, p= 0.0028/2 =0.0014. You reject the null hypothesis and conclude that a significant weight loss occurs because this p-value is less than the nominal significance level of $\alpha = 0.05$.

In SAS Releases 6.12 and earlier, PROC TTEST cannot be used to conduct paired t-tests. Instead, use PROC MEANS with the T and PRT options on the variable WTLOSS. The SAS statements for this example would be:

```
PROC MEANS MEAN STD N T PRT DATA=OBESE;
    VAR WTLOSS;
RUN;
```

SAS Code for Example 4.2

```
DATA OBESE;
    INPUT SUBJ WTPRE WTPST @@;
    WTLOSS = WTPRE - WTPST;                                    ❿
    DATALINES;
 1 165 160    2 202 200    3 256 259    4 155 156
 5 135 134    6 175 162    7 180 187    8 174 172
 9 136 138   10 168 162   11 207 197   12 155 155
13 220 205   14 163 153   15 159 150   16 253 255
17 138 128   18 287 280   19 177 171   20 181 170
21 148 154   22 167 170   23 190 180   24 165 154
25 155 150   26 153 145   27 205 206   28 186 184
29 178 166   30 129 132   31 125 127   32 165 169
33 156 158   34 170 161   35 145 152
;
```

```
PROC PRINT DATA = OBESE;                                    ⑪
    VAR SUBJ WTPRE WTPST WTLOSS;
    TITLE1 'One-Sample t-Test';
    TITLE2 'EXAMPLE 4.2: Paired-Difference in Weight
      Loss';
RUN;
PROC TTEST DATA = OBESE;
    PAIRED WTPRE*WTPST;                                     ⑫
RUN;
```

Output 4.2. SAS Output for Example 4.2

```
                         One-Sample t-Test
              EXAMPLE 4.2: Paired-Difference in Weight Loss

          OBS      SUBJ      WTPRE      WTPST      WTLOSS

           1         1        165        160         5
           2         2        202        200         2
           3         3        256        259        -3
           4         4        155        156        -1
           5         5        135        134         1
           6         6        175        162        13
           7         7        180        187        -7
           8         8        174        172         2       ⑪
           .         .         .          .          .
           .         .         .          .          .
           .         .         .          .          .
          33        33        156        158        -2
          34        34        170        161         9
          35        35        145        152        -7


                         The TTEST Procedure

                           Statistics

                    Lower CL              Upper CL  Lower CL            Upper CL
Variable         N     Mean     Mean        Mean    Std Dev  Std Dev   Std Dev
WTPRE - WTPST   35   1.2792    3.4571      5.635    5.1283   6.3401    8.3068

                           Statistics

              Variable        Std Err   Minimum    Maximum
              WTPRE - WTPST    1.0717      -7          15

                             T-Tests

              Variable         DF    t Value      Pr > |t|
              WTPRE - WTPST    34      3.23  ⑬    0.0028  ⑭
```

4.4   Details & Notes

▶ **4.4.1.**   The main difference between the *Z-test* (Chapter 2) and the *t-test* is that the Z-statistic is based on a known standard deviation, σ, while the t-statistic uses the sample standard deviation, s, as an estimate of σ. With the assumption of normally distributed data, the variance σ^2 is more closely estimated by the sample variance s^2 as n gets large. It can be shown that the *t-test* is equivalent to the *Z-test* for infinite degrees of freedom. In practice, a 'large' sample is usually considered $n \geq 30$. The distributional relationship between the Z- and t-statistics is shown in Appendix B.

If the assumption of normally distributed data cannot be made, the mean might not represent the best measure of central tendency. In such cases, a non-parametric rank test, such as the *Wilcoxon signed-rank test* (Chapter 12), might be more appropriate. The UNIVARIATE procedure in SAS can be used to test for normality.

▶ **4.4.2.**   Because Example 4.1 tests for *any* difference from a hypothesized value, a *two-tailed test* is used. A *one-tailed test* would be used when you want to test whether the population mean is strictly greater than *or* strictly less than the hypothesized threshold level (μ_0), such as in Example 4.2. We use the rejection region according to the alternative hypothesis as follows:

Type of Test	Alternative Hypothesis	Corresponding Rejection Region
two-tailed	H_A: $\mu \neq \mu_0$	reject H_0 if $t > t_{\alpha/2,n-1}$ or $t < -t_{\alpha/2,n-1}$
one-tailed (right)	H_A: $\mu > \mu_0$	reject H_0 if $t > t_{\alpha,n-1}$
one-tailed (left)	H_A: $\mu < \mu_0$	reject H_0 if $t < -t_{\alpha,n-1}$

▶ **4.4.3.**   Most statistics text books have tables of the t-distribution in an Appendix. These tables often provide the critical t-values for levels of $\alpha = 0.10, 0.05, 0.025, 0.01$, and 0.005, as in Appendix A.2. Critical t-values can also be found from many statistical programs. In SAS, you use the function TINV(1–a,n–1), where $a = \alpha$ for a *one-tailed test* and $a = \alpha/2$ for a *two-tailed test*. In Example 4.1, the critical t-value of 2.131 with n=16 (15 degrees of freedom) can be found with the SAS function TINV(0.975,15).

Alternatively, the p-value associated with the test statistic, t, based on υ degrees of freedom, can be found by using the SAS function PROBT(t,υ), which gives the cumulative probability of the Student-t distribution. Because you want the tail probabilities, the associated two-tailed p-value is $2\times(1-\text{PROBT}(t, \upsilon))$. In Example 4.1, the p-value 0.041 can be confirmed by using the SAS expression $2\times(1-\text{PROBT}(2.23,15))$. In Example 4.2, the one-tailed p-value 0.0014 can be confirmed by using the SAS expression $1-\text{PROBT}(3.226,34)$.

▶ **4.4.4.**   A non-significant result does not necessarily imply that the null hypothesis is true, only that insufficient evidence exists to contradict it. Larger sample sizes are often needed and an investigation of the power curve (see Chapter 2) is necessary for 'equivalency studies'.

▶ **4.4.5.**   Significance does not imply causality. In Example 4.2, concluding that the treatment *caused* the significant weight loss would be presumptuous. Causality can better be investigated using a concurrent untreated or control group in the study, and strictly controlling other experimental conditions. In controlled studies, comparison of responses among groups is carried out with tests such as the *two-sample t-test* (Chapter 5) or analysis of variance methods (Chapters 6-8).

▶ **4.4.6.**   Known values of n measurements uniquely determine the sample mean $\bar{y}$. But given $\bar{y}$, the n measurements cannot uniquely be determined. In fact, n–1 of the measurements can be freely selected, with the nth determined by $\bar{y}$. Thus the term n–1 degrees of freedom.

Note: The number of degrees of freedom, often denoted by the Greek letter υ (nu), is a parameter of the Student-t probability distribution.

The *Two-Sample t-Test*

5.1   Introduction

The *two-sample t-test* is used to compare the means of two independent populations, denoted μ_1 and μ_2. This test has ubiquitous application in the analysis of controlled clinical trials. Examples might include the comparison of mean decreases in diastolic blood pressure between two groups of patients receiving different antihypertensive agents, or estimating pain relief from a new treatment relative to that of a placebo based on subjective assessment of percent-improvement in two parallel groups.

Assume that the two populations are normally distributed and have the same variance (σ^2).

5.2   Synopsis

Samples of n_1 and n_2 observations are randomly selected from the two populations, with the measurements from Population i denoted by y_{i1}, y_{i2}, ..., y_{in_i} (for i = 1, 2). The unknown means, μ_1 and μ_2, are estimated by the sample means, $\overline{y}_1$ and $\overline{y}_2$, respectively. The greater the difference between the sample means, the greater the evidence that the hypothesis of equality of population means (H_0) is untrue.

The test statistic, t, is a function of this difference standardized by its standard error, namely $s(1/n_1 + 1/n_2)^{1/2}$. Large values of t will lead to rejection of the null hypothesis. When H_0 is true, t has the Student-t distribution with N–2 degrees of freedom, where $N = n_1+n_2$.

The best estimate of the common unknown population variance (σ^2), is the 'pooled' variance (s_p^2), computed as the weighted average of the sample variances using the formula:

$$s_p^2 = \frac{(n_1 - 1) \cdot s_1^2 + (n_2 - 1) \cdot s_2^2}{(n_1 + n_2 - 2)}$$

The *two-sample t-test* is summarized as follows:

---

null hypothesis: H_0: $\mu_1 = \mu_2$
alt. hypothesis: H_A: $\mu_1 \neq \mu_2$

test statistic:

$$t = \frac{\overline{y}_1 - \overline{y}_2}{\sqrt{s_p^2 \left(\dfrac{1}{n_1} + \dfrac{1}{n_2} \right)}}$$

decision rule: reject H_0 if $|t| > t_{\alpha/2, N-1}$

5.3   Examples

Example 5.1 -- FEV_1 Changes

A new compound, ABC-123, is being developed for long-term treatment of patients with chronic asthma. Asthmatic patients were enrolled in a double-blind study and randomized to receive daily oral doses of ABC-123 or a placebo for 6 weeks. The primary measurement of interest is the resting FEV_1 (forced expiratory volume during the first second of expiration), which is measured before and at the end of the 6-week treatment period. Data (in liters) are shown in the table which follows. Does administration of ABC-123 appear to have any effect on FEV_1 ?

TABLE 5.1. Raw Data for Example 5.1

Patient Number	Baseline	Week 6	Patient Number	Baseline	Week 6
ABC-123 Group			**Placebo Group**		
101	1.35	n/a	102	3.01	3.90
103	3.22	3.55	104	2.24	3.01
106	2.78	3.15	105	2.25	2.47
108	2.45	2.30	107	1.65	1.99
109	1.84	2.37	111	1.95	n/a
110	2.81	3.20	112	3.05	3.26
113	1.90	2.65	114	2.75	2.55
116	3.00	3.96	115	1.60	2.20
118	2.25	2.97	117	2.77	2.56
120	2.86	2.28	119	2.06	2.90
121	1.56	2.67	122	1.71	n/a
124	2.66	3.76	123	3.54	2.92

Solution

Let μ_1 and μ_2 represent the mean increases in FEV_1 for the ABC-123 and the placebo groups, respectively. The first step is to calculate each patient's increase in FEV_1 from baseline to Week 6 (shown in Output 5.1). Patients 101, 111, and 122 are excluded from this analysis because no Week-6 measurements are available. The FEV_1 increases (in liters) are summarized by treatment group as follows:

TABLE 5.2. Treatment Group Summary Statistics for Example 5.1

		ABC-123	Placebo
Mean	($\bar{y}_i$)	0.503	0.284
SD	(s_i)	0.520	0.508
Sample Size	(n_i)	11	10

The pooled variance is

$$s_p^2 = \frac{(11-1) \cdot 0.520^2 + (10-1) \cdot 0.508^2}{21-2} = 0.265$$

Because you are looking for any effect, use a *two-tailed test* as follows:

null hypothesis: H_0: $\mu_1 = \mu_2$

alt. hypothesis: H_A: $\mu_1 \neq \mu_2$

test statistic: $t = \dfrac{0.503 - 0.284}{\sqrt{0.265\left(\dfrac{1}{11} + \dfrac{1}{10}\right)}} = 0.974$

decision rule: reject H_0 if $|\,t\,| > t_{0.025,19} = 2.093$

conclusion: Because 0.974 is not > 2.093, you cannot reject H_0. You conclude that the samples fail to provide significant evidence of any effect of ABC-123 on FEV_1. This test is based on a significance level of $\alpha = 0.05$.

SAS Analysis of Example 5.1

The SAS code for analyzing this data set and the resulting output are shown on the next three pages. The program computes the pre- to post-study changes in FEV_1 ('CHG') ❶, then prints a listing of the data by using PROC PRINT ❷.

PROC MEANS is used in this example to obtain the summary statistics for the baseline and Week-6 response values for each group ❸. The T and PRT options are specified in the PROC MEANS statement to illustrate the *one-sample t-tests* for the significance of the within-group changes (variable=CHG) ❹. As demonstrated in Chapter 4, the *one-sample t-test* can also be conducted using the TTEST procedure in SAS, Version 8 or later. Note that the ABC-123 Group shows a significant increase in mean FEV_1 (p=0.0094), while the Placebo Group does not (p=0.1107).

The *two-sample t-test* is carried out by using PROC TTEST with the class variable, TRTGRP, specified in a CLASS statement. Assuming equal variances, you use the t-value and p-value (Pr>|t|) corresponding to 'Equal' under the 'Variances' column ❺. The t-statistic 0.97 confirms the result from the manual calculation above. The p-value 0.3425 (>0.05) indicates no significant difference in the FEV_1 increases between groups.

> SAS prints summary statistics for each level of the class variable, and beginning with Version 8, the upper- and lower-confidence limits for the means and standard deviations are also printed, by default. The confidence limits can be suppressed by using the CI=NONE option in PROC TTEST.

SAS Code for Example 5.1

```
DATA FEV;
    INPUT PATNO TRTGRP $ FEV0 FEV6 @@;
    CHG = FEV6 - FEV0;                          ❶
    IF CHG = . THEN DELETE;
    DATALINES;
101 A 1.35  .      103 A 3.22 3.55   106 A 2.78 3.15
108 A 2.45 2.30    109 A 1.84 2.37   110 A 2.81 3.20
113 A 1.90 2.65    116 A 3.00 3.96   118 A 2.25 2.97
120 A 2.86 2.28    121 A 1.56 2.67   124 A 2.66 3.76
102 P 3.01 3.90    104 P 2.24 3.01   105 P 2.25 2.47
107 P 1.65 1.99    111 P 1.95  .     112 P 3.05 3.26
114 P 2.75 2.55    115 P 1.60 2.20   117 P 2.77 2.56
119 P 2.06 2.90    122 P 1.71  .     123 P 3.54 2.92
;

PROC FORMAT;
    VALUE $TRT 'A' = 'ABC-123'
               'P' = 'PLACEBO';
RUN;

PROC PRINT DATA = FEV;                          ❷
    VAR PATNO TRTGRP FEV0 FEV6 CHG;
    FORMAT TRTGRP $TRT.  FEV0 FEV6 CHG 5.2;
    TITLE1 'Two-Sample t-Test';
    TITLE2 'EXAMPLE 5.1: FEV1 Changes';
RUN;

PROC MEANS MEAN STD N T PRT DATA = FEV;         ❸
    BY TRTGRP;
    VAR FEV0 FEV6 CHG;
    FORMAT TRTGRP $TRT.;
RUN;

PROC TTEST DATA = FEV;
    CLASS TRTGRP;
    VAR CHG;
    FORMAT TRTGRP $TRT.;
RUN;
```

OUTPUT 5.1. SAS Output for Example 5.1

```
                          Two-Sample t-Test
                        EXAMPLE 5.1: FEV1 Changes

        Obs    PATNO    TRTGRP       FEV0     FEV6     CHG

         1     103     ABC-123      3.22     3.55     0.33
         2     106     ABC-123      2.78     3.15     0.37
         3     108     ABC-123      2.45     2.30    -0.15
         4     109     ABC-123      1.84     2.37     0.53
         5     110     ABC-123      2.81     3.20     0.39
         6     113     ABC-123      1.90     2.65     0.75
         7     116     ABC-123      3.00     3.96     0.96
         8     118     ABC-123      2.25     2.97     0.72
         9     120     ABC-123      2.86     2.28    -0.58
        10     121     ABC-123      1.56     2.67     1.11
        11     124     ABC-123      2.66     3.76     1.10
        12     102     PLACEBO      3.01     3.90     0.89
        13     104     PLACEBO      2.24     3.01     0.77
        14     105     PLACEBO      2.25     2.47     0.22
        15     107     PLACEBO      1.65     1.99     0.34
        16     112     PLACEBO      3.05     3.26     0.21
        17     114     PLACEBO      2.75     2.55    -0.20
        18     115     PLACEBO      1.60     2.20     0.60
        19     117     PLACEBO      2.77     2.56    -0.21
        20     119     PLACEBO      2.06     2.90     0.84
        21     123     PLACEBO      3.54     2.92    -0.62
```

❷

```
                          Two-Sample t-Test
                        EXAMPLE 5.1: FEV1 Changes

    ------------------- TRTGRP=ABC-123 ------------------------------

                      The MEANS Procedure         ❸

    Variable          Mean        Std Dev    N   t Value   Pr > |t|
    ----------------------------------------------------------------
    FEV0           2.4845455      0.5328858  11    15.46    <.0001
    FEV6           2.9872727      0.5916095  11    16.75    <.0001
    CHG            0.5027273      0.5198286  11     3.21     0.0094   ❹
    ----------------------------------------------  --------------------


    ------------------- TRTGRP=PLACEBO ------------------------------

    Variable          Mean        Std Dev    N   t Value   Pr > |t|
    ----------------------------------------------------------------
    FEV0           2.4920000      0.6355365  10    12.40    <.0001
    FEV6           2.7760000      0.5507006  10    15.94    <.0001
    CHG            0.2840000      0.5077882  10     1.77     0.1107   ❹
    ----------------------------------------------------------------
```

OUTPUT 5.1. SAS Output for Example 5.1 (*continued*)

```
                        Two-Sample t-Test
                      EXAMPLE 5.1: FEV1 Changes

                        The TTEST Procedure

                             Statistics

                     Lower CL    Upper CL  Lower CL      Upper CL
Variable  Class    N   Mean   Mean   Mean   Std Dev  Std Dev  Std Dev

CHG       ABC-123  11  0.1535  0.5027  0.852   0.3632  0.5198   0.9123
CHG       PLACEBO  10  -0.079  0.284   0.6472  0.3493  0.5078   0.927
CHG       Diff (1-2)   -0.251  0.2187  0.6889  0.391   0.5142   0.751


                             Statistics

            Variable     Class     Std Err   Minimum    Maximum

            CHG          ABC-123    0.1567    -0.58      1.11
            CHG          PLACEBO    0.1606    -0.62      0.89
            CHG          Diff (1-2) 0.2247


                              T-Tests

    Variable      Method      Variances     DF    t Value     Pr > |t|

    CHG           Pooled        Equal       19     0.97    ❺  0.3425
    CHG       Satterthwaite    Unequal     18.9    0.97    ❼  0.3420


                      Equality of Variances
    Variable     Method     Num DF    Den DF    F Value    Pr > F

    CHG          Folded F      10        9       1.05     0.9532 ❻
```

5.4   Details & Notes

▶ **5.4.1.**   The assumption of equal variances can be tested using the *F-test*. An *F-test* generally arises as a ratio of variances. When the hypothesis of equal variances is true, the ratio of sample variances should be about 1. The probability distribution of this ratio is known as the F-distribution (which is widely used in the *analysis of variance*).

The test for comparing two variances can be made as follows:

---

null hypothesis: H_0: $\sigma_1^2 = \sigma_2^2$
alt. hypothesis: H_A: $\sigma_1^2 \neq \sigma_2^2$

test statistic: $F = s_U^2 / s_L^2$

decision rule: reject H_0 if $F > F_c(\alpha/2)$

The subscripts U and L denote 'upper' and 'lower'. The sample with the larger sample variance (s_U^2) is considered the 'upper' sample, and the sample with the smaller sample variance (s_L^2) is the 'lower'. Large values of F indicate a large disparity in sample variances and would lead to rejection of H_0. The critical F value, F_c, can be obtained from the F-tables in most elementary statistics books or many computer packages, based on n_{U-1} upper and n_{L-1} lower degrees of freedom. In SAS, the critical F value is found by using the FINV function:

$$F_c(\alpha/2) = \text{FINV}(1 - \alpha/2, n_{U-1}, n_{L-1})$$

In Example 5.1, compute $F = 0.520^2 / 0.508^2 = 1.048$, which leads to non-rejection of the null hypothesis of equal variances at $\alpha = 0.05$ based on $F_c(0.025) = 3.96$. As noted in Output 5.1, the p-value associated with this preliminary test is 0.9532 ❻, which can also be obtained using the PROBF function in SAS: $2*(1-\text{PROBF}(1.048,10,9))$. You can proceed with the *t-test* assuming equal variances because the evidence fails to contradict that assumption.

If the hypothesis of equal variances is rejected, the *t-test* might give erroneous results. In such cases, a modified version of the *t-test* proposed by Satterthwaite is often used. The 'Satterthwaite adjustment' consists of using the statistic similar to the *t-test* but with an approximate degrees of freedom, carried out as follows:

---

test statistic: $t' = \dfrac{\overline{y}_1 - \overline{y}_2}{\sqrt{\dfrac{s_1^2}{n_1} + \dfrac{s_2^2}{n_2}}}$

decision rule: reject H_0 if $|t'| > t_{\alpha/2, q}$

---

where q represents the approximate degrees of freedom computed as follows (with $w_i = s_i^2 / n_i$):

$$q = \frac{(w_1 + w_2)^2}{\dfrac{w_1^2}{(n_1 - 1)} + \dfrac{w_2^2}{(n_2 - 1)}}$$

Although Satterthwaite's adjustment is not needed for Example 5.1, it can be used to illustrate the computational methods as follows. Compute

$$w_1 = 0.520^2 / 11 = 0.0246$$

and

$$w_2 = 0.508^2 / 10 = 0.0258$$

so that

$$q = \frac{(0.0246 + 0.0258)^2}{\dfrac{0.0246^2}{10} + \dfrac{0.0258^2}{9}} = 18.9$$

and

$$t' = \frac{0.503 - 0.284}{\sqrt{\dfrac{0.520^2}{11} + \dfrac{0.508^2}{10}}} = 0.975$$

SAS computes these quantities automatically in the output of PROC TTEST (See Output 5.1). Satterthwaite's t-value and approximate degrees of freedom are given for Unequal under Variances in the SAS output. (See ❼ in Output 5.1.) These results should be used when the *F-test* for equal variances is significant, or when it is known that the population variances differ.

▶ **5.4.2.** The significance level of a statistical test will be altered if it is conditioned on the results of a preliminary test. Therefore, if a *t-test* depends on the results of a preliminary *F-test* for variance homogeneity, the actual significance level might be slightly different than what is reported. This difference gets smaller as the significance level of the preliminary test increases. With this in mind, you might want to conduct the preliminary *F-test* for variance homogeneity at a significance level greater than 0.05, usually 0.10, 0.15, or even 0.20. For example, if 0.15 were used, Satterthwaites adjustment would be used if the *F-test* were significant at $p < 0.15$.

▶ **5.4.3.**   The assumption of normality can be tested by using the *Shapiro-Wilk test* or the *Kolmogorov-Smirnov test* executed with the NORMAL option in PROC UNIVARIATE in SAS. Rejection of the assumption of normality in the small sample case precludes the use of the *t-test*. As n_1 and n_2 become large (generally$\geq$30), you don't need to rely so heavily on the assumption that the data have an underlying normal distribution in order to apply the *two-sample t-test*. However, with non-normal data, the mean might not represent the most appropriate measure of central tendency. With a skewed distribution, for example, the median might be more representative of the distributional center than the mean. In such cases, a rank test, such as the *Wilcoxon rank-sum test* (Chapter 13) or the *log-rank test* (Chapter 21), should be considered.

▶ **5.4.4.**   Note that, if within-group tests are used for the analysis *instead* of the *two-sample t-test*, the researcher might reach a different, erroneous conclusion. In Example 5.1, you might hastily conclude that a significant treatment-related increase in mean FEV_1 exists just by looking at the within-group results. The *two-sample t-test*, however, is the more appropriate test for the comparison of between-group changes because the control group response must be factored out of the response from the active group.

In interpreting the changes, you might argue that the mean change in FEV_1 for the active group is comprised of two additive effects, namely the placebo effect plus a therapeutic benefit. If it can be established that randomization to the treatment groups provides effectively homogeneous groups, you might conclude that the FEV_1 mean change for the active group in Example 5.1 can be broken down as follows:

$$0.503 \quad = \quad 0.284 \quad + \quad 0.219$$
(Total Effect)   (Placebo Effect)   (Therapeutic Effect)

To validate such interpretations of the data, you would first establish baseline comparability of the two groups. The *two-sample t-test* can also be applied for this purpose by analyzing the baseline values in the same way the changes were analyzed in Example 5.1.

▶ **5.4.5.**   While larger p-values (> 0.10) give greater credence to the null hypothesis of equality, such a conclusion should not be made without considering the test's power function, especially with small sample sizes. Statistical power is the probability of rejecting the null hypothesis when it is *not* true. This probability is based on the value of the parameter assumed as the alternative and, with many alternatives, a power function can be constructed. This concept is discussed briefly in Chapter 2.

▶ **5.4.6.**   In checking for differences between means in either direction, Example 5.1 uses a *two-tailed test*. If interest is restricted to differences in only one direction, a *one-tailed test* can be applied in the same manner as described for the *one-sample t-test* (Chapter 4). The probability given in the SAS output, Pr>|t|, can be halved to obtain the corresponding one-tailed p-value.

One-Way ANOVA

6.1   Introduction

One-way ANOVA (*analysis of variance*) is used to simultaneously compare two or more group means based on independent samples from each group. The bigger the variation among sample group means relative to the variation of individual measurements within the groups, the greater the evidence that the hypothesis of equal group means is untrue. This concept is illustrated in Appendix C (Section C.1), which discusses some basic concepts of *ANOVA*.

In clinical trials, this *ANOVA* method might be appropriate for comparing mean responses among a number of parallel-dose groups or among various strata based on patients' background information, such as race, age group, or disease severity.

In this chapter, assume the samples are from normally distributed populations, all with the same variance, σ^2.

6.2   Synopsis

In general, there are k (k $\geq$ 2) levels of the factor GROUP. From each, independently sample a number of observations, letting y_{ij} represent the jth measurement from the ith group and n_i represent the number of measurements within Group i (i = 1, 2,..., k). Data are collected as shown in Table 6.1.

TABLE 6.1. Typical Layout for the One-Way ANOVA

GROUP			
Group 1	**Group 2**	**...**	**Group k**
y_{11}	y_{21}	...	y_{k1}
y_{12}	y_{22}	...	y_{k2}
...	...	...	...
y_{1n_1}	y_{2n_2}	...	y_{kn_k}

The null hypothesis is that of "no Group effect" (i.e., no difference in mean responses among groups). The alternative hypothesis is that "the Group effect is important" (i.e., at least one pair of Group means differs). When H_0 is true, the variation among groups and the variation within groups are independent estimates of the same measurement variation, σ^2, and their ratio should be close to 1. This ratio is used as the test statistic F, which has the F-distribution with $k-1$ upper and $N-k$ lower degrees of freedom ($N = n_1 + n_2 + ... + n_k$).

The test summary is given as

null hypothesis: $H_0:\ \mu_1 = \mu_2 = ... = \mu_k$
alt. hypothesis: $H_A:\ \text{not } H_0$

test statistic: $F = \dfrac{MSG}{MSE}$

decision rule: reject H_0 if $F > F_{N-k}^{k-1}(\alpha)$

MSG is an estimate of the variability among groups, and MSE is an estimate of the variability within groups.

In *ANOVA*, you assume 'variance homogeneity', which means that the within-group variance is constant across groups. This can be expressed as

$$\sigma_1^2 = \sigma_2^2 = ... = \sigma_k^2 = \sigma^2$$

where σ_i^2 denotes the unknown variance of the ith population. The common variance σ^2 is estimated by s^2, which is a weighted average of the k sample variances:

$$s^2 = \frac{(n_1 - 1) \cdot s_1^2 + (n_2 - 1) \cdot s_2^2 + ... + (n_k - 1) \cdot s_k^2}{(n_1 + n_2 + ... + n_k) - k}$$

Recall the formula for the sample variance for Group i (Table 1.3) to be

$$s_i^2 = \sum_{j=1}^{n_i} \frac{(y_{ij} - \bar{y}_i)^2}{n_i - 1}$$

Because s_i^2 is the estimated variance within Group i, s^2 represents an average within-group variation over all groups. In *ANOVA*, s^2 is called the mean square error (MSE), and its numerator is the sum of squares for error (SSE). The 'error' is the deviation of each observation from its group mean. If SSE is expressed as the sum of squared errors,

$$SSE = \sum_{i=1}^{k} \sum_{j=1}^{n_i} (y_{ij} - \bar{y}_i)^2$$

then the pooled variance s^2 is just SSE / (N–k). The denominator N–k, where N = $n_1 + n_2 + ... + n_k$, is the total sample size over all samples and is known as the degrees of freedom associated with the error.

The variability among groups can be measured by the deviation of the average observation in each group from the overall average, $\bar{y}$. That is, the overall variance obtained by replacing each observation with its group mean ($\bar{y}_i$), represents the between-group variability MSG. Its numerator is the sum of squares for groups (SSG), computed as

$$SSG = \sum_{i=1}^{k} n_i (\bar{y}_i - \bar{y})^2$$

where $\bar{y}$ is the mean of all N observations. Each group mean is treated as a single observation, so there are k–1 degrees of freedom associated with the SSG. The mean square for the GROUP effect is the sum of squares divided by its degrees of freedom

$$MSG = SSG / (k-1)$$

When the null hypothesis is true, the variation between groups should be the same as the variation within groups. Therefore, under H_0, the test statistic F should be close to 1 and has an F-distribution with k–1 upper degrees of freedom and N–k lower degrees of freedom. Critical F-values based on the F-distribution are used to determine the rejection region (See Section 6.4.1).

6.3   Examples

⚋ Example 6.1 -- HAM-A Scores in GAD

A new serotonin-uptake inhibiting agent, SN-X95, is being studied in subjects with general anxiety disorder (GAD). Fifty-two subjects diagnosed with GAD of moderate or greater severity consistent with the "Diagnostic and Statistical Manual, 3rd Edition" (DSMIIIR) were enrolled and randomly assigned to one of three treatment groups: 25 mg SN-X95, 100 mg SN-X95, or placebo. After 10 weeks of once-daily oral dosing in a double-blind fashion, a test based on the Hamilton Rating Scale for Anxiety (HAM-A) was administered. This test consists of 14 anxiety-related items (e.g., 'anxious mood', 'tension', 'insomnia', 'fears', etc.), each rated by the subject as 'not present', 'mild', 'moderate', 'severe', or 'very severe'. HAM-A test scores were found by summing the coded values of all 14 items using the numeric coding scheme of 0 for 'not present', 1 for 'mild', 2 for 'moderate', 3 for 'severe', and 4 for 'very severe'. The data are presented in Table 6.2. Are there any differences in mean HAM-A test scores among the three groups?

TABLE 6.2.   Raw Data for Example 6.1

Lo-Dose (25mg)		Hi-Dose (100mg)		Placebo	
Patient Number	HAM-A	Patient Number	HAM-A	Patient Number	HAM-A
101	21	103	16	102	22
104	18	105	21	107	26
106	19	109	31	108	29
110	n/a	111	25	114	19
112	28	113	23	115	n/a
116	22	119	25	117	33
120	30	123	18	118	37
121	27	127	20	122	25
124	28	128	18	126	28
125	19	131	16	129	26
130	23	135	24	132	n/a
136	22	138	22	133	31
137	20	140	21	134	27
141	19	142	16	139	30
143	26	146	33	144	25
148	35	150	21	145	22
152	n/a	151	17	147	36
				149	32

Solution

Patients who dropped out with no data (Nos. 110, 115, 132, 152) are excluded from the analysis. Arbitrarily assigning subscripts 1 for Lo-Dose, 2 for Hi-Dose, and 3 for Placebo, the group summary statistics for the HAM-A scores are shown in Table 6.3.

TABLE 6.3. Summary Statistics by Treatment Group for Example 6.1

| | -------------- GROUP -------------- | | | |
	Lo-Dose (i=1)	Hi-Dose (i=2)	Placebo (i=3)	Overall
$\bar{y}_i$	23.800	21.588	28.000	24.417
s_i	4.974	4.963	5.033	5.588
n_i	15	17	16	48

Compute

$$
\begin{aligned}
SSG = \; & 15\,(23.800 - 24.417)^2 + \\
& 17\,(21.588 - 24.417)^2 + \\
& 16\,(28.000 - 24.417)^2 \quad = \; 347.1
\end{aligned}
$$

with k = 3 groups, so that

$$MSG = SSG/(k-1) = 347.1\,/\,2 = 173.6$$

Also,

$$
\begin{aligned}
SSE = \; & (21-23.800)^2 + (18-23.800)^2 + \ldots + (35-23.800)^2 + \\
& (16-21.588)^2 + (21-21.588)^2 + \ldots + (17-21.588)^2 + \\
& (22-28.000)^2 + (26-28.000)^2 + \ldots + (32-28.000)^2 = 1120.5
\end{aligned}
$$

with N–k = 48 – 3 = 45 degrees of freedom, so that MSE = 1120.5 / 45 = 24.9.

To check the calculations, you can also compute the MSE, alternatively, as the weighted average of the group variances:

$$MSE = \frac{14 \cdot (4.974^2) + 16 \cdot (4.963^2) + 15 \cdot (5.033^2)}{45} = 24.9$$

The test summary, conducted at a significance level of $\alpha = 0.05$ is shown as

null hypothesis: $H_0: \mu_1 = \mu_2 = \mu_3$

alt. hypothesis: H_A: not H_0

test statistic: $F = 173.6 / 24.9 = 6.97$

decision rule: reject H_0 if $F > F_{45}^2(0.05) = 3.2$

conclusion: because $6.97 > 3.2$, you reject H_0 and conclude that there is a significant difference in mean HAM-A scores among the 3 dose groups.

SAS Analysis of Example 6.1

The next four pages provide the code and output for the analysis of Example 6.1 using the GLM procedure in SAS.

The summary statistics are first obtained for each dose group by using PROC MEANS ❶. These statistics are also summarized in Table 6.3.

The key to using PROC GLM is in correctly specifying the MODEL statement, which lists the response variable on the left side of the equal sign and the model factors on the right side of the equal sign. In the *one-way ANOVA*, there is only one model factor. In this case, the model factor is Dose Group (variable=DOSEGRP). The model factor must also be specified in the CLASS statement to indicate it is a classification factor rather than a numeric covariate.

The output shows the MSE ❷, the MSG ❸, and the *F-test* for the Dose Group effect of 6.97 ❹, which corroborate the manual calculations. The p-value ❺ of 0.0023 (<0.05) indicates that the mean HAM-A scores differ significantly among Dose Groups. The MEANS statement ❻ is used to obtain multiple comparison results using both the pairwise *t-test* ❼ and *Dunnett's test* ❽. Both of these methods reveal significant differences between each active group and placebo. A CONTRAST statement is also included ❾ to illustrate a customized test (see Section 6.4.5).

SAS Code for Example 6.1

```
DATA GAD;
    INPUT PATNO DOSEGRP $ HAMA @@;
    DATALINES;
101 LO 21   104 LO 18
106 LO 19   110 LO  .
112 LO 28   116 LO 22
120 LO 30   121 LO 27
124 LO 28   125 LO 19
130 LO 23   136 LO 22
137 LO 20   141 LO 19
143 LO 26   148 LO 35
152 LO  .   103 HI 16
105 HI 21   109 HI 31
111 HI 25   113 HI 23
119 HI 25   123 HI 18
127 HI 20   128 HI 18
131 HI 16   135 HI 24
138 HI 22   140 HI 21
142 HI 16   146 HI 33
150 HI 21   151 HI 17
102 PB 22   107 PB 26
108 PB 29   114 PB 19
115 PB  .   117 PB 33
118 PB 37   122 PB 25
126 PB 28   129 PB 26
132 PB  .   133 PB 31
134 PB 27   139 PB 30
144 PB 25   145 PB 22
147 PB 36   149 PB 32
;

PROC SORT DATA = GAD; BY DOSEGRP;
PROC MEANS MEAN STD N DATA = GAD;                        ❶
    BY DOSEGRP;
    VAR HAMA;
    TITLE1 'One-Way ANOVA';
    TITLE2 'EXAMPLE 6.1: HAM-A Scores in GAD';
RUN;

PROC GLM DATA = GAD;
    CLASS DOSEGRP;
    MODEL HAMA = DOSEGRP;
    MEANS DOSEGRP/T DUNNETT('PB');                       ❻
    CONTRAST 'ACTIVE vs. PLACEBO' DOSEGRP 0.5 0.5 -1;    ❾
RUN;
```

OUTPUT 6.1. SAS Output for Example 6.1

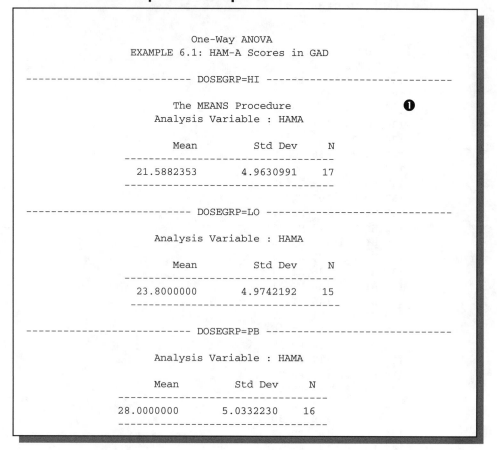

```
                        One-Way ANOVA
                EXAMPLE 6.1: HAM-A Scores in GAD

------------------------- DOSEGRP=HI --------------------------------

                    The MEANS Procedure                        ❶
                 Analysis Variable : HAMA

                Mean           Std Dev       N
        ----------------------------------------
             21.5882353        4.9630991      17
        ----------------------------------------


------------------------- DOSEGRP=LO --------------------------------

                 Analysis Variable : HAMA

                Mean           Std Dev       N
        ----------------------------------------
             23.8000000        4.9742192      15
        ----------------------------------------


------------------------- DOSEGRP=PB --------------------------------

                 Analysis Variable : HAMA

              Mean           Std Dev       N
        ----------------------------------------
           28.0000000         5.0332230      16
        ----------------------------------------
```

```
                   The GLM Procedure

                Class Level Information

        Class          Levels     Values

        DOSEGRP           3        HI LO PB


              Number of observations    52

NOTE: Due to missing values, only 48 observations can be used in
      this analysis.
```

OUTPUT 6.1. SAS Output for Example 6.1 (*continued*)

```
                          One-Way ANOVA
                  EXAMPLE 6.1: HAM-A Scores in GAD

                        The GLM Procedure
Dependent Variable: HAMA


                         Sum of
Source            DF     Squares      Mean Square    F Value    Pr > F

Model              2    347.149020    173.574510       6.97     0.0023
Error             45   1120.517647     24.900392 ❷
Corrected Total   47   1467.666667


            R-Square       Coeff Var       Root MSE      HAMA Mean
            0.236531       20.43698        4.990029      24.41667


Source            DF     Type I SS    Mean Square    F Value    Pr > F
DOSEGRP            2   347.1490196    173.5745098       6.97     0.0023


Source            DF    Type III SS   Mean Square    F Value    Pr > F
DOSEGRP            2   347.1490196    173.5745098       6.97     0.0023
                                           ❸           ❹        ❺



                  t Tests (LSD) for HAMA                           ❼

NOTE: This test controls the Type I comparisonwise error rate, not the
experimentwise error rate.


                    Alpha                         0.05
                    Error Degrees of Freedom        45
                    Error Mean Square          24.90039
                    Critical Value of t         2.01410


   Comparisons significant at the 0.05 level are indicated by ***.

                              Difference
                 DOSEGRP       Between      95% Confidence
                 Comparison      Means          Limits

                 PB   - LO        4.200      0.588    7.812   ***
                 PB   - HI        6.412      2.911    9.912   ***
                 LO   - PB       -4.200     -7.812   -0.588   ***
                 LO   - HI        2.212     -1.349    5.772
                 HI   - PB       -6.412     -9.912   -2.911   ***
                 HI   - LO       -2.212     -5.772    1.349
```

OUTPUT 6.1. SAS Output for Example 6.1 (*continued*)

```
                        One-Way ANOVA
                EXAMPLE 6.1: HAM-A Scores in GAD

                      The GLM Procedure

                Dunnett's t Tests for HAMA                    ❽

    NOTE: This test controls the Type I experimentwise error for
  comparisons of all treatments against a control.

          Alpha                              0.05
          Error Degrees of Freedom             45
          Error Mean Square             24.90039
          Critical Value of Dunnett's t  2.28361

  Comparisons significant at the 0.05 level are indicated by ***.


                      Difference      Simultaneous
            DOSEGRP     Between      95% Confidence
           Comparison    Means           Limits


           LO   - PB     -4.200     -8.295   -0.105   ***
           HI   - PB     -6.412    -10.381   -2.443   ***



  Dependent Variable: HAMA

  Contrast              DF Contrast SS  Mean Square   F Value   Pr > F

  ACTIVE vs. PLACEBO    1 299.9001075   299.9001075    12.04    0.0012  ❾
```

6.4   Details & Notes

▶ **6.4.1**   The parameters associated with the F-distribution are the upper and lower degrees of freedom. Many elementary statistical texts provide tables of critical F-values associated with a fixed significance level (usually 0.10, 0.05, 0.01) for various combinations of values for the upper and lower degrees of freedom. F-values or associated probabilities for known degrees of freedom can also be found by using most statistical programs. In SAS, the FINV function ($1-\alpha$, udf, ldf), where udf and ldf represent the upper and lower degrees of freedom, respectively, is used to obtain the critical F-values for a significance level of α.

▶ **6.4.2**   When conducting *analysis of variance*, using an ANOVA table is a traditional and widely used method of summarizing the results. The *ANOVA* summary identifies each source of variation, the degrees of freedom, the sum of squares, the mean square, and the F-statistic. An ANOVA table is a conventional way of organizing results for analyses that use many factors. In Example 6.1, there is only one model factor (Dose Group), but it is still convenient to use the ANOVA table format to summarize the results. The ANOVA table for this example is

ANOVA

Source	df	SS	MS	F
Dose Group	2	347.15	173.57	6.97 *
Error	45	1120.52	24.90	
Total	47	1467.67		

* Significant (p < 0.05)

▶ **6.4.3** A *one-way ANOVA* requires the assumptions of

- normally distributed data
- independent samples from each group
- variance homogeneity among groups.

The *Shapiro-Wilk test* or *Kolmogorov-Smirnoff test* for normality and *Bartlett's test* for variance homogeneity are some of the many formal tests available for determining whether the sample data are consistent with these assumptions. These tests can be conducted in SAS using options available in PROC UNIVARIATE and PROC GLM. Graphics of the data, such as histograms or plots of the residuals, often provide an informal but convenient means of identifying departures from the ANOVA assumptions.

In the event of significant preliminary tests that identify departures from the assumptions, a data transformation might be appropriate. Logarithmic and rank transformations are popular transformations used in clinical data analysis (see Appendix F). The *Kruskal-Wallis test* (Chapter 14) may be used as an alternative to the *one-way ANOVA* when normality cannot be assumed.

▶ **6.4.4**   When comparing more than two means ($k > 2$), a significant *F-test* indicates that at least one pair of means differs, but which pair (or pairs) is not identified by *ANOVA*. If the null hypothesis of equal means is rejected, further analysis must be undertaken to investigate where the differences lie. Numerous multiple comparison procedures are available for conducting such investigations.

For now, attention is confined to two commonly-used multiple comparison methods: one method is a very simple approach to all-pairwise tests, and one method is a very useful way to compare numerous groups with a control. Multiple comparisons are discussed in more detail in Appendix E. The simplest approach to multiple comparisons is to conduct pairwise *t-tests* for each pair of treatments. This method uses the approach of the *two-sample t-test* discussed in Chapter 5, but rather than using the pooled standard deviation of only the two groups being compared, the pooled standard deviation of all k groups is used (i.e., the square root of the MSE from the *ANOVA*). This method can be carried out in SAS using the T option in the MEANS statement in PROC GLM.

Another approach to multiple comparisons, which compares treatment means with a control group, is called *Dunnett's test*. Special tables are needed to conduct this test manually. The results are printed by SAS if you use the DUNNETT option in the MEANS statement in PROC GLM, or use the PROBMC function in the DATA step.

The T and DUNNETT options are shown in Example 6.1. The output for the pairwise *t-tests* (LSD) ❼ shows significant differences in mean HAM-A scores between the placebo group and each of the active-dose groups, but no difference between the low- and high-dose groups. The results using DUNNETT ❽ also show significant comparisons of each active treatment group versus the control group (placebo).

The biggest drawback of using pairwise *t-tests* is the effect on the overall significance level (as described in Chapter 2). If each pairwise test is conducted at a significance level of $\alpha=0.05$, the chance of having at least one erroneous conclusion, among all the comparisons performed, increases with the number of groups, k. Approaches to multiple comparisons that control the overall error rate have been developed, and it is important to consider the use of these methods when the study uses a larger number of groups. *Dunnett's test* controls the overall significance level because it uses an 'experiment-wise error rate', as noted in Output 6.1.

> Note: For a comprehensive discussion of the numerous other approaches to multiple comparisons, an excellent reference is *"Multiple Comparisons and Multiple Tests Using the SAS System"* by Westfall, Tobias, Rom, and Wolfinger, which is part of the SAS BBU library.

▶ **6.4.5**   When conducting an *ANOVA*, customized comparisons among combinations of the group means can be made. This is done by testing whether specific linear combinations of the group means (called 'linear contrasts') differ from 0.

In Example 6.1, a CONTRAST statement is included in the SAS analysis to compare mean scores between 'Active' and 'Placebo' ❾. 'Active' represents the pooled results from both active-dose groups, and this overall mean is compared to the results from the placebo group. The CONTRAST statement in PROC GLM is followed by a descriptive label (in this case, ACTIVE vs. PLACEBO), then the name of the effect (DOSEGRP) and, finally, the contrast specification. The contrast is simply a vector whose elements are coefficients of the parameters, which represent the levels of the effect being tested. Because the effect DOSEGRP has three levels, we include the 3 coefficients 0.5, 0.5, and −1.0, the order of which must correspond to the order that SAS uses, either alphabetical (e.g., HI, LO, PB) or as specified in an ORDER statement. This specification tells SAS to test

H_0: (Hi-Dose mean + Lo-Dose mean) / 2 = Placebo mean

The output shows a significant contrast with an F-value of 12.04 (p=0.0012).

▶ **6.4.6**   Multiple comparison results can sometimes be contrary to your intuition. For example, let $\bar{y}_A < \bar{y}_B < \bar{y}_C$, and suppose the analysis determines that the Group A mean is not statistically different from that of Group B, which is not different from C. You might infer that there is no difference among any of the 3 groups, while in fact, there might be a significant difference between Groups A and C. Remember that 'no difference' means 'insufficient evidence to detect a difference'.

▶ **6.4.7**   Sometimes, when a significant *F-test* for groups is found, it is preferable to report the confidence intervals for the group mean responses rather than perform multiple comparisons. A 95% confidence interval for the mean of Group i is found by

$$\bar{y}_i \pm t_{0.025,N-k} \cdot \sqrt{\frac{MSE}{n_i}}$$

In Example 6.1, a 95% confidence interval for the Hi-Dose group is

$$21.588 \pm 2.014 \cdot \sqrt{\frac{24.9}{17}} = (19.2 - 24.0)$$

Similarly, 95% confidence intervals can be found for the Lo-Dose group (21.2 – 26.4) and for the Placebo group (25.5 – 30.5). Such intervals are often depicted in graphics in medical journal articles.

▶ **6.4.8**   95% confidence intervals can also be obtained for the mean difference between any pair of groups (e.g., Group i vs. Group j) by using the formula

$$(\bar{y}_i - \bar{y}_j) \pm t_{0.025,N-k} \sqrt{MSE(\frac{1}{n_i} + \frac{1}{n_j})}$$

In Example 6.1, a 95% confidence interval for the difference in mean HAM-A scores between the Placebo and Lo-Dose groups is

$$(28.00 - 23.80) \pm 2.014 \cdot \sqrt{24.9\left(\frac{1}{16} + \frac{1}{15}\right)}$$

or

(0.59 to 7.81)

A confidence interval for the difference in means that does not contain 0 is indicative of significantly different means.

Making inferences based on a series of confidence intervals can lead to the same type of inflation of the overall significance level as was discussed with hypothesis testing. Adjustments to the interval widths can be made when using simultaneous confidence intervals by resorting to the same methodology developed for multiple comparison inferences.

▶ **6.4.9**   If there are only two groups (k = 2), the p-value for Group effect using an *ANOVA* is the same as that of a *two-sample t-test*. The F- and t-distributions enjoy the relationship that, with 1 upper degree of freedom, the F-statistic is the square of the t-statistic. When k = 2, the MSE (computed as a pooled combination of the group sample means) is identical to the pooled variance s_p^2, which is used in the *two-sample t-test* (Chapter 5).

▶ **6.4.10**   Manual computations (with a hand calculator) can be facilitated with standard computing formulas as follows:

Total for Group i
$$G_i = \sum Y_i$$

Overall Total
$$G = \sum_i G_i$$

Correction Factor
$$C = \frac{G^2}{N}$$

Total Sum of Squares
$$TOT(SS) = \sum_i \sum_j y_{ij}^2 - C$$

Sum of Squares for Groups
$$SSG = \sum_i \frac{G_i^2}{n_i} - C$$

Sum of Squares for Error
$$SSE = TOT(SS) - SSG$$

▶ **6.4.11**   SAS computes the sum of squares in four ways. These are called the Type I, II, III, and IV sums of squares. Computational differences among these types are based on the model used and the missing value structure. For the *one-way ANOVA*, all four types of sums of squares are identical, so it does not matter which type is selected. SAS prints the Type I and III results by default. These different types of sums of squares are discussed in Chapter 7 and Appendix D.

CHAPTER 7

Two-Way ANOVA

7.1 Introduction

The *two-way ANOVA* is a method for simultaneously analyzing two factors that affect a response. As in the *one-way ANOVA*, there is a group effect, such as treatment group or dose level. The *two-way ANOVA* also includes another identifiable source of variation called a blocking factor, whose variation can be separated from the error variation to give more precise group comparisons. For this reason, the *two-way ANOVA* layout is sometimes called a 'randomized block design'.

Because clinical studies often use factors such as study center, gender, diagnostic group, or disease severity as a stratification or blocking factor, the *two-way ANOVA* is one of the most common ANOVA methods used in clinical data analysis.

The basic ideas underlying the *two-way ANOVA* are given in Appendix C (Section C.2).

7.2 Synopsis

In general, the randomized block design has g ($g \geq 2$) levels of a 'group' factor and b ($b \geq 2$) levels of a 'block' factor. An independent sample of measurements is taken from each of the $g \times b$ cells formed by the group-block combinations. Let n_{ij} represent the number of measurements taken in Group i and Block j (Cell i–j), and let N represent the number of measurements over all $g \times b$ cells. Letting y_{ijk} denote the kth response in Cell i–j (k = 1, 2, ..., n_{ij}), the general layout of the randomized block design is shown in Table 7.1.

TABLE 7.1. Randomized Block Layout

	Group 1	**Group 2**	...	**Group g**
Block 1	$y_{111}, y_{112}, \ldots, y_{11n_{11}}$	$y_{211}, y_{212}, \ldots, y_{21n_{21}}$	...	$y_{g11}, y_{g12}, \ldots, y_{g1n_{g1}}$
Block 2	$y_{121}, y_{122}, \ldots, y_{12n_{12}}$	$y_{221}, y_{222}, \ldots, y_{22n_{22}}$	...	$y_{g21}, y_{g22}, \ldots, y_{g2n_{g2}}$
...	...	...	...	...
Block b	$y_{1b1}, y_{1b2}, \ldots, y_{1bn_{1b}}$	$y_{2b1}, y_{2b2}, \ldots, y_{2bn_{2b}}$	...	$y_{gb1}, y_{gb2}, \ldots, y_{gbn_{gb}}$

The general entries in a *two-way ANOVA* summary table are represented as shown in Table 7.2.

TABLE 7.2 ANOVA Summary Table for the *Two-Way ANOVA*

Source	df	SS	MS	F
Group (G)	$g-1$	SSG	MSG	$F_G = MSG/MSE$
Block (B)	$b-1$	SSB	MSB	$F_B = MSB/MSE$
G x B (interaction)	$(g-1)(b-1)$	SSGB	MSGB	$F_{GB} = MSGB/MSE$
Error	$N-gb$	SSE	MSE	
Total	$N-1$	TOT(SS)		

SS represents the sum of squared deviations associated with the factor listed under Source. These are computed in a way similar to that shown in Chapter 6 for the *one-way ANOVA*.

The mean square (MS) is found by dividing the SS by the degrees of freedom. The MS represents a measure of variability associated with the factor listed under source. When there is no effect due to the specified factor, this variability reflects measurement error variability, σ^2, which is also estimated by MSE.

The F-values are ratios of the effect mean squares to the mean square error (MSE). Under the null hypothesis of no effect, the F-ratio should be close to 1. These F-values are used as the test statistics for testing the null hypothesis of no mean differences among the levels of the factor.

The *F-test* for group (F_G) tests the primary hypothesis of no group effect. Denoting the mean for the ith group by μ_i, the test summary is

null hypothesis:	H_0: $\mu_1 = \mu_2 = ... = \mu_g$
alt. hypothesis:	H_A: NOT H_0
test statistic:	$F_G = \dfrac{MSG}{MSE}$
decision rule:	reject H_0 if $F_G > F_{N-g}^{g-1}(\alpha)$

The F-test for the block effect (F_B) provides a secondary test, which is used in a similar way to determine if the mean responses differ among blocking levels. A significant block effect often results in a smaller error variance (MSE) and greater precision for testing the primary hypothesis of "no group effect" than if the block effect were ignored.

The GroupxBlock factor (GxB) represents the statistical interaction between the two main effects. If the *F-test* for interaction is significant, this result indicates that trends across groups differ among the levels of the blocking factor. This is usually the first test of interest in a *two-way ANOVA* because the test for group effects might not be meaningful in the presence of a significant interaction. If the interaction is significant, further analysis might be required, such as application of a *one-way ANOVA* to compare groups within each level of the blocking factor.

In a *two-way ANOVA*, you assume that the samples within each cell are normally distributed with the same variance. You can estimate this common variance, σ^2, by the mean square error (MSE), which is a pooled combination of the cell sample variances, s_{ij}^2

$$s^2 = \frac{\sum\limits_{i=1}^{g}\sum\limits_{j=1}^{b}(n_{ij}-1) \cdot s_{ij}^2}{N - (g \cdot b)}$$

The numerator of this quantity is the sum of squares for error (SSE) based on $N-(g \cdot b)$ degrees of freedom.

Generally, the effect sums of squares (SS) are computed in a way that is similar to that shown for the *one-way ANOVA*. For example, the sum of squares for 'Group' (SSG), which represents the variability among group levels, is based on the sum of squared deviations of the group means from the overall mean. In the same way, the sum of squares for 'Block' (SSB), which represents the variability among the block levels, is based on the sum of squared deviations of the block means from the overall mean. The interaction sum of squares (SS(GB)) is based on the sum of squared deviations of the cell means from the overall mean. The computations are shown in Example 7.1.

7.3   Examples

Example 7.1 -- Hemoglobin Changes in Anemia

A new synthetic erythropoietin-type hormone, Rebligen, which is used to treat chemotherapy-induced anemia in cancer patients, was tested in a study of 48 adult cancer patients undergoing chemo-therapeutic treatment. Half the patients received low-dose administration of Rebligen via intramuscular injection three times at 2-day intervals; half the patients received a placebo in a similar fashion. Patients were stratified according to their type of cancer: cervical, prostate, or colorectal. For study admission, patients were required to have a baseline hemoglobin less than 10 mg/dl and a decrease in hemoglobin of at least 1 mg/dl following the last chemotherapy. Changes in hemoglobin (in mg/dl) from pre-first injection to one week after last injection (as shown in Table 7.3) were obtained for analysis. Does Rebligen have any effect on the hemoglobin (Hgb) levels?

TABLE 7.3. Raw Data for Example 7.1

Cancer Type	--- ACTIVE ---		-- PLACEBO --	
	Patient Number	Hgb Change	Patient Number	Hgb Change
CERVICAL	1	1.7	2	2.3
	3	-0.2	4	1.2
	6	1.7	5	-0.6
	7	2.3	8	1.3
	10	2.7	9	-1.1
	12	0.4	11	1.6
	13	1.3	14	-0.2
	15	0.6	16	1.9
PROSTATE	22	2.7	21	0.6
	24	1.6	23	1.7
	26	2.5	25	0.8
	28	0.5	27	1.7
	29	2.6	30	1.4
	31	3.7	32	0.7
	34	2.7	33	0.8
	36	1.3	35	1.5
COLORECTAL	42	-0.3	41	1.6
	45	1.9	43	-2.2
	46	1.7	44	1.9
	47	0.5	48	-1.6
	49	2.1	50	0.8
	51	-0.4	53	-0.9
	52	0.1	55	1.5
	54	1.0	56	2.1

Solution

You use a *two-way ANOVA*, with main effects 'Treatment' and 'Cancer Type', and the interaction 'Treatment-by-Type'. Treatment has two levels: Active and Placebo. Cancer Type has three levels: Cervical, Prostate, and Colorectal. Of primary interest is whether the Active treatment shows any effect on hemoglobin relative to any effects shown by the Placebo group.

First, obtain the summary statistics. These are shown in a table of cell and marginal means in Table 7.4.

TABLE 7.4. Summary Statistics by Treatment Group for Example 7.1

| Cancer Type | ---------- Treatment Group ---------- | | Row Mean |
	ACTIVE	PLACEBO	N
CERVICAL	1.313 (0.988)	0.800 (1.258)	1.056
	N=8	N=8	16
PROSTATE	2.200 (1.004)	1.150 (0.469)	1.675
	N=8	N=8	16
COLORECTAL	0.825 (0.998)	0.400 (1.707)	0.613
	N=8	N=8	16
Column Mean	1.446	0.783	1.115
N	24	24	48

Entries in Table 7.4 are Cell mean, (SD), and sample size, N

The sum of squares for the main effects, Treatment and Cancer Type, are computed as

$$SS(TRT) = 24 \cdot (1.446 - 1.115)^2 + 24 \cdot (0.783 - 1.115)^2 = 5.27$$

$$SS(TYPE) = 16 \cdot (1.056 - 1.115)^2 + 16 \cdot (1.675 - 1.115)^2 + 16 \cdot (0.613 - 1.115)^2 = 9.11$$

The interaction sum of squares can be computed as

$$
\begin{aligned}
\text{SS(TRT-by-TYPE)} = 8 \cdot (1.313 - 1.115)^2 & + \\
8 \cdot (0.800 - 1.115)^2 & + \\
8 \cdot (2.200 - 1.115)^2 & + \\
8 \cdot (1.150 - 1.115)^2 & + \\
8 \cdot (0.825 - 1.115)^2 & + \\
8 \cdot (0.400 - 1.115)^2 & - \\
\text{SS(TRT)} - \text{SS(TYPE)} & = 0.92
\end{aligned}
$$

The total sum of squares is simply the numerator of the sample variance based on all observations.

$$
\text{SS(TOT)} = (1.7 - 1.115)^2 + (-0.2 - 1.115)^2 + \ldots + (2.1 - 1.115)^2 = 69.18
$$

Finally, the error sum of squares (SSE) can be found by subtracting the sum of squares of each of the effects from the total sum of squares.

$$
\begin{aligned}
\text{SSE} &= \text{SS(TOT)} - \text{SS(TRT)} - \text{SS(TYPE)} - \text{SS(TRT-by-TYPE)} \\
&= 69.18 - 5.27 - 9.11 - 0.92 = 53.88
\end{aligned}
$$

As a check, you can also compute SSE from the cell standard deviations.

$$
\begin{aligned}
\text{SSE} = 7 \cdot (0.988)^2 & + \\
7 \cdot (1.258)^2 & + \\
7 \cdot (1.004)^2 & + \\
7 \cdot (0.469)^2 & + \\
7 \cdot (0.998)^2 & + \\
7 \cdot (1.707)^2 & = 53.88
\end{aligned}
$$

Now you can complete the ANOVA table and compute the F-statistics. See Table 7.5.

TABLE 7.5. ANOVA Summary for Example 7.1

Source	df	SS	MS	F	p-Value
Treatment (TRT)	1	5.27	5.27	4.11	0.049 *
Cancer (TYPE)	2	9.11	4.55	3.55	0.038 *
TRT-by-TYPE	2	0.92	0.46	0.36	0.702
Error	42	53.88	1.28		
Total	47	69.18			

* Significant ($p < 0.05$)   (p-values obtained from SAS)

At a significance level of α, the F-statistic is compared with the critical F-value, which can be obtained from widely tabulated F-tables or from SAS, by using the FINV(1-α,U,L) function. The upper degrees of freedom correspond to the MS in the numerator; the error degrees of freedom, which correspond to the MSE, are used as the lower degrees of freedom. The F-value for Treatment effect in example 7.1 is the ratio, MS(TRT)/MSE, based on 1 upper and 42 lower degrees of freedom.

The ANOVA summary indicates a non-significant interaction, which suggests that the differences between Treatment levels are consistent over Cancer Types. The *F-test* for Treatment is significant (p = 0.049), which indicates that the mean hemoglobin response for the Active group differs from that of the Placebo group averaged over all Cancer Types.

The Cancer Type effect is also significant at the 0.05 level, which suggests differing mean response levels among the Cancer Types. Such information might be useful in designing future studies or in guiding further analyses.

SAS Analysis of Example 7.1

The SAS code and output for analyzing these data with the *two-way ANOVA* are shown on the next four pages. The cell summary statistics are first printed using the MEANS procedure ❶. The GLM procedure is used with the main effects, Treatment (TRT) and Cancer Type (TYPE), specified as class variables in the CLASS statement and as factors in the MODEL statement ❷. The interaction (TRT*TYPE) is also included in the MODEL statement.

For a balanced layout as shown in this example (same sample size in each cell), the SAS Types I, II, III, and IV sums of squares are identical. The Type III results ❸ (specified by the SS3 option in the MODEL statement) corroborate the results obtained by manual computations.

While the primary concern is the treatment effect (TRT), which is seen to be significant (p=0.0491) ❹, there is also a significant difference in response among Cancer Types (p=0.0376) ❺. Because there are more than two levels of this effect, further analyses are needed to determine where the differences exist. To use pairwise *t-tests* for multiple comparisons, include the MEANS statement with the T option after the MODEL statement in the SAS code. This provides comparisons between each pair of Cancer Types, as described in Chapter 6. As seen in Output 7.1, mean hemoglobin response differs significantly between the prostate and colerectal Cancer Types ❻.

The LSMEANS statement is also included to illustrate another way of obtaining pairwise comparisons. When the PDIFF option is used, SAS prints out a matrix of p-values for all pairwise comparisons ❼. As indicated by a p-value less than 0.05, mean responses for the colerectal (no.2 mean) and prostate (no.3 mean) Cancer Types differ significantly (p = 0.0112).

SAS Code for Example 7.1

```
DATA HGBDS;
    INPUT TRT $  TYPE $  PATNO HGBCH @@;
    DATALINES;
ACT C  1  1.7   ACT C  3 -0.2   ACT C  6  1.7
ACT C  7  2.3   ACT C 10  2.7   ACT C 12  0.4
ACT C 13  1.3   ACT C 15  0.6   ACT P 22  2.7
ACT P 24  1.6   ACT P 26  2.5   ACT P 28  0.5
ACT P 29  2.6   ACT P 31  3.7   ACT P 34  2.7
ACT P 36  1.3   ACT R 42 -0.3   ACT R 45  1.9
ACT R 46  1.7   ACT R 47  0.5   ACT R 49  2.1
ACT R 51 -0.4   ACT R 52  0.1   ACT R 54  1.0
PBO C  2  2.3   PBO C  4  1.2   PBO C  5 -0.6
PBO C  8  1.3   PBO C  9 -1.1   PBO C 11  1.6
PBO C 14 -0.2   PBO C 16  1.9   PBO P 21  0.6
PBO P 23  1.7   PBO P 25  0.8   PBO P 27  1.7
PBO P 30  1.4   PBO P 32  0.7   PBO P 33  0.8
PBO P 35  1.5   PBO R 41  1.6   PBO R 43 -2.2
PBO R 44  1.9   PBO R 48 -1.6   PBO R 50  0.8
PBO R 53 -0.9   PBO R 55  1.5   PBO R 56  2.1
;

PROC FORMAT;
    VALUE $TYPFMT 'C' = 'CERVICAL   '
                  'P' = 'PROSTATE   '
                  'R' = 'COLORECTAL' ;
RUN;

PROC SORT DATA = HGBDS;
    BY TRT TYPE;

PROC MEANS MEAN STD N;                                    ❶
    VAR HGBCH;
    BY TRT TYPE;
    FORMAT TYPE $TYPFMT.;
    TITLE1 'Two-Way ANOVA';
    TITLE2 'EXAMPLE 7.1: Hemoglobin Changes in Anemia';
RUN;

PROC GLM DATA = HGBDS;
    CLASS TRT TYPE;
    MODEL HGBCH = TRT TYPE TRT*TYPE / SS3;               ❷
        MEANS TYPE / T;
        LSMEANS TYPE / PDIFF STDERR;
    FORMAT TYPE $TYPFMT.;
RUN;
```

Output 7.1. SAS Output for Example 7.1

```
                        Two-Way ANOVA
           EXAMPLE 7.1: Hemoglobin Changes in Anemia


                    The MEANS Procedure
                 Analysis Variable : HGBCH


---------------------- TRT=ACT TYPE=CERVICAL ----------------------

              Mean          Std Dev      N
        -------------------------------------
           1.3125000       0.9876921     8
        -------------------------------------


---------------------- TRT=ACT TYPE=PROSTATE ----------------------

              Mean          Std Dev      N
        -------------------------------------
           2.2000000       1.0042766     8
        -------------------------------------


---------           ----------- TRT=ACT TYPE=COLORECTAL ----------------------

              Mean          Std Dev      N
        -------------------------------------
           0.8250000       0.9982127     8
        -------------------------------------


---------------------- TRT=PBO TYPE=CERVICAL ----------------------

              Mean          Std Dev      N
        -------------------------------------
           0.8000000       1.2581165     8
        -------------------------------------


---------------------- TRT=PBO TYPE=PROSTATE ----------------------

              Mean          Std Dev      N
        -------------------------------------
           1.1500000       0.4690416     8
        -------------------------------------


---------------------- TRT=PBO TYPE=COLORECTAL ----------------------

              Mean          Std Dev      N
        -------------------------------------
           0.4000000       1.7071279     8
        -------------------------------------
```

❶

Output 7.1. SAS Output for Example 7.1 (*continued*)

```
                          Two-Way ANOVA
              EXAMPLE 7.1: Hemoglobin Changes in Anemia

                       The GLM Procedure

                    Class Level Information

            Class          Levels   Values

            TRT               2      ACT PBO
            TYPE              3      CERVICAL COLORECTAL PROSTATE

                   Number of observations    48

     Dependent Variable: HGBCH


                          Sum of
      Source        DF    Squares     Mean Square   F Value   Pr > F

   Model            5   15.29604167   3.05920833     2.38     0.0543
   Error           42   53.88375000   1.28294643
   Corrected Total 47   69.17979167


              R-Square    Coeff Var     Root MSE    HGBCH Mean

              0.221106    101.6229      1.132672     1.114583



      Source     DF    Type III SS   Mean Square   F Value   Pr > F

      TRT         1    5.26687500    5.26687500     4.11     0.0491  ❹
      TYPE        2    9.11291667    4.55645833     3.55     0.0376  ❺
      TRT*TYPE    2    0.91625000    0.45812500     0.36     0.7018
                                ❸
```

Output 7.1. SAS Output for Example 7.1 (*continued*)

```
                              Two-Way ANOVA
                EXAMPLE 7.1: Hemoglobin Changes in Anemia

                            The GLM Procedure

                         t Tests (LSD) for HGBCH

NOTE: This test controls the Type I comparisonwise error rate,
      not the experimentwise error rate.

              Alpha                              0.05
              Error Degrees of Freedom             42
              Error Mean Square               1.282946
              Critical Value of t             2.01808
              Least Significant Difference     0.8082


        Means with the same letter are not significantly different.

          t Grouping          Mean      N     TYPE

                    A        1.6750     16     PROSTATE
                    A
              B     A        1.0563     16     CERVICAL          ❻
              B
              B              0.6125     16     COLORECTAL


                          Least Squares Means

                                   Standard              LSMEAN
      TYPE          HGBCH LSMEAN      Error    Pr > |t|   Number

      CERVICAL       1.05625000    0.28316806   0.0006      1
      COLORECTAL     0.61250000    0.28316806   0.0363      2
      PROSTATE       1.67500000    0.28316806   <.0001      3

                 Least Squares Means for effect TYPE
                 Pr > |t| for H0: LSMean(i)=LSMean(j)

                      Dependent Variable: HGBCH

          i/j         1            2            3

           1                     0.2741       0.1298
           2       0.2741                     0.0112          ❼
           3       0.1298       0.0112

NOTE: To ensure overall protection level, only probabilities associated
with pre-planned comparisons should be used.
```

To better understand the interaction effect, it is helpful to visualize the trends with graphics. Usually, an interaction is indicated if the response profiles cross or have markedly different slopes among the levels of the blocking factor. In Figure 7.1, graphs a, b, and c show no interaction; graphs d, e, and f depict an interaction between the group and block main effects.

FIGURE 7.1. No Interaction (a,b,c) and Interaction (d,e,f) Effects

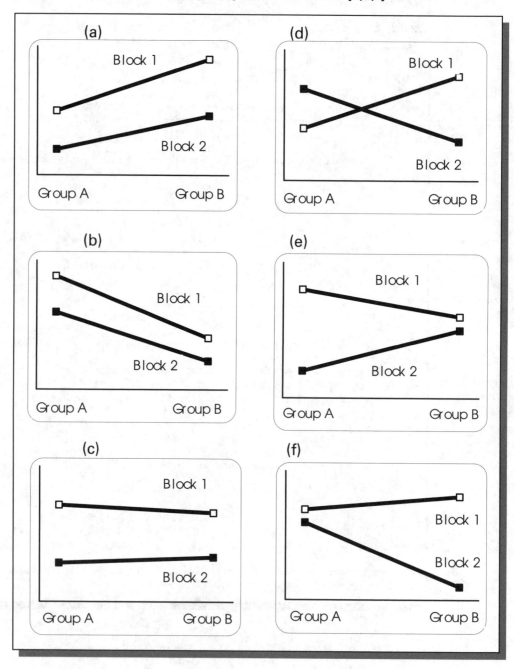

Example 7.2 shows the *two-way ANOVA* for an unbalanced layout with three treatment groups and a significant interaction.

⫽ **Example 7.2** -- Memory Function

Two investigators conducted a clinical trial to determine the effect of two doses of a new therapeutic agent on short-term memory function. A single oral dose of the test preparation was administered to subjects, who were then asked to recall items one hour after exposure to a list consisting of 15 items. The number of items correctly identified are shown in Table 7.6. A placebo group was included as a control in a parallel-group design.

TABLE 7.6. Raw Data for Example 7.2

CENTER	Placebo		30 mg		60 mg	
Dr. Abel	6	5	8	6	11	10
	5	6	12	9	7	12
	6	5	7	6	7	9
	8	5	8	11	11	15
	3	7			9	
	4	8				
Dr. Best	7	5	5	8	9	12
	4	9	6	6	12	14
	7	11	6	9	13	15
	6	4	5	11	9	12
	7	7	3	5	13	
	8					

SOLUTION

The summary statistics and ANOVA table are shown in Table 7.7:

TABLE 7.7. Summary Statistics by Dose Group for Example 7.2

| CENTER | DOSE GROUP | | |
	Placebo	30 mg	60 mg
Dr. Abel	5.67 (1.50) 12	8.38 (2.20) 8	10.11 (2.52) 9
Dr. Best	6.82 (2.09) 11	6.40 (2.32) 10	12.11 (2.03) 9

Entries in Table 7.7 are mean, (SD), and sample size.

SAS Analysis of Example 7.2

This is an unbalanced layout, and the computation of the effect sums of squares as illustrated in Example 7.1 might not produce the most appropriate tests. With an unbalanced layout, the SAS Types I, II, and III sums of squares differ, as discussed in Appendix D. This analysis focuses only on the Type III results.

The ANOVA summary table from the SAS output is shown in Table 7.8. The SAS code for generating the *two-way ANOVA* is shown following the table.

TABLE 7.8. ANOVA Summary for Example 7.2

Source	df	SS	MS	F	p-Value
Dose	2	251.42	125.71	28.43	<0.001 *
Center	1	2.23	2.23	0.50	0.481
Center-by-Dose	2	39.77	19.88	4.50	0.016 *
Error	53	234.36	4.42		
Total	58	533.93			

* Significant (p < 0.05)

SAS Code for Example 7.2

```
DATA MEMRY;
    INPUT DOSE $  CENTER $  Y @@;
    DATALINES;
 0 A  6    0 A  5    0 A  6    0 A  8    0 A  3
 0 A  4    0 A  5    0 A  6    0 A  5    0 A  5
 0 A  7    0 A  8    0 B  7    0 B  4    0 B  7
 0 B  6    0 B  7    0 B  8    0 B  5    0 B  9
 0 B 11    0 B  4    0 B  7   30 A  8   30 A 12
30 A  7   30 A  8   30 A  6   30 A  9   30 A  6
30 A 11   30 B  5   30 B  6   30 B  6   30 B  5
30 B  3   30 B  8   30 B  6   30 B  9   30 B 11
30 B  5   60 A 11   60 A  7   60 A  7   60 A 11
60 A  9   60 A 10   60 A 12   60 A  9   60 A 15
60 B  9   60 B 12   60 B 13   60 B  9   60 B 13
60 B 12   60 B 14   60 B 15   60 B 12
;

PROC GLM DATA = MEMRY;
    CLASS CENTER DOSE;
    MODEL Y = DOSE CENTER CENTER*DOSE;
        LSMEANS DOSE/PDIFF STDERR;
    TITLE1 'Two-Way ANOVA';
    TITLE2 'EXAMPLE 7.2: Memory Function';
RUN;
```

Output 7.2. SAS Output for Example 7.2

```
                        Two-Way ANOVA
                EXAMPLE 7.2: Memory Function

                    The GLM Procedure
                  Class Level Information

            Class           Levels    Values
            CENTER             2      A B
            DOSE               3      0 30 60


                Number of observations     59


Dependent Variable: Y
                            Sum of
Source              DF      Squares     Mean Square   F Value   Pr > F
Model                5   299.5763953     59.9152791     13.55   <.0001
Error               53   234.3558081      4.4218077
Corrected Total     58   533.9322034


          R-Square    Coeff Var    Root MSE     Y Mean
          0.561076    26.17421     2.102809     8.033898


Source          DF     Type I SS    Mean Square   F Value    Pr > F
DOSE             2   256.6302710    128.3151355     29.02    <.0001
CENTER           1     3.1777983      3.1777983      0.72    0.4004
CENTER*DOSE      2    39.7683260     19.8841630      4.50    0.0157


Source          DF   Type III SS    Mean Square   F Value    Pr > F
DOSE             2   251.4197307    125.7098653     28.43    <.0001     ❽
CENTER           1     2.2272995      2.2272995      0.50    0.4810
CENTER*DOSE      2    39.7683260     19.8841630      4.50    0.0157     ❾


                    Least Squares Means

                               Standard               LSMEAN
    DOSE      Y LSMEAN           Error    Pr > |t|     Number

     0       6.2424242        0.4388811   <.0001          1
    30       7.3875000        0.4987251   <.0001          2
    60      11.1111111        0.4956369   <.0001          3

            Least Squares Means for effect DOSE
                Pr > |t| for H0: LSMean(i)=LSMean(j)

                    Dependent Variable: Y
         i/j          1            2            3
          1                      0.0906       <.0001
          2       0.0906                      <.0001
          3       <.0001       <.0001

NOTE: To ensure overall protection level, only probabilities associated
      with pre-planned comparisons should be used.
```

The Dose effect is seen to be highly significant (p=<.0001) ❽, which indicates differences among the dose groups. However, whenever the interaction term is significant, caution must be used in the interpretation of the main effects. In this example, the F-value for the Center-by-Dose interaction is significant (p=0.0157) ❾, which indicates that the Dose response is not the same for each study center. This interaction is shown in Figure 7.2.

FIGURE 7.2. Interaction in Example 7.2

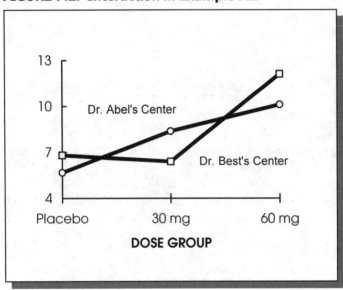

In the presence of such an interaction, you would typically perform analyses separately within each center. To do this, *a one-way ANOVA* (Chapter 6) can be used for Example 7.2. Such an analysis results in a significant Dose effect for both centers with pairwise comparisons. (See Table 7.9.)

TABLE 7.9. Results of Pairwise Dose Comparisons for Example 7.2

CENTER	----------- Pairwise Comparisons ------------		
	Placebo vs. 30 mg	Placebo vs. 60 mg	30 mg vs. 60 mg
Dr. Abel	*	*	NS
Dr. Best	NS	*	*

Asterisk (*)=significant (p < 0.05), NS = not significant (p > 0.05)

From Table 7.9, you can conclude that a difference exists between the 60 mg dose and the placebo, but the overall efficacy of the 30 mg dose is in question. When significant interactions are found, the analyst can use exploratory analyses to try to better understand or to explain the interaction. In this case, further analyses might reveal, for example, that Dr. Best's patients are older and have greater difficulty with short-term memory, thereby requiring a higher dose of medication.

7.4   Details & Notes

▶ **7.4.1.**   In Example 7.1, the main benefit of including Cancer Type as an ANOVA factor in the analysis is to improve the precision of the treatment comparisons by identifying the large variations among Cancer Types and removing them from the estimate of the error variation (MSE). Indeed, if the *one-way ANOVA* had been used to compare treatments (ignoring Cancer Type), you might verify that the result would be non-rejection of the hypothesis of equal treatment means based on an *F-test* of 3.79 (p = 0.058). This analysis produces an inflated estimate of the MSE of 1.39, compared with an MSE of 1.28 when using the more appropriate *two-way ANOVA*.

▶ **7.4.2.**   In developing the concept of analysis of variance in this and other chapters, manual calculations are demonstrated for balanced layouts to emphasize how the within- and between-group variability estimates arise and how the results are interpreted. The computing methods shown in Example 7.1 show the deviations used in obtaining the effect sums of squares. Formulas similar to those used in the *one-way ANOVA* (see Section 6.4.10) can also be used for the *two-way* (and higher) *ANOVA* with balanced layouts. However, such equations are not often used. Statistical packages obviate the need for manual calculations in the balanced case and are mandatory for most practical applications that involve unbalanced layouts.

▶ **7.4.3**   In clinical trials, there is almost always imbalance in two-way layouts, even if the study were designed as a balanced one. This might be due to patients who dropped out or missed visits, data exclusion, or some other reason that results in missing data. In such cases, there might be more than one way to compute the sum of squares for the ANOVA effects, as seen by the different SAS types of sums of squares.

In the unbalanced case, the total sum of squares cannot be broken down as easily into additive components due to the sources of variation. A number of statistical methods have been devised to circumvent the problems that arise with sample size imbalance. The method of 'fitting constants' and the method of 'weighted squares of means' are two classical approaches, which can be explored further by the interested reader (Bancroft, 1968). Each method tests a slightly different hypothesis, as framed in terms of cell means. The method that should be used is the method that corresponds most closely to the assumptions and hypotheses relevant to the given problem.

In SAS, Type III corresponds to the method of weighted squares of means and is often the method of choice for the analysis of clinical data. The hypothesis tested by using Type III results is the equality of treatment group means, where each group mean is the unweighted average of the cell means that comprise that group. The group mean does not depend on the cell sample sizes (LS-mean), as is the case with Type I and II. In cases of extreme imbalance, such as a large number of patients in some centers and a very small number of patients in other centers, the use of Type III results for the treatment effect when center is used as a blocking factor should be questioned when finite populations must be assumed. LS-means are discussed in Appendix C (Section C.3), and interpretation of the various types of sums of squares is discussed in Appendix D.

▶ **7.4.4.**   In a multi-center trial, there might be differences among study centers due to such things as geography, climate, general population characteristics, or specialty differences at specific centers. If you ignore these differences, the variation due to Study Centers will be included in the estimate of experimental error (MSE). As seen in Chapter 6, "*One-Way ANOVA*", potential treatment differences become obscured with large values of MSE. Therefore, you want to try to identify all important sources of variation that can be factored out of the experimental error to yield a more precise test for treatment effect. In the case of a multi-center study, 'Study Center' is usually considered an important factor in analyzing treatment differences because of known or suspected differences among centers.

▶ **7.4.5.**   Sometimes, including a block effect with a *two-way ANOVA* results in a less precise treatment comparison of the group means than would result by ignoring the blocking factor and using the *one-way ANOVA*. Because the error degrees of freedom are reduced when including the Block variable as a source of variation in the *ANOVA*, the MSE might increase appreciably if among-block variation is small and the number of levels of the blocking factor is large. With an increased MSE, the *F-test* for GROUP is smaller due to the reduced degrees of freedom for error, therefore, the precision of the group comparisons decreases. Thus, using ANOVA should avoid including blocking factors that have a large number of homogeneous levels.

▶ **7.4.6.**   Pairwise comparisons of group means are often conducted by using the PDIFF option in the LSMEANS statement in PROC GLM, as shown in Examples 7.1 and 7.2. This method compares the LS-means of the levels of the factor specified in the LSMEANS statement using '*t-test* type' procedures. To avoid greatly altering the tests' significance levels, only pre-planned comparisons should be made. Multiple comparison procedures controlling for the overall significance level should be used when the number of comparisons becomes large (see Appendix E).

▶ **7.4.7.** The MSE is an estimate of the variance among similar patients. Because patients are most similar within Group-by-Block cells, the MSE is an average or pooled variance over all cells of the within-cell variances. However, if each cell has only one measurement ($n_{ij} = 1$ for all i,j), the within-cell variability cannot be estimated. In such cases, the analysis can proceed by assuming there is no interaction and using the interaction sum of squares as the SSE.

Even in layouts with cells that have more than one measurement, if it is known or can be safely assumed that there is no interaction between main effects, the interaction can be ignored as a source in the *ANOVA*. The sum of squares for interaction is then absorbed into the SSE. Although this increases the SSE, the number of degrees of freedom also increases. If the interaction effect is really insignificant, then increasing the degrees of freedom for MSE might more than offset the SSE increase with the possible net effect of gaining sensitivity in testing the main effects.

▶ **7.4.8.** An *ANOVA* can be easily extended to include more than two factors with the analyses by following the same pattern as demonstrated in this chapter. For example, you can conduct a *three-way ANOVA* on the data set TRIAL in Chapter 3 by using the factors Treatment Group (TRT), Study Center (CENTER), and patient gender (SEX). Using the GLM procedure, the following SAS statements show a model that includes all two-way and the three-way interactions:

```
PROC GLM DATA = TRIAL;
    CLASS TRT CENTER SEX;
    MODEL SCORE = TRT CENTER SEX
                  TRT*CENTER TRT*SEX CENTER*SEX
                  TRT*CENTER*SEX;
```

The number of possible interactions increases markedly as new main effects are added to the model. Higher-order interactions and even some two-way interactions might not be meaningful or might be difficult to explain, and including a large number of interactions can decrease the degrees of freedom available for estimation of the error (MSE). For these reasons, only meaningful interactions or interactions that might lead to important subgroup differences should be considered when performing the final analysis.

▶ **7.4.9.** There are two types of effects in an ANOVA model, the 'fixed' effect and the 'random' effect. All the effects in the examples in this chapter are assumed to be fixed, that is, having pre-specified levels, with the goal of comparing specific levels of that effect. Treatment Group, for example, is normally a fixed effect since you want to compare responses among the fixed groups or dose levels. A random effect is one whose levels are randomly selected from a large population of levels and are not amenable to *a priori* specification. Study Center, for example, might be considered a random effect if a sample of centers is randomly selected from a large number of centers available to conduct the study.

A statistical model associated with a *two-way* or *higher-order ANOVA* is called a 'fixed-effects' model if all effects are fixed, a 'random-effects' model if all effects are random, and a 'mixed' model if there is a mixture of fixed and random effects. The *two-way ANOVA* that includes Treatment Group and Study Center as factors is generally considered a fixed-effects model, especially if only a small number of centers is used. If the centers that are included are selected from a large number of centers that might qualify to conduct the study, Study Center can be considered a random effect, in which case, the *two-way ANOVA* model is mixed.

When there is no interest in the interaction in the *two-way ANOVA*, the analysis of treatment comparisons is identical whether Study Center is considered fixed or random. If, however, Study Center is considered a random effect and the interaction term is included (interaction also being considered a random effect), then the test for treatment effect requires more work. In the balanced model, the *F-test* for Treatment Group is the ratio of the mean square for Treatment to the mean square for interaction. The *F-test* can be performed by using the TEST statement in PROC GLM in SAS. This is because model assumptions are different for fixed and random effects, and the *F-tests* are based on expected mean-squares.

A RANDOM statement following the MODEL statement specifies which effects are random. When one or more effects are identified as random, the SAS output will show the form of the expected mean-squares. In the unbalanced model, the analyst should use these forms to determine the most appropriate effects to use in the TEST statement.

The complexities involved in the analysis of higher order unbalanced mixed models are best handled by using PROC MIXED in SAS.

> Note: An excellent reference for the analysis of mixed models for the more advanced reader is "*SAS System for Mixed Models*" by Littell, Milliken, Stroup, and Wolfinger, which was written under the SAS Books by Users program.

CHAPTER 8

Repeated Measures ANOVA

8.1 Introduction

Repeated measures refer to multiple measurements taken from the same experimental unit, such as serial evaluations over time on the same patient. Special attention is given to these types of measurements because they cannot be considered independent. In particular, the analysis must make provisions for the correlation structure.

Most clinical studies require outpatients to return to the clinic for multiple visits during the trial with response measurements made at each. This is the most common example of *repeated measures*, sometimes called 'longitudinal' data. These repeated response measurements can be used to characterize a response profile over time. One of the main questions the researcher asks is whether the mean response profile for one treatment group is the same as for another treatment group or a placebo group. This situation might arise, for example, when trying to determine if the onset of effect or rate of improvement due to a new treatment is faster than that of a competitor's treatment. Comparison of response profiles can be tested with a single *F-test* from a *repeated measures analysis*.

8.2 Synopsis

In general, you have g independent groups of patients each of whom are subjected to repeated measurements of the same response variable, y, at t equally spaced time periods. Letting n_i represent the number of patients in Group i (i=1,2,...,g), the layout for g=3 groups is shown in Table 8.1. In comparative trials, the groups often represent different parallel treatment groups or dose levels of a drug.

TABLE 8.1. Layout for a Repeated Measures Design with 3 Groups

Group	Patient	Time 1	2	...	t
1	1	y_{111}	y_{112}	...	y_{11t}
	2	y_{121}	y_{122}	...	y_{12t}
	...	...	...	...	...
	n_1	y_{1n_11}	y_{1n_12}	...	y_{1n_1t}
2	1	y_{211}	y_{212}	...	y_{21t}
	2	y_{221}	y_{222}	...	y_{22t}
	...	...	...	...	...
	n_2	y_{2n_21}	y_{2n_22}	...	y_{2n_2t}
3	1	y_{311}	y_{312}	...	y_{31t}
	2	y_{321}	y_{322}	...	y_{32t}
	...	...	...	...	...
	n_3	y_{3n_31}	y_{3n_32}	...	y_{3n_3t}

There are a number of analytic approaches for handling *repeated measures*. First, examine a 'univariate' method that uses the same *ANOVA* concepts discussed in Chapter 7. A 'multivariate' method, which treats the repeated measurements as a multivariate response vector, may also be used in many circumstances. You might also want to look at modeling techniques that use the MIXED and GENMOD procedures in SAS, which are often preferable if there are missing data.

The 'Univariate' Approach

Consider the Group, Patient, and Time effects shown in Table 8.1 as three factors in an *ANOVA*. Using the ideas discussed in Chapter 7, you can examine the variability within and among these factors, noting that the Time effect represents correlated measurements. Notice that the response might vary among groups, among patients within groups, and among the different measurement times. Therefore, you include a Group effect, a Patient (within-Group) effect, and a Time effect as sources of variation in the *ANOVA*. In addition, the *repeated measures analysis* using a univariate approach includes the Group-by-Time interaction.

As with other *ANOVA* methods, you assume normality of the response measurements and variance homogeneity among groups. In addition, the univariate *ANOVA* requires that each pair of repeated measures has the same correlation, a feature known as 'compound symmetry'.

A significant interaction means that changes in response over time differ among groups, i.e., a significant difference in response profiles, as illustrated in Figure 8.1. When the profiles are similar among groups (i.e., no Group-by-Time interaction), tests for the Group effect measure the deviation from the hypothesis of equality of mean responses among groups, 'averaged' over time. This test using the *repeated measures analysis* method might be more sensitive to detecting group differences than using a *one-way ANOVA* to compare groups at a single time point. However, the Group effect might not be meaningful if there is a significant Time effect. The Time effect is a measure of deviation from the hypothesis of equality of mean responses among the measurement times for all groups combined. *Repeated measures ANOVA* also provides a test of this hypothesis.

In the simplest case of *repeated measures ANOVA*, which is presented here, the Group and the evaluation Time are cross-classified main effects. However, the samples are not independent among the Group-Time cells, because measurements over time that are taken from the same patient are correlated. To account for this correlation, the Patient effect must be included as a source of variation in the *ANOVA*.

With $N = n_1 + n_2 + ... + n_g$, the *repeated measures ANOVA* summary table takes the following form:

TABLE 8.2. ANOVA Summary for Repeated-Measures Design

SOURCE	df	SS	MS	F
GROUP	g-1	SSG	MSG	$F_G = MSG / MSP(G)$
PATIENT (within GROUP)	N-g	SSP(G)	MSP(G)	--
TIME	t-1	SST	MST	$F_T = MST / MSE$
GROUP-by-TIME	(g-1)(t-1)	SSGT	MSGT	$F_{GT} = MSGT / MSE$
Error	(N-g)(t-1)	SSE	MSE	--
Total	Nt-1	TOT(SS)		

For the balanced layout ($n_1 = n_2 = ... = n_g$), the sums of squares can be computed in a manner similar to that used for the *two-way ANOVA* (Chapter 7). These computations are shown in Example 8.1. As usual, the mean squares (MS) are found by dividing the sums of squares (SS) by the corresponding degrees of freedom.

Variation from patient-to-patient is one type of random error, as estimated by the mean square for Patient (within Group). If there is no difference among groups, the between-group variation merely reflects patient-to-patient variation. Therefore, under the null hypothesis of no Group effect, MSG and MSP(G) are independent estimates of the among-patient variability, so that F_G has the F-distribution with g-1 upper and N-g lower degrees of freedom.

If there is no Time effect, the mean square for Time (MST) is an estimate of within-patient variability, as is the error variation, MSE. The ratio of these independent estimates (F_T) is the F-statistic used to test the hypothesis of no Time effect. Similarly, the interaction mean square, which is also a measure of within-patient variation under H_0, is compared to the MSE to test for a significant Group-by-Time interaction.

Sample response profiles are shown in Figure 8.1 for 2 drug groups and 4 time periods. As depicted, treatment differences depend on time if the profiles differ.

FIGURE 8.1. Sample Profiles of Drug Response

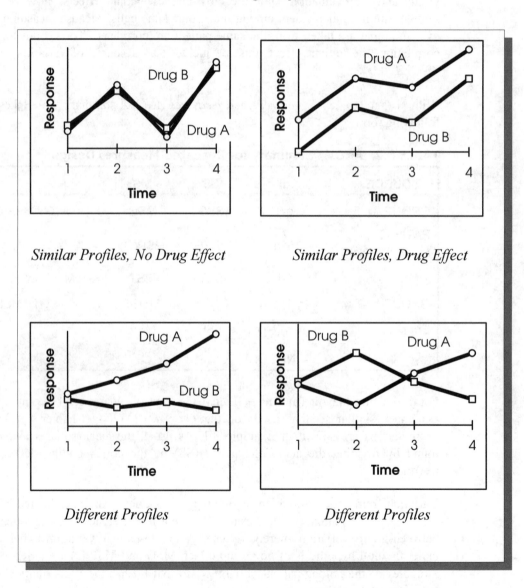

8.3   Examples

The following example is used to demonstrate the 'univariate' approach to the *repeated measures ANOVA* in the balanced case.

⁄⁄ **Example 8.1** -- Arthritic Discomfort Following Vaccine

A pilot study was conducted in 8 patients to evaluate the effect of a new vaccine on discomfort due to arthritic outbreaks. Four patients were randomly assigned to receive an active vaccine, and 4 patients were to receive a placebo. The patients were asked to return to the clinic monthly for 3 months and evaluate their comfort level with routine daily chores during the preceding month using a scale of 0 (no discomfort) to 10 (maximum discomfort). Eligibility criteria required patients to have a rating of at least an 8 in the month prior to vaccination. The rating data are shown in Table 8.3. Is there any evidence of a difference in response profiles between the active and placebo vaccines?

TABLE 8.3.   Raw Data for Example 8.1

Vaccine	Patient Number	Month 1	Month 2	Month 3
Active	101	6	3	0
	103	7	3	1
	104	4	1	2
	107	8	4	3
Placebo	102	6	5	5
	105	9	4	6
	106	5	3	4
	108	6	2	3

(Visit)

Solution

Using a 'univariate' *repeated measures ANOVA*, you identify Vaccine as the Group effect and Visit as the Time effect. The Patient-within-Vaccine and Vaccine-by-Visit effects are also include in the *ANOVA*. The sum of squares for each of these sources can be computed in the same manner as demonstrated previously (Chapters 6 and 7). First, you obtain the marginal means, as shown in Table 8.4.

TABLE 8.4. Marginal Summary Statistics for Example 8.1

Vaccine	Patient Number	Month 1	Month 2	Month 3	Mean
		---------------- Visit ----------------			
Active	101	6	3	0	3.000
	103	7	3	1	3.667
	104	4	1	2	2.333
	107	8	4	3	5.000
	Mean	6.25	2.75	1.50	3.500
	(SD)	(1.71)	(1.26)	(1.29)	
Placebo	102	6	5	5	5.333
	105	9	4	6	6.333
	106	5	3	4	4.000
	108	6	2	3	3.667
	Mean	6.50	3.50	4.50	4.833
	(SD)	(1.73)	(1.29)	(1.29)	
	Combined Mean	6.375	3.125	3.000	4.167

The Vaccine sum of squares is proportional to the sum of squared deviations of the group means from the overall mean:

$$SS(\text{Vaccine}) = (12 \cdot (3.500 - 4.167)^2) +$$
$$(12 \cdot (4.833 - 4.167)^2) = 10.667$$

This is based on 1 degree of freedom because there are two levels of the Group factor Vaccine.

The sum of squares for Visit, based on 2 degrees of freedom, and the Vaccine-by-Visit interaction, also with 2 degrees of freedom, can be computed as follows:

$$SS(\text{Visit}) = (8 \cdot (6.375 - 4.167)^2) +$$
$$(8 \cdot (3.125 - 4.167)^2) +$$
$$(8 \cdot (3.000 - 4.167)^2) = 58.583$$

$$SS(\text{Vaccine-by-Visit}) = (4 \cdot (6.25 - 4.167)^2) +$$
$$(4 \cdot (2.75 - 4.167)^2) +$$
$$(4 \cdot (1.50 - 4.167)^2) +$$
$$(4 \cdot (6.50 - 4.167)^2) +$$
$$(4 \cdot (3.50 - 4.167)^2) +$$
$$(4 \cdot (4.50 - 4.167)^2) -$$
$$SS(\text{Vaccine}) - SS(\text{Visit})$$

$$= 77.833 - 10.667 - 58.583 = 8.583$$

The Patient (within Vaccine) sum of squares is found by summing the squared deviations between the mean response for each patient and the Vaccine Group mean within which that patient is nested. Within each Vaccine Group, the factor Patient has 3 degrees of freedom, so for the two vaccine groups, you have 6 degrees of freedom for Patient(Vaccine).

$$
\begin{aligned}
\text{SS(Patient(Vaccine))} = \; & (3 \cdot (3.000 - 3.500)^2) \; + \\
& (3 \cdot (3.667 - 3.500)^2) \; + \\
& (3 \cdot (2.333 - 3.500)^2) \; + \\
& (3 \cdot (5.000 - 3.500)^2) \; + \\
& (3 \cdot (5.333 - 4.833)^2) \; + \\
& (3 \cdot (6.333 - 4.833)^2) \; + \\
& (3 \cdot (4.000 - 4.833)^2) \; + \\
& (3 \cdot (3.667 - 4.833)^2) \\
\\
= \; & 25.333
\end{aligned}
$$

The total sum of squares (based on 23 degrees of freedom) is found by summing the squared deviations of each observation from the overall mean.

$$
\begin{aligned}
\text{SS(Total)} \quad = \quad & (\,(6 - 4.167)^2) \; + \\
& (\,(3 - 4.167)^2) \; + \\
& (\,(0 - 4.167)^2) \; + \\
& (\,(7 - 4.167)^2) \; + \\
& \quad \ldots \qquad + \\
& (\,(3 - 4.167)^2) \\
\\
= \quad & 115.333
\end{aligned}
$$

Finally, because this is a balanced layout, the error sum of squares (SSE) can be found by subtraction.

$$
\begin{aligned}
\text{SSE} \quad = \quad & \text{SS(Total)} \\
& - \text{SS(Vaccine)} \\
& - \text{SS(Patient(Vaccine))} \\
& - \text{SS(Visit)} \\
& - \text{SS(Vaccine-by-Visit)} \\
\\
& = 115.333 - 10.667 - 25.333 - 58.583 - 8.583 \\
& = 12.167
\end{aligned}
$$

The ANOVA table can now be completed as shown in Table 8.5. The mean squares for each effect are found by dividing the sum of squares (SS) by the degrees of freedom. The *F-tests* are the ratios of the effect mean squares to the appropriate error associated with that effect.

TABLE 8.5. ANOVA Summary for Example 8.1

SOURCE	df	SS	MS	F
Vaccine	1	10.667	10.667	2.53
Patient(Vaccine)	6	25.333	4.222	--
Visit	2	58.583	29.292	28.89*
Vaccine-by-Visit	2	8.583	4.292	4.23*
Error	12	12.167	1.014	--
Total	23	115.333		

* Significant (p < 0.05)

The *F-test* for the Vaccine effect is the ratio of the mean square for Vaccine to the mean square for Patient(Vaccine), F = 10.667/4.222 = 2.53. The F-values for Visit and Vaccine-by-Visit are found by the ratios of the mean squares for these effects to the mean square error (MSE = 1.014).

The null hypothesis of similar response profiles over time for each of the vaccine groups is tested by the Vaccine-by-Visit interaction. For two treatment groups as used in this example, the hypothesis can be expressed as the simultaneous equality of Treatment Group differences at each time point. That is, if Δ_j represents the difference in mean responses between the active and placebo groups at Month j (e.g., $\Delta_j = \mu_{1j} - \mu_{2j}$) for j = 1, 2, or 3, then the test summary can be expressed as

null hypothesis: H_0: $\Delta_1 = \Delta_2 = \Delta_3$

alt. hypothesis: H_A: not H_0

test statistic: F = MS(Vaccine-by-Visit) / MSE = 4.23

decision rule: reject H_0 if $F > F_{12}^{2}(0.05) = 3.89$

conclusion: Because 4.23 > 3.89, you reject H_0 and conclude that there is a significant Vaccine Group-by-Visit interaction.

Because Vaccine Group differences are based on the study month, further analyses can be performed by depicting the mean responses over time in graphical format (see Figure 8.2) and by using linear contrasts to compare differences between vaccine groups in the changes from successive time points. A *one-way ANOVA* (Chapter 6) can also be used to test for the Vaccine effect at each visit.

In the ANOVA summary table, the Visit effect is also seen to be significant. This means that the average responses for the combined vaccine groups differ among evaluation months. The *F-test* for the Vaccine effect can be interpreted as a comparison of mean responses between vaccine groups, 'averaged' over all measurement times. With a non-significant F-value of 2.53 for the Vaccine effect and a significant interaction, further analyses, as suggested above, are required prior to forming any conclusions with regard to the main effects.

SAS Analysis of Example 8.1

In the SAS code for analyzing the data for Example 8.1, the input data set ARTHR is transformed to a new format with 1 observation per record in the data set DISCOM. This data set is displayed by using PROC PRINT (see Output 8.1) ❶.

PROC GLM in SAS is applied to this data set by using a MODEL statement that includes effects for Vaccine Group (VACGRP), Time (VISIT), and Patient (PAT) nested within Vaccine Group. These effects must be designated as class variables in the CLASS statement ❷. The interaction is specified in the MODEL statement as VACGRP*VISIT. The SS3 option is used in the MODEL statement to request only the Type III sums of squares.

As shown in Output 8.1, the MSE verifies the computation 1.014 ❸. Notice that SAS automatically computes F-values for each model effect by using the MSE as the denominator, unless otherwise specified. The programmer must tell SAS to test the Group effect (VACGRP) against the Patient-within-Group (PAT(VACGRP)) 'error' by using the TEST statement ❹. The resulting F-value of 2.53 ❺ is the appropriate *F-test* for the null hypothesis of no Vaccine Group effect. The F-value 10.52 for VACGRP, which is shown in the output, is not meaningful for a *repeated measures ANOVA*. The F-value 4.16 for PAT(VACGRP) can also be ignored because this tests for a difference among patients within each group and will often be inconsequentially significant. The significant Vaccine-by-Visit interaction ❻ suggests that the difference between treatments is time-related, as was previously discovered.

SAS Code for Example 8.1

```
DATA ARTHR;
    INPUT VACGRP $  PAT MO1 MO2 MO3 ;
    DATALINES;
ACT 101 6 3 0
ACT 103 7 3 1
ACT 104 4 1 2
ACT 107 8 4 3
PBO 102 6 5 5
PBO 105 9 4 6
PBO 106 5 3 4
PBO 108 6 2 3
;
```

```
DATA DISCOM; SET ARTHR;
    KEEP VACGRP PAT VISIT SCORE;
    SCORE = MO1; VISIT = 1; OUTPUT;
    SCORE = MO2; VISIT = 2; OUTPUT;
    SCORE = MO3; VISIT = 3; OUTPUT;
RUN;

PROC PRINT DATA = DISCOM;                               ❶
    VAR VACGRP PAT VISIT SCORE;
    TITLE1 'Repeated-Measures ANOVA';
    TITLE2 'Example 8.1: Arthritic Discomfort Following Vaccine';
RUN;

PROC GLM DATA = DISCOM;
    CLASS VACGRP PAT VISIT;                             ❷
    MODEL SCORE = VACGRP PAT(VACGRP) VISIT VACGRP*VISIT/SS3;
    RANDOM PAT(VACGRP);
    TEST H=VACGRP E=PAT(VACGRP);                        ❹
    QUIT;
RUN;
```

OUTPUT 8.1. SAS Output for Example 8.1

```
                    Repeated-Measures ANOVA
         Example 8.1:  Arthritic Discomfort Following Vaccine

            Obs    VACGRP    PAT    VISIT    SCORE

              1     ACT      101      1        6
              2     ACT      101      2        3
              3     ACT      101      3        0
              4     ACT      103      1        7
              5     ACT      103      2        3
              6     ACT      103      3        1
              7     ACT      104      1        4
              8     ACT      104      2        1
              9     ACT      104      3        2
             10     ACT      107      1        8
             11     ACT      107      2        4
             12     ACT      107      3        3      ❶
             13     PBO      102      1        6
             14     PBO      102      2        5
             15     PBO      102      3        5
             16     PBO      105      1        9
             17     PBO      105      2        4
             18     PBO      105      3        6
             19     PBO      106      1        5
             20     PBO      106      2        3
             21     PBO      106      3        4
             22     PBO      108      1        6
             23     PBO      108      2        2
             24     PBO      108      3        3
```

OUTPUT 8.1. SAS Output for Example 8.1 (*continued*)

```
                    Repeated-Measures ANOVA
        Example 8.1:  Arthritic Discomfort Following Vaccine

                      The GLM Procedure

                   Class Level Information

        Class          Levels    Values

        VACGRP             2      ACT PBO
        PAT                8      101 102 103 104 105 106 107 108
        VISIT              3      1 2 3

                Number of observations    24


Dependent Variable: SCORE
                            Sum of
Source            DF        Squares    Mean Square    F Value    Pr > F

Model             11      103.1666667    9.3787879       9.25    0.0003
Error             12       12.1666667    1.0138889  ❸
Corrected Total   23      115.3333333


           R-Square     Coeff Var     Root MSE     SCORE Mean
           0.894509     24.16609      1.006920     4.166667


Source            DF     Type III SS    Mean Square    F Value    Pr > F

VACGRP             1    10.66666667    10.66666667      10.52    0.0070
PAT(VACGRP)        6    25.33333333     4.22222222       4.16    0.0171
VISIT              2    58.58333333    29.29166667      28.89    <.0001
VACGRP*VISIT       2     8.58333333     4.29166667       4.23  ❻ 0.0406


Source                    Type III Expected Mean Square

VACGRP                    Var(Error) + 3 Var(PAT(VACGRP)) +  ❼
                          Q(VACGRP,VACGRP*VISIT)
PAT(VACGRP)               Var(Error) + 3 Var(PAT(VACGRP))
VISIT                     Var(Error) + Q(VISIT,VACGRP*VISIT)
VACGRP*VISIT              Var(Error) + Q(VACGRP*VISIT)


Tests of Hypotheses Using the Type III MS for PAT(VACGRP) as an
Error Term

Source     DF    Type III SS    Mean Square    F Value      Pr > F

VACGRP      1    10.66666667    10.66666667       2.53  ❺ 0.1631
```

The 'Multivariate' Approach

The methodology demonstrated in Example 8.1 is a 'univariate' approach to *repeated measures analysis* and, as noted, requires the assumption of compound symmetry. This assumption is often not valid, especially if the trial is lengthy or time points are unequally spaced, because measurements taken farther apart in time might be less correlated than those taken closer together. Erroneous conclusions might result if the 'univariate' approach is used under violation of the assumption of compound symmetry.

A 'multivariate' approach can sometimes be used to circumvent this situation. This approach uses the repeated measurements as multivariate response vectors, and is more robust when the assumption of compound symmetry is violated.

The SAS code needed to analyze Example 8.1 using the 'multivariate' approach is shown next. This analysis uses the data set ARTHR, which is in the correct format for multivariate analysis. Notice that the ODS statement is used to customize the output (see Section 8.4.16).

> Note: For details about using ODS, see "The Complete Guide to the SAS Output Delivery System, Version 8".

SAS Code for Example 8.1 – 'Multivariate' Approach

```
PROC PRINT DATA = ARTHR;                              ❽
    VAR VACGRP PAT MO1 MO2 MO3;
RUN;

ODS EXCLUDE
    PartialCorr
    ErrorSSCP;

PROC GLM DATA = ARTHR;
    CLASS VACGRP;
    MODEL MO1 MO2 MO3 = VACGRP / SS3;  ❾
    REPEATED VISIT PROFILE / PRINTE SUMMARY;
    TITLE3 '[Multivariate Approach]';
    QUIT;
RUN;
```

PROC PRINT is used to display the data set shown in Output 8.2 ❽. The analysis is performed with the GLM procedure, which can be used for the 'multivariate' as well as the 'univariate' approach. The MODEL statement is specified using the responses at each time point (MO1, MO2, MO3) as dependent variables (i.e., included before the equal sign(=)) ❾. The REPEATED statement specifies that these dependent variables are repeated observations and provides SAS with a name for the repeated factor, in this case, VISIT. The PROFILE option is used to compare successive changes among groups (see details in Section 8.4.7). When the PRINTE option is specified in the REPEATED statement, the SAS output includes a *sphericity test* (indicated as Mauchly's Criterion) applied to a set of orthogonal components. This test is based on a chi-square approximation, and significant values indicate departure from the assumption of compound symmetry. For this example, the *sphericity tests* are not significant ❿.

When there is no evidence to contradict the assumption of compound symmetry, as in this case, the 'univariate' results previously obtained can and should be used. The 'multivariate' approach is known to produce overly conservative results when the compound symmetry assumption is satisfied, especially with small sample sizes. The output confirms this, as both the VISIT ⓫ and the VISIT*VACGRP ⓬ effects have less significance (i.e., greater p-values) than obtained by the 'univariate' approach, namely 0.0033 vs. 0.0001 for VISIT and 0.1317 vs. 0.0406 for VISIT*VACGRP. In fact, the interaction depicted by a plot of the means (shown in Figure 8.2) goes undetected when the 'multivariate' approach is used.

FIGURE 8.2. Response Profiles (Example 8.1)

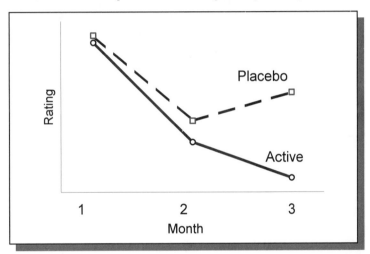

OUTPUT 8.2. SAS Output for Example 8.1 – 'Multivariate' Approach

```
                    Repeated-Measures ANOVA
       Example 8.1:  Arthritic Discomfort Following Vaccine
                                  [Multivariate Approach]



          Obs     VACGRP     PAT     MO1     MO2     MO3

           1       ACT       101      6       3       0
           2       ACT       103      7       3       1
           3       ACT       104      4       1       2
           4       ACT       107      8       4       3          ❽
           5       PBO       102      6       5       5
           6       PBO       105      9       4       6
           7       PBO       106      5       3       4
           8       PBO       108      6       2       3
```

OUTPUT 8.2. SAS Output for Example 8.1 – 'Multivariate' Approach
(*continued*)

```
                         The GLM Procedure

                      Class Level Information

                  Class        Levels     Values
                  VACGRP          2        ACT PBO

                   Number of observations     8
Dependent Variable: MO1
                               Sum of
Source                DF       Squares     Mean Square   F Value   Pr > F

Model                  1     0.12500000    0.12500000      0.04    0.8439
Error                  6    17.75000000    2.95833333
Corrected Total        7    17.87500000


        R-Square      Coeff Var     Root MSE      MO1 Mean
        0.006993      26.98009      1.719981      6.375000



Source                DF     Type III SS   Mean Square   F Value   Pr > F

VACGRP                 1     0.12500000    0.12500000      0.04    0.8439




Dependent Variable: MO2
                               Sum of
Source                DF       Squares     Mean Square   F Value   Pr > F

Model                  1     1.12500000    1.12500000      0.69    0.4372
Error                  6     9.75000000    1.62500000
Corrected Total        7    10.87500000


        R-Square      Coeff Var     Root MSE      MO2 Mean
        0.103448      40.79216      1.274755      3.125000



Source                DF     Type III SS   Mean Square   F Value   Pr > F
VACGRP                 1     1.12500000    1.12500000      0.69    0.4372




Dependent Variable: MO3

                               Sum of
Source                DF       Squares     Mean Square   F Value   Pr > F

Model                  1    18.00000000   18.00000000     10.80    0.0167
Error                  6    10.00000000    1.66666667
Corrected Total        7    28.00000000

        R-Square      Coeff Var     Root MSE      MO3 Mean
        0.642857      43.03315      1.290994      3.000000



Source                DF     Type III SS   Mean Square   F Value   Pr > F

VACGRP                 1    18.00000000   18.00000000     10.80    0.0167
```

OUTPUT 8.2. SAS Output for Example 8.1 – 'Multivariate' Approach (*continued*)

```
                       Repeated-Measures ANOVA
         Example 8.1:  Arthritic Discomfort Following Vaccine
                          [Multivariate Approach]

                          The GLM Procedure

                  Repeated Measures Analysis of Variance

                  Repeated Measures Level Information

          Dependent Variable        MO1       MO2       MO3
               Level of VISIT         1         2         3


                            Sphericity Tests

                                Mauchly's
        Variables            DF   Criterion      Chi-Square     Pr > ChiSq

        Transformed Variates  2   0.8962875      0.5474703       0.7605
        Orthogonal Components 2   0.9547758  ❿  0.2313939       0.8907


                Manova Test Criteria and Exact F Statistics
                   for the Hypothesis of no VISIT Effect
                H = Type III SSCP Matrix for VISIT            ⓫
                      E = Error SSCP Matrix


                      S=1      M=0      N=1.5


        Statistic               Value    F Value   Num DF   Den DF   Pr > F

        Wilks' Lambda         0.10207029   21.99      2        5     0.0033
        Pillai's Trace        0.89792971   21.99      2        5     0.0033
        Hotelling-Lawley Trace 8.79716981  21.99      2        5     0.0033
        Roy's Greatest Root   8.79716981   21.99      2        5     0.0033


                Manova Test Criteria and Exact F Statistics
                for the Hypothesis of no VISIT*VACGRP Effect
                H = Type III SSCP Matrix for VISIT*VACGRP      ⓬

                      E = Error SSCP Matrix

                      S=1      M=0      N=1.5

        Statistic               Value    F Value   Num DF   Den DF   Pr > F

        Wilks' Lambda         0.44444444    3.13      2        5     0.1317
        Pillai's Trace        0.55555556    3.13      2        5     0.1317
        Hotelling-Lawley Trace 1.25000000   3.13      2        5     0.1317
        Roy's Greatest Root   1.25000000    3.13      2        5     0.1317
```

OUTPUT 8.2. SAS Output for Example 8.1 – 'Multivariate' Approach (*continued*)

```
                            Repeated-Measures ANOVA
              Example 8.1:  Arthritic Discomfort Following Vaccine
                              [Multivariate Approach]


                              The GLM Procedure


                     Repeated Measures Analysis of Variance
                  Tests of Hypotheses for Between Subjects Effects

     Source            DF      Type III SS     Mean Square  F Value    Pr > F

     VACGRP             1      10.66666667     10.66666667     2.53    ⓭  0.1631
     Error              6      25.33333333      4.22222222


               Univariate Tests of Hypotheses for Within Subject Effects

     Source            DF      Type III SS     Mean Square   F Value   Pr > F

     VISIT             2       58.58333333     29.29166667    28.89    <.0001
     VISIT*VACGRP      2        8.58333333      4.29166667     4.23    0.0406
     Error(VISIT)      12      12.16666667      1.01388889

                                                    Adj Pr > F
                        Source                    G - G      H - F

                        VISIT                    <.0001     <.0001
                        VISIT*VACGRP             0.0433     0.0406
                        Error(VISIT)

                         Greenhouse-Geisser Epsilon     0.9567  ⓮
                         Huynh-Feldt Epsilon            1.6282


                     Analysis of Variance of Contrast Variables

     VISIT_N represents the nth successive difference in VISIT

     Contrast Variable: VISIT_1

     Source            DF      Type III SS     Mean Square   F Value   Pr > F

     Mean              1       84.50000000     84.50000000    46.09    0.0005
     VACGRP            1        0.50000000      0.50000000     0.27    0.6202 ⓯
     Error             6       11.00000000      1.83333333

     Contrast Variable: VISIT_2

     Source            DF      Type III SS     Mean Square   F Value   Pr > F

     Mean              1        0.12500000      0.12500000     0.07    0.8005
     VACGRP            1       10.12500000     10.12500000     5.65    0.0550 ⓯
     Error             6       10.75000000      1.79166667
```

Four multivariate methods due to Wilks, Pillai, Hotelling, and Roy (see Section 8.4.5) are used to obtain the *F-test* statistic for these within-patient effects. Notice that the test for the group effect (VACGRP) ❸ is the same as in the 'univariate' analysis ❺.

This example illustrates the method by which the 'multivariate' approach can be conducted, although it is not the best approach for analyzing the data in this case because of the small sample sizes and consistency with compound symmetry. Output 8.2 further shows how the 'multivariate' approach provides a series of *one-way ANOVA*'s at each time point (dependent variables MO1, MO2, and MO3), and how changes across time points can be compared. A simple execution of the ODS statement in SAS to customize the output is also shown. These points are further discussed in Section 8.4.

Additional factors can also be used in the *repeated measures analysis*. Example 8.2 shows how Study Center can be used as a blocking effect in an unbalanced *repeated measures* layout and further illustrates the 'multivariate' approach.

⁂ **Example 8.2** -- Treadmill Walking Distance in Intermittent Claudication

Patients were randomly assigned to receive either the new drug Novafylline, thought to reduce the symptoms of intermittent claudication, or a placebo in a 4-month double-blind study. The primary measurement of efficacy is the walking distance on a treadmill until discontinuation due to claudication pain. In two study centers, 38 patients underwent treadmill testing at baseline (Month-0) and at each of 4 monthly, follow-up visits. The treadmill walking distances (in meters) are shown in Table 8.6. Is there any distinction in exercise tolerance profiles between patients who receive Novafylline and those on placebo? (The 100-series patient numbers are from Center 1; the 200-series patient numbers are from Center 2).

Solution

A summary of the mean walking distances (in meters) and sample sizes is shown in Table 8.7.

Because of the sample size imbalance, the methods illustrated in Example 8.1 for manually computing the sums of squares cannot be used. In such cases, the Type III sums of squares are most efficiently computed by using matrix algebra with a program such as SAS. The 'multivariate' approach is used with PROC GLM for this example.

TABLE 8.6. Raw Data for Example 8.2

Novafylline Group						Placebo Group					
Patient Number	Treatment Month					Patient Number	Treatment Month				
	0	1	2	3	4		0	1	2	3	4
101	190	212	213	195	248	103	187	177	200	190	206
102	98	137	185	215	225	106	205	230	172	196	232
104	155	145	196	189	176	108	165	142	195	185	170
105	245	228	280	274	260	109	256	232	252	326	292
107	182	205	218	194	193	112	197	182	160	210	185
110	140	138	187	195	205	114	134	115	150	165	170
111	196	185	185	227	180	115	196	166	166	188	205
113	162	176	192	230	215	119	167	144	176	155	158
116	195	232	199	185	200	121	98	102	89	128	130
117	167	187	228	192	210						
118	123	165	145	185	215	201	167	175	122	162	125
120	105	144	119	168	165	203	123	136	147	130	135
						206	95	102	154	105	112
202	161	177	162	185	192	207	181	177	140	212	230
204	255	242	330	284	319	210	237	232	245	193	245
205	144	195	180	184	213	212	144	172	163	158	188
208	180	218	224	165	200	213	182	202	254	185	173
209	126	145	173	175	140	216	165	140	153	180	155
211	175	155	154	164	154	217	196	195	204	188	178
214	227	218	245	235	257						
215	175	197	195	182	193						

TABLE 8.7. Summary Statistics for Example 8.2

Treatment	Center	Month 0	1	2	3	4
Active	1	163.2 12	179.5 12	195.6 12	204.1 12	207.7 12
	2	180.4 8	193.4 8	207.9 8	196.8 8	208.5 8
	Combined	170.1 20	185.1 20	200.5 20	201.2 20	208.0 20
Placebo	1	178.3 9	165.6 9	173.3 9	193.7 9	194.2 9
	2	165.6 9	170.1 9	175.8 9	168.1 9	171.2 9
	Combined	171.9 18	167.8 18	174.6 18	180.9 18	182.7 18
	Total	38	38	38	38	38

In this example, patients are nested within each Treatment-by-Center cell, so that the factors Treatment, Center, and Treatment-by-Center all represent between-patient effects. The *F-tests* for these effects, therefore, are based on the Patient(within Treatment-by-Center) 'error'.

SAS Analysis of Example 8.2

As shown in the SAS code that follows, the *repeated measures* are specified as dependent variables on the left side of the equal sign (=) in the MODEL statement[16], and the between-patient effects are specified to the right of the equal sign. The REPEATED statement tells SAS that these dependent variables are *repeated measures*, and labels the time factor as MONTH [17]. The PRINTE option is used to obtain the *sphericity test* for compound symmetry. Only selected portions of the entire output are reproduced here, using one of the ODS features in SAS (see Section 8.4.16).

Unless suppressed with the NOUNI option in the MODEL statement, SAS prints the results of a *two-way ANOVA* for each time point, denoted by the dependent variables WD0, WD1, WD2, WD3, and WD4. Output 8.3 indicates no significant Treatment or Center main effects and no Treatment-by-Center interaction at any of the individual measurement times ($p > 0.05$ for each) [18].

SAS Code for Example 8.2

```
DATA WDVIS;
    INPUT TREATMNT $  PAT WD0 WD1 WD2 WD3 WD4;
    CENTER = INT(PAT/100);
    DATALINES;
ACT 101 190 212 213 195 248
ACT 102  98 137 185 215 225
ACT 104 155 145 196 189 176

(more data lines)...

PBO 216 165 140 153 180 155
PBO 217 196 195 204 188 178
;

ODS EXCLUDE
    GLM.Repeated.MANOVA.Model.Error.ErrorSSCP
    GLM.Repeated.MANOVA.Model.Error.PartialCorr
    GLM.Repeated.WithinSubject.ModelANOVA
    GLM.Repeated.WithinSubject.Epsilons;

PROC GLM DATA = WDVIS;
    CLASS TREATMNT CENTER;
    MODEL WD0 WD1 WD2 WD3 WD4 =                          ⓰
        TREATMNT CENTER TREATMNT*CENTER / SS3;
        REPEATED MONTH CONTRAST(1) / PRINTE SUMMARY;    ⓱
    TITLE1 'Repeated-Measures ANOVA';
    TITLE2 'Example 8.2:  Treadmill Walking Distance in
            Intermittent Claudication';
    QUIT;
RUN;
```

The 'multivariate' analysis indicates a significant test for compound symmetry based on the *sphericity tests* (p=0.0103) ⓳, which would invalidate the 'univariate' approach as demonstrated in Example 8.1. The MONTH and MONTH*TREATMNT effects are significant based on the 'multivariate' tests (shown as *Wilks Lambda, Pillai's Trace, Hotelling-Lawley Trace*, and *Roy's Greatest Root*). These tests all yield the same F-values for each effect that involves MONTH for this data set. The p-value of 0.0182 ⓴ for the MONTH * TREATMNT interaction indicates that the response profiles differ between groups. This difference is depicted in Figure 8.3, which shows the mean response at each month for the two treatment groups.

The Treatment effect, with an F-value of 2.11, is not significant ㉑ when 'averaged' over all measurement times (p=0.1556). The Center and Treatment-by-Center effects are also non-significant ㉒. The time effect (MONTH) is significant ㉓ for the combined treatment groups and study centers (p=0.0011). However, this should not be interpreted alone without consideration of the significant interaction, which indicates a treatment profile difference.

In the REPEATED statement, CONTRAST(1) is specified in addition to the SUMMARY option ❼, to tell SAS to provide an analysis of the *changes* in mean response from the first time period used. Because the first time period is 'Month 0', which refers to baseline (prior to medication), the CONTRAST(1) option provides between-treatment group comparisons of the mean changes from baseline to each time point ㉔. These results indicate a significant ($p < 0.05$) difference between the active and placebo groups in mean walking distance changes from baseline at each of the 4 follow-up months (p-values of 0.0077, 0.0090, 0.0358, and 0.0176). (Notice that the REPEATED statement labels Months 1, 2, 3, and 4 as MONTH_2, MONTH_3, MONTH_4, and MONTH_5, respectively.)

OUTPUT 8.3. SAS Output for Example 8.2

```
                          Repeated-Measures ANOVA
          Example 8.2:  Treadmill Walking Distance in Intermittent Claudication

                             The GLM Procedure
                           Class Level Information
                      Class          Levels     Values

                      TREATMNT          2        ACT PBO
                      CENTER            2        1 2


                      Number of observations     38
```

Dependent Variable: WD0

Source	DF	Sum of Squares	Mean Square	F Value	Pr > F
Model	3	2190.13085	730.04362	0.40	0.7545
Error	34	62181.76389	1828.87541		
Corrected Total	37	64371.89474			

R-Square	Coeff Var	Root MSE	WD0 Mean
0.034023	25.01668	42.76535	170.9474

Source	DF	Type III SS	Mean Square	F Value	Pr > F
TREATMNT	1	0.280018	0.280018	0.00	0.9902
CENTER	1	45.591846	45.591846	0.02	0.8755 ⑱
TREATMNT*CENTER	1	2088.387545	2088.387545	1.14	0.2928

Dependent Variable: WD1

Source	DF	Sum of Squares	Mean Square	F Value	Pr > F
Model	3	3825.59284	1275.19761	0.87	0.4642
Error	34	49611.98611	1459.17606		
Corrected Total	37	53437.57895			

R-Square	Coeff Var	Root MSE	WD1 Mean
0.071590	21.59429	38.19916	176.8947

Source	DF	Type III SS	Mean Square	F Value	Pr > F
TREATMNT	1	3215.520161	3215.520161	2.20	0.1469
CENTER	1	788.946685	788.946685	0.54	0.4672 ⑱
TREATMNT*CENTER	1	201.720878	201.720878	0.14	0.7123

OUTPUT 8.3. SAS Output for Example 8.2 (*continued*)

```
                        Repeated-Measures ANOVA
      Example 8.2:  Treadmill Walking Distance in Intermittent Claudication

                          The GLM Procedure

Dependent Variable: WD2
                              Sum of
Source              DF       Squares      Mean Square    F Value    Pr > F

Model                3     7128.96857     2376.32286       1.08     0.3693
Error               34    74577.34722     2193.45139
Corrected Total     37    81706.31579

            R-Square      Coeff Var      Root MSE      WD2 Mean
            0.087251      24.88399       46.83430      188.2105

Source              DF     Type III SS    Mean Square    F Value    Pr > F

TREATMNT             1     6860.021953    6860.021953      3.13     0.0860
CENTER               1      504.355287     504.355287      0.23     0.6346
TREATMNT*CENTER      1      225.215502     225.215502      0.10     0.7506


Dependent Variable: WD3
                              Sum of
Source              DF       Squares      Mean Square    F Value    Pr > F

Model                3     7086.08918     2362.02973       1.47     0.2391
Error               34    54499.30556     1602.92075
Corrected Total     37    61585.39474

            R-Square      Coeff Var      Root MSE      WD3 Mean
            0.115061      20.90104       40.03649      191.5526

Source              DF     Type III SS    Mean Square    F Value    Pr > F

TREATMNT             1     3542.716846    3542.716846      2.21     0.1463
CENTER               1     2512.286738    2512.286738      1.57     0.2191
TREATMNT*CENTER      1      771.211470     771.211470      0.48     0.4926


Dependent Variable: WD4
                              Sum of
Source              DF       Squares      Mean Square    F Value    Pr > F

Model                3     8437.19591     2812.39864       1.45     0.2450
Error               34    65863.77778     1937.16993
Corrected Total     37    74300.97368

            R-Square      Coeff Var      Root MSE      WD4 Mean
            0.113554      22.45275       44.01329      196.0263

Source              DF     Type III SS    Mean Square    F Value    Pr > F

TREATMNT             1     5975.405018    5975.405018      3.08     0.0880
CENTER               1     1141.225806    1141.225806      0.59     0.4481
TREATMNT*CENTER      1     1319.290323    1319.290323      0.68     0.4150
```

The annotation marker **18** appears to the right of the Pr > F column for the CENTER rows in each of the three dependent variable sections (at 0.6346, 0.2191, and 0.4481).

OUTPUT 8.3. SAS Output for Example 8.2 (*continued*)

```
                         Repeated-Measures ANOVA
        Example 8.2:  Treadmill Walking Distance in Intermittent Claudication

                            The GLM Procedure


                    Repeated Measures Level Information

        Dependent Variable      WD0     WD1     WD2     WD3     WD4
                Level of MONTH    1       2       3       4       5


Partial Correlation Coefficients from the Error SSCP Matrix / Prob > |r|

DF = 34         WD0          WD1          WD2          WD3          WD4

WD0       1.000000     0.881446     0.778029     0.781755     0.742002
                        <.0001       <.0001       <.0001       <.0001

WD1       0.881446     1.000000     0.703789     0.663442     0.754124
          <.0001                     <.0001       <.0001       <.0001

WD2       0.778029     0.703789     1.000000     0.695239     0.724997
          <.0001       <.0001                     <.0001       <.0001

WD3       0.781755     0.663442     0.695239     1.000000     0.826616
          <.0001       <.0001       <.0001                     <.0001

WD4       0.742002     0.754124     0.724997     0.826616     1.000000
          <.0001       <.0001       <.0001       <.0001


                            Sphericity Tests

                                 Mauchly's
        Variables            DF  Criterion   Chi-Square   Pr > ChiSq

        Transformed Variates  9  0.3190188   37.036211    <.0001
        Orthogonal Components  9  0.5139265   21.578963    0.0103
```
❶❾

OUTPUT 8.3. SAS Output for Example 8.2 (*continued*)

```
                        Repeated-Measures ANOVA
       Example 8.2:   Treadmill Walking Distance in Intermittent Claudication

                     Manova Test Criteria and Exact F Statistics
                       for the Hypothesis of no MONTH Effect
                        H = Type III SSCP Matrix for MONTH
                              E = Error SSCP Matrix


                          S=1      M=1      N=14.5


    Statistic                     Value   F Value   Num DF   Den DF   Pr > F
    Wilks' Lambda              0.56579676   5.95       4        31    0.0011
    Pillai's Trace             0.43420324   5.95       4        31    0.0011  ㉓
    Hotelling-Lawley Trace     0.76741911   5.95       4        31    0.0011
    Roy's Greatest Root        0.76741911   5.95       4        31    0.0011


                     Manova Test Criteria and Exact F Statistics for
                        the Hypothesis of no MONTH*TREATMNT Effect
                        H = Type III SSCP Matrix for MONTH*TREATMNT
                              E = Error SSCP Matrix


                          S=1      M=1      N=14.5


    Statistic                     Value   F Value   Num DF   Den DF   Pr > F
    Wilks' Lambda              0.68930532   3.49       4        31    0.0182
    Pillai's Trace             0.31069468   3.49       4        31    0.0182  ⑳
    Hotelling-Lawley Trace     0.45073593   3.49       4        31    0.0182
    Roy's Greatest Root        0.45073593   3.49       4        31    0.0182


                     Manova Test Criteria and Exact F Statistics
                      for the Hypothesis of no MONTH*CENTER Effect
                        H = Type III SSCP Matrix for MONTH*CENTER
                              E = Error SSCP Matrix


                          S=1      M=1      N=14.5


    Statistic                     Value   F Value   Num DF   Den DF   Pr > F
    Wilks' Lambda              0.81294393   1.78       4        31    0.1574
    Pillai's Trace             0.18705607   1.78       4        31    0.1574
    Hotelling-Lawley Trace     0.23009714   1.78       4        31    0.1574
    Roy's Greatest Root        0.23009714   1.78       4        31    0.1574


                   Manova Test Criteria and Exact F Statistics for the
                      Hypothesis of no MONTH*TREATMNT*CENTER Effect
                    H = Type III SSCP Matrix for MONTH*TREATMNT*CENTER
                              E = Error SSCP Matrix


                          S=1      M=1      N=14.5


    Statistic                     Value   F Value   Num DF   Den DF   Pr > F
    Wilks' Lambda              0.88498645   1.01       4        31    0.4188
    Pillai's Trace             0.11501355   1.01       4        31    0.4188
    Hotelling-Lawley Trace     0.12996081   1.01       4        31    0.4188
    Roy's Greatest Root        0.12996081   1.01       4        31    0.4188
```

OUTPUT 8.3. SAS Output for Example 8.2 (*continued*)

```
                      Repeated-Measures ANOVA
      Example 8.2:  Treadmill Walking Distance in Intermittent Claudication

                          The GLM Procedure
                 Repeated Measures Analysis of Variance
              Tests of Hypotheses for Between Subjects Effects


      Source              DF     Type III SS    Mean Square   F Value   Pr > F


      TREATMNT             1     15215.6775     15215.6775     2.11    0.1556 ㉑
      CENTER               1       141.5815       141.5815     0.02    0.8894
      TREATMNT*CENTER      1      3864.2911      3864.2911     0.54    0.4693 ㉒
      Error               34    245350.6639      7216.1960


              Analysis of Variance of Contrast Variables


 MONTH_N represents the contrast between the nth level of MONTH and the 1st


 Contrast Variable: MONTH_2
 Source              DF     Type III SS    Mean Square   F Value   Pr > F


 Mean                 1      1035.12545     1035.12545     2.54    0.1205
 TREATMNT             1      3275.81362     3275.81362     8.03    0.0077 ㉔
 CENTER               1       455.22581      455.22581     1.12    0.2984
 TREATMNT*CENTER      1       992.00000      992.00000     2.43    0.1283
 Error               34     13878.44444      408.18954


 Contrast Variable: MONTH_3
 Source              DF     Type III SS    Mean Square   F Value   Pr > F


 Mean                 1      9854.88351     9854.88351    10.88    0.0023
 TREATMNT             1      6947.95878     6947.95878     7.67    0.0090 ㉔
 CENTER               1       246.66846      246.66846     0.27    0.6051
 TREATMNT*CENTER      1       941.98029      941.98029     1.04    0.3150
 Error               34     30794.47222      905.71977


 Contrast Variable: MONTH_4
 Source              DF     Type III SS    Mean Square   F Value   Pr > F


 Mean                 1     13127.49507    13127.49507    17.39    0.0002
 TREATMNT             1      3605.98970     3605.98970     4.78    0.0358 ㉔
 CENTER               1      3234.75314     3234.75314     4.29    0.0461
 TREATMNT*CENTER      1       321.41980      321.41980     0.43    0.5184
 Error               34     25663.01389      754.79453


 Contrast Variable: MONTH_5
 Source              DF     Type III SS    Mean Square   F Value   Pr > F


 Mean                 1     20601.23701    20601.23701    21.18    <.0001
 TREATMNT             1      6057.49507     6057.49507     6.23    0.0176 ㉔
 CENTER               1      1643.02195     1643.02195     1.69    0.2025
 TREATMNT*CENTER      1        87.92518       87.92518     0.09    0.7655
 Error               34     33074.76389      972.78717
```

FIGURE 8.3. Mean Walking Distances for Example 8.2

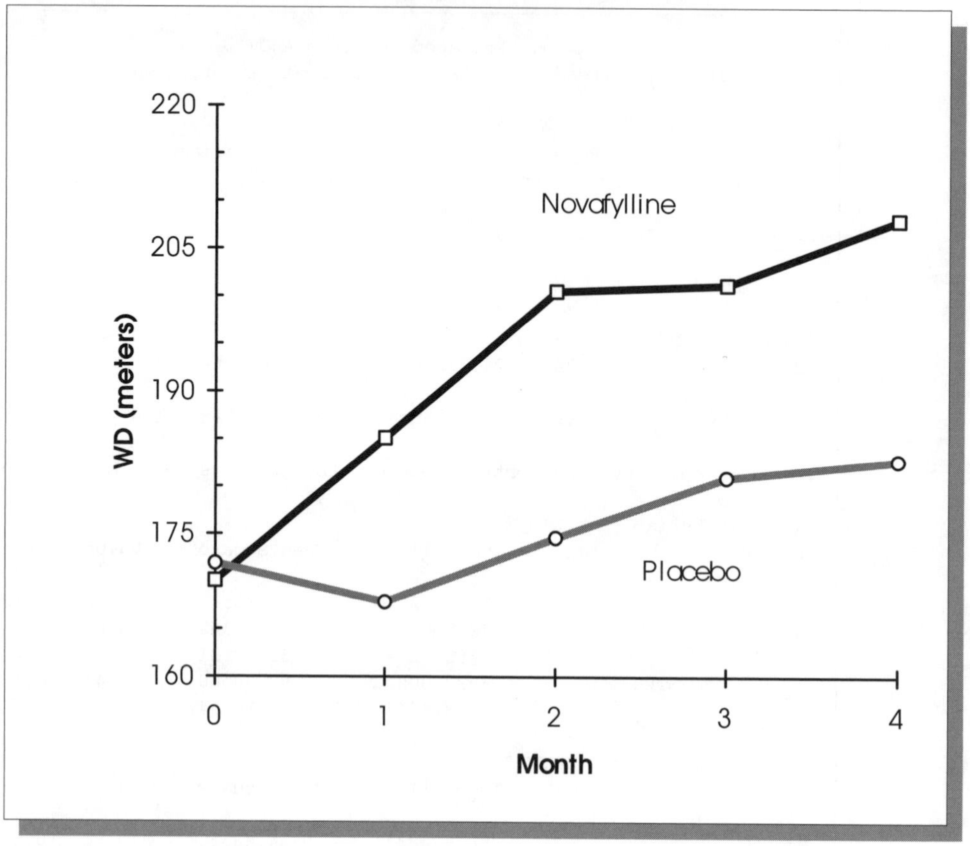

Missing Data

Analyses of *repeated measures* using the general linear model (GLM) in SAS can be disconcerting in the presence of missing data (see Section 8.4.9). If the 'multivariate' approach is used, only 1 missing value from each of several subjects can lead to the exclusion of large amounts of data, not only lowering the power of the statistical tests, but also removing information from the analysis that could be valuable in interpreting the trends of the data.

PROC MIXED in SAS handles missing values more efficiently than PROC GLM, allowing the inclusion of subjects with missing data. In addition, the assumption of compound symmetry is not required with PROC MIXED. In fact, the analyst can specify a model that uses the most appropriate correlation patterns among pairs of measurements across time.

Example 8.3 demonstrates the use of PROC MIXED to analyze *repeated measures* in the presence of missing values.

// **Example 8.3** -- Disease Progression in Alzheimer's Trial

Patients were randomized to receive one of two daily doses (L=low dose or H=high dose) of a new treatment for Alzheimer's disease (AD) or a placebo (P) in a parallel study design. Each patient was to return to the clinic every 2 months for 1 year for assessment of disease progression based on cognitive measurements on the Alzheimer's Disease Assessment Scale (ADAS-cog). This test evaluates memory, language, and praxis function, and is based on the sum of scores from an 11-item scale, with a potential range of 0 to 70, higher scores indicative of greater disease severity. The primary goal is to determine if the rate of disease progression is slowed with active treatment compared with a placebo. The data are shown in Table 8.8 (a decimal point (.) represents missing values). Is there a difference in response profiles over time among the three groups?

TABLE 8.8. Raw Data for Example 8.3

Treatment Group	Patient Number	Study Month					
		2	4	6	8	10	12
H	2	31	36	35	31	31	31
H	6	24	27	28	21	27	26
H	7	31	31	39	37	41	.
H	14	45	48	46	52	48	42
H	17	24	28	26	23	24	29
H	20	21	32	39	36	33	30
H	22	32	34	45	42	37	32
H	25	18	22	26	26	27	24
H	27	51	47	.	43	43	43
H	33	20	22	29	24	29	30
H	38	41	34	37	29	35	33
H	42	24	35	39	32	24	.
H	45	23	.	33	36	33	30
H	50	25	28	25	28	28	30
H	52	31	34	.	33	34	35
H	56	27	31	26	33	33	34
H	60	37	43	39	42	43	36
H	62	41	42	51	45	46	51
H	66	35	33	34	35	36	41
H	69	30	31	27	34	33	36
H	72	54	60	55	58	.	65
H	75	35	37	39	41	39	44
H	79	18	21	19	19	20	27
H	80	40	35	33	39	38	41
L	1	22	30	.	33	28	30
L	5	34	35	46	37	31	35
L	8	40	41	41	46	52	48
L	12	24	.	21	28	30	27
L	13	29	26	29	26	.	36
L	15	31	36	41	46	52	57
L	19	22	27	28	24	27	28
L	21	43	49	42	48	48	46
L	24	18	28	29	.	25	28

TABLE 8.8. Raw Data for Example 8.3 (*continued*)

Treatment Group	Patient Number	Study Month 2	4	6	8	10	12
L	28	25	24	27	18	21	22
L	31	37	35	35	38	42	.
L	34	24	27	28	24	27	25
L	37	45	50	58	59	60	58
L	40	33	32	35	30	31	35
L	44	34	37	43	44	39	38
L	47	25	27	29	28	31	.
L	51	30	.	36	32	34	38
L	54	23	.	33	28	32	32
L	57	35	37	39	38	41	43
L	59	44	48	48	45	50	52
L	63	28	30	32	31	35	32
L	67	24	22	23	24	27	30
L	68	.	49	51	48	55	54
L	73	26	28	30	27	30	33
L	76	30	32	35	35	36	38
L	78	40	42	44	43	45	46
P	3	31	36	37	41	39	44
P	4	20	26	32	35	25	29
P	9	33	33	29	33	39	41
P	10	35	39	40	38	40	38
P	11	26	24	31	42	50	.
P	16	44	48	44	37	36	47
P	18	25	31	21	27	41	32
P	23	28	34	26	26	36	35
P	26	27	.	28	35	40	.
P	29	20	30	30	27	33	29
P	30	49	.	43	48	44	53
P	32	26	29	31	30	35	38
P	35	30	33	41	.	41	44
P	36	31	34	44	44	50	56
P	39	42	46	36	43	48	48
P	41	31	30	31	.	41	38
P	43	27	22	36	45	54	60
P	46	24	37	41	31	36	44
P	48	33	31	38	41	31	.
P	49	27	30	36	36	32	33
P	53	35	34	45	44	38	40
P	55	39	40	38	44	43	44
P	58	32	34	40	45	36	38
P	61	45	50	.	54	50	53
P	64	21	23	31	34	27	27
P	65	26	30	37	37	30	32
P	70	53	50	55	57	.	.
P	71	32	34	27	30	36	35
P	74	.	50	52	56	52	54
P	77	24	32	31	37	35	30

Solution

The mean ADAS-cog scores are shown by Treatment and Month in Table 8.9 and Figure 8.4. Mean scores show an increasing trend across time within each Treatment Group, indicative of disease progression. The question is whether the rate of increase has been slowed by using an active treatment compared with a placebo. Statistically, this is addressed by examining the Treatment-by-Month interaction effect.

TABLE 8.9. Summary Statistics for Example 8.3

Treatment		Month					
		2	4	6	8	10	12
Placebo	Mean	31.6	34.6	36.2	39.2	39.2	40.8
	(SD)	(8.4)	(8.0)	(7.7)	(8.4)	(7.4)	(9.2)
(N=30)	N	29	28	29	28	29	26
Low Dose	Mean	30.6	34.4	36.1	35.2	37.2	38.0
	(SD)	(7.6)	(8.5)	(9.1)	(10.0)	(10.7)	(10.3)
(N=26)	N	25	23	25	25	25	24
High Dose	Mean	31.6	34.4	35.0	35.0	34.0	35.9
	(SD)	(10.0)	(9.1)	(9.0)	(9.5)	(7.3)	(9.4)
(N=24)	N	24	23	22	24	23	22
Combined	Mean	31.3	34.5	35.8	36.6	37.0	38.4
	(SD)	(8.6)	(8.4)	(8.5)	(9.4)	(8.7)	(9.7)
(N=80)	N	78	74	76	77	77	72

FIGURE 8.4. ADAS-cog Response Profiles (Example 8.3)

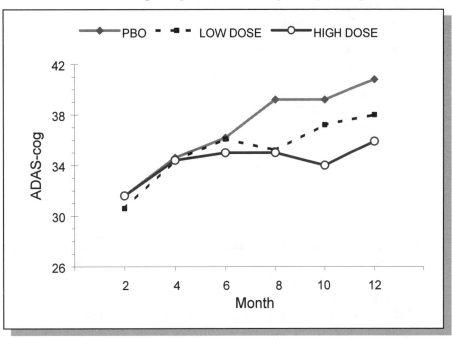

SAS Analysis of Example 8.3

Initially, you might proceed with a *repeated measures* analysis using a 'multivariate' approach. The SAS statements for doing this are shown in the code that follows. The data are read into the data set ALZHMRS. Each patient's repeated measurements comprise a separate record. This format allows direct multivariate model specification in PROC GLM, as shown **㉕**. The REPEATED statement identifies MONTH as the time factor and requests *sphericity tests* (PRINTE option) and within-patient effects summaries (SUMMARY option) **㉖**.

SAS Code for Example 8.3 (PROC GLM)

```
DATA ALZHMRS;
    INPUT TREAT $ PAT ADAS02 ADAS04 ADAS06 ADAS08 ADAS10 ADAS12;
    DATALINES;
L  1  22  30   .  33  28  30
L  5  34  35  46  37  31  35
L  8  40  41  41  46  52  48

. . .(more data lines). . .


P 71  32  34  27  30  36  35
P 74   .  50  52  56  52  54
P 77  24  32  31  37  35  30
;

ODS SELECT
    GLM.Repeated.PartialCorr
    GLM.Repeated.MANOVA.Model.Error.Sphericity
    GLM.Repeated.MANOVA.Model.MONTH.MultStat
  GLM.Repeated.MANOVA.Model.MONTH_TREAT.MultStat
    GLM.Repeated.WithinSubject.ModelANOVA;

PROC GLM DATA = ALZHMRS;
    CLASS TREAT;
        MODEL ADAS02 ADAS04 ADAS06 ADAS08 ADAS10 ADAS12 =    ㉕
            TREAT / NOUNI;
        REPEATED MONTH / PRINTE SUMMARY;        ㉖
    TITLE1 'Repeated-Measures ANOVA';
    TITLE2 'Example 8.3: Disease Progression in Alzheimer's;
    TITLE3 ' ';
    TITLE4 'Multivariate Approach Using GLM';
    QUIT;
RUN;
```

In Output 8.4, the section labeled Sphericity Tests **㉗** indicates a significant departure from the assumption of compound symmetry ($p < 0.0001$). Therefore, the 'univariate' approach described earlier in this chapter would not be appropriate. Looking further in the output, you see that the multivariate tests (*Wilks' Lambda*, *Pillai's Trace* and *Hotelling-Lawley Trace*) for the Month-by-Treatment interaction are not significant with p-values of 0.316 **㉘**. The 'univariate' test for the Month-by-Treatment interaction **㉙** provides the result (p=0.204) you would get by using the 'univariate' approach to *repeated measures* after excluding all patients who have one or more missing values and assuming compound symmetry. Because it was already concluded that this would not be an appropriate method of analysis, you might look at the Greenhouse-Geiser adjusted values (see Section 8.4.6). The p-value for the interaction effect using the Greenhouse-Geiser adjustment is 0.227 **㉚**.

OUTPUT 8.4. SAS Output for Example 8.3 – PROC GLM

```
                      Repeated-Measures ANOVA
             Example 8.3: Disease Progression in Alzheimer's

                     Multivariate Approach Using GLM

                         The GLM Procedure
                 Repeated Measures Analysis of Variance

Partial Correlation Coefficients from the Error SSCP Matrix / Prob > |r|  ㊷

DF = 53    ADAS02     ADAS04     ADAS06     ADAS08     ADAS10     ADAS12

ADAS02   1.000000   0.892847   0.715396   0.743266   0.734904   0.703999
                     <.0001      <.0001     <.0001     <.0001     <.0001

ADAS04   0.892847   1.000000   0.750344   0.745911   0.731188   0.653269
          <.0001                 <.0001     <.0001     <.0001     <.0001

ADAS06   0.715396   0.750344   1.000000   0.852443   0.690418   0.690489
          <.0001     <.0001                 <.0001     <.0001     <.0001

ADAS08   0.743266   0.745911   0.852443   1.000000   0.847485   0.784974
          <.0001     <.0001     <.0001                 <.0001     <.0001

ADAS10   0.734904   0.731188   0.690418   0.847485   1.000000   0.900155
          <.0001     <.0001     <.0001     <.0001                 <.0001

ADAS12   0.703999   0.653269   0.690489   0.784974   0.900155   1.000000
          <.0001     <.0001     <.0001     <.0001     <.0001


                         Sphericity Tests
                                                          ㉗
                             Mauchly's
Variables               DF   Criterion   Chi-Square   Pr > ChiSq

Transformed Variates    14   0.022696    193.4424       <.0001
Orthogonal Components   14   0.2211441    77.106867      <.0001
```

OUTPUT 8.4. SAS Output for Example 8.3 – PROC GLM (*continued*)

```
                    Repeated-Measures ANOVA
           Example 8.3: Disease Progression in Alzheimer's


              Manova Test Criteria and Exact F Statistics
                 for the Hypothesis of no MONTH Effect
                 H = Type III SSCP Matrix for MONTH
                       E = Error SSCP Matrix


                   S=1     M=1.5    N=23.5

Statistic                     Value   F Value  Num DF  Den DF  Pr > F

Wilks' Lambda              0.38811297   15.45      5      49   <.0001
Pillai's Trace             0.61188703   15.45      5      49   <.0001
Hotelling-Lawley Trace     1.57656938   15.45      5      49   <.0001
Roy's Greatest Root        1.57656938   15.45      5      49   <.0001


              Manova Test Criteria and F Approximations for
                the Hypothesis of no MONTH*TREAT Effect
                H = Type III SSCP Matrix for MONTH*TREAT
                       E = Error SSCP Matrix


                   S=2     M=1     N=23.5

 Statistic                    Value   F Value  Num DF  Den DF  Pr > F

Wilks' Lambda              0.79719596    1.18     10      98   0.3163
Pillai's Trace             0.21044586    1.18     10     100   0.3160  ㉘
Hotelling-Lawley Trace     0.24481085    1.18     10  70.804   0.3162
Roy's Greatest Root        0.19587117    1.96      5      50   0.1012

    NOTE: F Statistic for Roy's Greatest Root is an upper bound.
          NOTE: F Statistic for Wilks' Lambda is exact.


     Univariate Tests of Hypotheses for Within Subject Effects

Source         DF    Type III SS    Mean Square   F Value   Pr > F

MONTH           5   1529.760451    305.952090     18.57    <.0001
MONTH*TREAT    10    222.315729     22.231573      1.35    0.2044  ㉙
Error(MONTH)  265   4366.776533     16.478402

                                    Adj Pr > F
             Source                 G - G     H - F

             MONTH                 <.0001    <.0001
             MONTH*TREAT           0.2337    0.2271      ㉚
             Error(MONTH)
```

From this analysis alone, you might begin to believe that there is no statistical difference in AD progression among the treatment groups, even when you consider the encouraging depiction in Figure 8.4. However, as noted earlier, the 'multivariate' approach can be conservative, especially in the way it handles missing values. Any patient with one or more missing values is excluded from the analysis. Notice that, among the 80 patients studied, 24 patients have a total of 26 missing values. Thus, the *repeated measures analysis* using the 'multivariate' approach ignores $(24 \times 6) - 26 = 118$ valid data points.

Now, analyze the data by using PROC MIXED, which more efficiently handles missing values. The SAS code and output follow. As in previous examples, only selected output is shown by using ODS (see Section 8.4.16).

You see that the ALZHMRS data set is first rearranged to the 'univariate' format (see Example 8.1) in a new data set called UNIALZ. This is the same format used by PROC GLM, and you can also see that PROC MIXED uses the CLASS and MODEL statements similar to PROC GLM ❸①. The main difference is that you can specify a covariance structure rather than being bound by the assumption of compound symmetry. A vast array of different user-selected covariance structures is available in SAS (see the SAS Help and Documentation for PROC MIXED). Initially, the 'unstructured' covariance model, which allows SAS to estimate a working covariance matrix from the estimated correlations among study visits is used. The TYPE= option in the REPEATED statement specifies UN (for unstructured). Notice that, in PROC MIXED the PAT(TREAT) effect is specified in the SUBJECT= option in the REPEATED statement rather than in the MODEL statement ❸②.

SAS Code for Example 8.3 (PROC MIXED)

```
DATA UNIALZ; SET ALZHMRS;
    KEEP TREAT PAT MONTH ADASCOG;
    MONTH =  2; ADASCOG = ADAS02; OUTPUT;
    MONTH =  4; ADASCOG = ADAS04; OUTPUT;
    MONTH =  6; ADASCOG = ADAS06; OUTPUT;
    MONTH =  8; ADASCOG = ADAS08; OUTPUT;
    MONTH = 10; ADASCOG = ADAS10; OUTPUT;
    MONTH = 12; ADASCOG = ADAS12; OUTPUT;
RUN;

ODS SELECT
    Mixed.RCorr
    Mixed.Dimensions
    Mixed.FitStatistics
    Mixed.Tests3;


PROC MIXED DATA = UNIALZ;
    CLASS TREAT MONTH PAT;
    MODEL ADASCOG = TREAT MONTH TREAT*MONTH;            ❸①
        REPEATED / TYPE=UN  SUBJECT=PAT(TREAT) RCORR;   ❸②
    TITLE4 'PROC MIXED Using Unstructured Covariance (UN)';
RUN;
```

OUTPUT 8.5. SAS Output for Example 8.3 – PROC MIXED

```
                     Repeated-Measures ANOVA
            Example 8.3: Disease Progression in Alzheimer's

              PROC MIXED Using Unstructured Covariance (UN)

                        The Mixed Procedure

                            Dimensions

             Covariance Parameters          21
             Columns in X                   28
             Columns in Z                    0
             Subjects                       80
             Max Obs Per Subject             6
             Observations Used             454
             Observations Not Used          26
             Total Observations            480

        Estimated R Correlation Matrix for PAT(TREAT) 2 H          (41)

     Row    Col1     Col2     Col3     Col4     Col5     Col6

      1    1.0000   0.9005   0.7703   0.8002   0.7763   0.7773
      2    0.9005   1.0000   0.8179   0.7995   0.7521   0.7261
      3    0.7703   0.8179   1.0000   0.8738   0.7223   0.7418
      4    0.8002   0.7995   0.8738   1.0000   0.8628   0.8273
      5    0.7763   0.7521   0.7223   0.8628   1.0000   0.9206
      6    0.7773   0.7261   0.7418   0.8273   0.9206   1.0000

                         Fit Statistics          (34)

             -2 Res Log Likelihood          2649.9
             AIC (smaller is better)        2691.9
             AICC (smaller is better)       2694.1
             BIC (smaller is better)        2741.9


                  Type 3 Tests of Fixed Effects

                          Num      Den
             Effect        DF       DF     F Value    Pr > F

             TREAT          2       77       0.94     0.3967
             MONTH          5       77      21.55     <.0001
             TREAT*MONTH   10       77       2.08     0.0357    (33)
```

Output 8.5 shows a significant (p = 0.0357) Treatment-by-Month interaction [33] using the unstructured covariance. The section entitled Fit Statistics [34] provides an indication of relative goodness of fit, smaller values suggesting a better fit. You can specify other covariance structures by using the same MODEL statement in PROC MIXED and compare the fit statistics among them. To illustrate this, re-run the analysis for autoregressive (AR(1)), Toeplitz (TOEP), first order autoregressive moving average (ARMA(1,1)), and compound symmetric (CS) covariance structures by replacing the REPEATED statement with the following.

SAS Code for Example 8.3 (PROC MIXED) (*continued*)

```
...
    REPEATED / TYPE=AR(1) SUBJECT=PAT(TREAT);      ㉟
    TITLE4 'PROC MIXED Using First-Order Auto-Regressive
            Covariance (AR(1))';
...
    REPEATED / TYPE=TOEP SUBJECT=PAT(TREAT);       ㊱
    TITLE4 'PROC MIXED Using Toeplitz Covariance (TOEP)';
...
    REPEATED / TYPE=ARMA(1,1) SUBJECT=PAT(TREAT);   ㊲
    TITLE4 'PROC MIXED Using 1st-Order Auto-Regressive
            Moving Average Covariance (ARMA(1,1))';
...
    REPEATED / TYPE=CS SUBJECT=PAT(TREAT);        ㊳
    TITLE4 'PROC MIXED Using Compound Symmetric
            Covariance (CS)';
RUN;
```

OUTPUT 8.6. SAS Output for Example 8.3 — PROC MIXED (*continued*)

```
                    Repeated-Measures ANOVA
         Example 8.3: Disease Progression in Alzheimer's

 PROC MIXED Using First-Order Auto-Regressive Covariance (AR(1))

                     Fit Statistics
          -2 Res Log Likelihood          2698.2
          AIC (smaller is better)        2702.2
          AICC (smaller is better)       2702.2
          BIC (smaller is better)        2706.9

             Type 3 Tests of Fixed Effects           ㉟

                    Num      Den
         Effect      DF       DF      F Value    Pr > F

         TREAT        2       77        0.94     0.3952
         MONTH        5      359       11.21     <.0001
         TREAT*MONTH 10      359        1.43     0.1671
```

OUTPUT 8.6. SAS Output for Example 8.3 – PROC MIXED (*continued*)

```
                        Repeated-Measures ANOVA
              Example 8.3: Disease Progression in Alzheimer's

                PROC MIXED Using Toeplitz Covariance (TOEP)

                             Fit Statistics

                   -2 Res Log Likelihood          2671.1
                   AIC (smaller is better)        2683.1
                   AICC (smaller is better)       2683.3
                   BIC (smaller is better)        2697.4

                    Type 3 Tests of Fixed Effects
```

36

```
                      Num      Den
           Effect      DF       DF      F Value    Pr > F

           TREAT        2       77       0.91      0.4077
           MONTH        5      359      19.65      <.0001
           TREAT*MONTH 10      359       2.06      0.0266
```

```
       PROC MIXED Using 1st-Order Auto-Regressive-Moving Average
                         Covariance (ARMA(1,1))

                             Fit Statistics

                   -2 Res Log Likelihood          2691.2
                   AIC (smaller is better)        2697.2
                   AICC (smaller is better)       2697.2
                   BIC (smaller is better)        2704.3

                    Type 3 Tests of Fixed Effects
```

37

```
                      Num      Den
           Effect       DF       DF     F Value    Pr > F

           TREAT        2       77       0.90      0.4116
           MONTH        5      359      14.02      <.0001
           TREAT*MONTH 10      359       1.47      0.1478
```

```
       PROC MIXED Using Compound Symmetric Covariance (CS)

                             Fit Statistics

                   -2 Res Log Likelihood          2743.5
                   AIC (smaller is better)        2747.5
                   AICC (smaller is better)       2747.5
                   BIC (smaller is better)        2752.2

                    Type 3 Tests of Fixed Effects
```

38

```
                               Num      Den
           Effect      DF       DF      F Value    Pr > F

           TREAT        2       77       0.88      0.4172
           MONTH        5      359      26.69      <.0001
           TREAT*MONTH 10      359       2.30      0.0125
```

AIC stands for "Akaike's Information Criterion", which measures model fit. Based on Output 8.6, values for the AIC are consistent with the other fit statistics (AICC, BIC, –2 Res Log Likelihood). Toeplitz provides the best fit of the five covariance structures considered, based on the AIC, AICC, and BIC fit parameters (smallest values). The unstructured covariance ➌ is a close second based on these measures, and it is the preferred method based on the –2 Res Log Likelihood fit statistic. Both of these covariance structures result in a significant Treatment-by-Month interaction. Compound symmetry shows the worst fit and, as previously discovered ➋, is not a good assumption.

TABLE 8.10. Summary of PROC MIXED Results for Example 8.3 for Various Correlation Structures

Covariance Structure	SAS Name	AIC	–2 Res Log Likelihood	p-value for TREAT*MONTH
Unstructured	UN	2691.9	2649.9	0.0357
Autoregressive	AR(1)	2702.2	2698.2	0.1671
Toeplitz	TOEP	2683.1	2671.1	0.0266
Autoregressive MA	ARMA(1)	2697.2	2691.2	0.1478
Compound Symmetric	CS	2747.5	2743.5	0.0125

GEE Analysis

The use of generalized estimating equations (GEE) is another method for analyzing *repeated measures* data sets that have missing values. PROC GENMOD, which is used for GEE analysis in SAS, requires the specification of a 'working' correlation structure (such as compound symmetric (CS) or unstructured (UN)), which represents the correlations among the repeated measurements. The GEE modeling methodology will usually produce good estimates of the model parameters even if the correlation structure is misspecified. In this sense, a GEE analysis is more robust than using the generalized linear modeling methods of PROC GLM or PROC MIXED.

The SAS statements that follow this section illustrate how to conduct a GEE analysis of the data in Example 8.3 by using the autoregressive (TYPE = AR(1)) working correlation matrix ➒. The DIST option in the MODEL statement specifies the assumption of normal distribution of the data (DIST = NORMAL). In this case, the DIST option is not required because the normal distribution is the default. The TYPE3 option in the MODEL statement requests tests (analogous to the PROC GLM SAS Type III tests) for each of the effects given in the MODEL statement. This approach also results in a significant Treatment-by-Month interaction (p=0.0164) ➍.

SAS Code for Example 8.3 (PROC GENMOD)

```
ODS SELECT
    Genmod.Type3;

PROC GENMOD DATA = UNIALZ;
    CLASS TREAT MONTH PAT;
    MODEL ADASCOG = TREAT MONTH TREAT*MONTH /
                    DIST = NORMAL TYPE3;
        REPEATED SUBJECT = PAT / TYPE = AR(1);      ㊴
    TITLE4 'GEE Analysis Using PROC GENMOD';
    TITLE5 'Autoregressive Correlation (AR(1)) Working
            Correlation';
RUN;
```

OUTPUT 8.7. SAS Output for Example 8.3 – PROC GENMOD

```
                Repeated-Measures ANOVA
        Example 8.3: Disease Progression in Alzheimer's

               GEE Analysis Using PROC GENMOD
    Autoregressive Correlation (AR(1)) Working Correlation

                 The GENMOD Procedure

        Score Statistics For Type 3 GEE Analysis
                               Chi-
        Source          DF    Square    Pr > ChiSq

        TREAT            2      2.02       0.3639
        MONTH            5     46.14      <.0001
        TREAT*MONTH     10     21.76       0.0164      ㊵
```

8.4   Details & Notes

▶   **8.4.1**   With only one group (g=1) in Table 8.1, the *repeated measures* layout is identical to that of a randomized block design. In this case, the analysis is carried out as described in Chapter 7 by using the repeated factor as the Group effect and Patient as the blocking factor.

▶   **8.4.2**   The manual computing methods demonstrated in Example 8.1 apply only to balanced designs (i.e., same number of patients per group). This demonstration is used to show which deviations are represented by each of the effect sum of squares and is not recommended in practice. Even if a suitable computer package is unavailable, easier computing formulas are available for manual computations with a balanced layout (see e.g., Winer, 1971).

▶ **8.4.3** For the balanced case, the *repeated measures ANOVA* error sum of squares (SSE) is simply the sum of the SSE's found by using *two-way ANOVA*'s (with no interaction) *within* each treatment group. In Example 8.1, the *two-way ANOVA* tables within each Vaccine Group are as follows:

ANOVA	Active Group				Placebo Group			
Source	df	SS	MS	F	df	SS	MS	F
PATIENT	3	11.667	3.889	3.41	3	13.667	4.556	5.12*
VISIT	2	48.500	24.250	21.29*	2	18.667	9.333	10.50*
Error	6	6.833	1.139		6	5.333	0.889	
Total	11	67.000			11	37.667		

* Significant (p < 0.05)

SSE for the *repeated measures ANOVA* is $6.833 + 5.333 = 12.167$ based on $6 + 6 = 12$ degrees of freedom. Similarly, the SS(Patient) can be added to obtain the SS(Patient(Vaccine)) for the *repeated measures ANOVA*, $11.667 + 13.667 = 25.333$ with $3 + 3 = 6$ degrees of freedom. Notice that the sums of squares for the Time effect (SS(Visit)) are not additive.

▶ **8.4.4** In the 'univariate' analysis of Example 8.1, Patient-within-Vaccine is considered a random effect because patients are selected from a large population of eligible patients, and you want to make inferences about that population, not just the selected patients. To indicate this, the RANDOM statement is used following the MODEL statement in the SAS code. Whenever the RANDOM statement is included in PROC GLM, SAS prints the form of the expected mean squares as functions of the variance components attributed to each source of variation. Output 8.1 ❼ shows that the expected mean square for the fixed Vaccine effect is composed of a component due to the Vaccine (i.e., VACGRP) and two additional components due to the random effects.

Under the null hypothesis of no Vaccine effect, the quadratic form involving Vaccine (i.e., Q(VACGRP,VACGRP*VISIT)) would be 0, reducing it to the same form as the expected mean square for Patient(Vaccine). Therefore, when H_0 is true, the ratio of these two mean squares would be 1, which confirms that this is the appropriate test for Vaccine.

In more complex *repeated measures* designs and those involving missing data, the structures of the expected mean squares are important in helping to determine how to construct the *F-tests*. As an exact test might not exist, the analyst must examine the variance structures to determine the ratio for the most appropriate *F-tests* as discussed above, and then use the TEST statement to carry out the test.

▶ **8.4.5**   The 'multivariate' approach to *repeated measures analysis* using SAS makes the within-patient tests using 4 criteria: *Wilks' Lambda, Pillai's Trace, Hotelling-Lawley Trace,* and *Roy's Greatest Root*. Each of these statistics is based on multivariate statistical analysis methods to obtain an *F-test* of significance for the given factor based on complex functions of sums of squares. The differences among these tests depend on the alternative hypothesis. *Wilks' Lambda*, for example, might be the most powerful test to use under some alternatives and the least powerful of the four tests under others. Research that compares these tests suggests that *Pillai's Trace* might be the most appropriate one for use under a wide range of applications. The reader is referred to other references for further discussion of these comparisons (e.g., Hand & Taylor, 1987). In any case, when there are only two groups (g=2), all four tests yield the same results, as shown in Examples 8.1 and 8.2.

▶ **8.4.6**   The 'univariate' approach to *repeated measures ANOVA* can sometimes be used even under violations to the assumption of compound symmetry by applying an adjustment to the analysis. A correction factor, called the Greenhouse-Geiser epsilon (ε), can be computed as a function of the variances and covariances of the repeated measurements. The adjustment is made by multiplying each of the degrees of freedom in the ANOVA table that is associated with the Time effect by ε to obtain the adjusted degrees of freedom. The Greenhouse-Geiser adjusted p-values are printed in Output 8.2 (G-G) for each effect that involves the Time factor, as illustrated in Example 8.1 'Multivariate' Approach[14]. When the *sphericity test* is highly significant, the 'univariate' approach is not recommended, even with the adjustment described.

▶ **8.4.7**   When there is a significant profile difference among groups, further analyses are required to determine at what time points these differences occur. For the 'multivariate' approach, using the SUMMARY option in the REPEATED statement in PROC GLM produces *ANOVA*'s at various sets of time points. Specifying CONTRAST(1) will give the same results as if an *ANOVA* were conducted on the changes in the response measure from the first time point, as shown in the REPEATED statement for Example 8.2 [17]. This can be useful if the first time point is a baseline value.

Alternatively, using the PROFILE option in the REPEATED statement provides the results as if an *ANOVA* were conducted on the changes between *successive* time points. This might be useful, for example, in determining at what time point the responses of two treatment groups first begin to converge or diverge. This is illustrated in the 'multivariate' approach for Example 8.1[15]. The first analysis shows a non-significant Treatment effect (p=0.6202) based on the changes from Month 1 to Month 2; the second analysis results in a marginally significant (p=0.0550) treatment effect based on the changes from Month 2 to Month 3.

Other contrasts can also be used with SAS (see the SAS Help and Documentation for details about the SUMMARY option in the REPEATED statement in PROC GLM).

▶ **8.4.8**   The error variation for between-group comparisons (averaged over time) is estimated by the mean square for Patients-within-Group (MSP(G)) with N–g degrees of freedom. The within-Patient error variation (over all groups) is estimated by MSE, with (N–g)(t–1) degrees of freedom. The error variation within the Group-by-Time cells is the pooled combination of these two sometimes disparate error estimates, namely,

$$\hat{\sigma}^2_{cell} = \frac{SSP(G) + SSE}{(N - g) + (N - g)(t - 1)} = \frac{SSP(G) + SSE}{t \cdot (N - g)}$$

This within-cell error variation is the within-time, among-patient variation, averaged over all time points. That is, if MSE_j represents the MSE from a *one-way ANOVA* conducted at time period j, the within-cell variance of the *repeated measures* layout is the average of these MSE's

$$\hat{\sigma}^2_{cell} = \frac{\sum_{j=1}^{t} MSE_j}{t}$$

This within-cell error variation can be used to compare cell means (e.g., Group i vs. Group j) for a specific time point or to form 95% confidence intervals for the cell means.

▶ **8.4.9**   The *repeated measures analysis* is not recommended when there are many missing values. A *repeated measures* layout with two time periods is similar to the paired-difference situation (Chapter 3). Patients who have a missing value at one of the two time periods might contribute information regarding between-patient variability, but nothing regarding the patients' response profile (within-patient variability). Similar problems, though not as extreme, occur when patients have missing data in layouts with more than two time periods.

When there are missing values, the 'univariate' approach to *repeated measures analysis* using SAS confounds hypotheses regarding treatment effects with other model effects that result in complex hypotheses and interpretation difficulties. Unless the analyst can clearly re-state the statistical hypothesis in clinical terms, this approach to *repeated measures analysis* should be avoided when the data set is plagued with missing data (just a few missing values in a large study should not present interpretation difficulties).

The 'multivariate' approach using SAS eliminates patients who have missing values from the analysis, thereby decreasing the test's power. Much of the data will be excluded from evaluation when using this analysis method if there are a large number of patients each having just one missing value.

PROC MIXED is capable of handling missing values and unbalanced cases for *repeated measures analysis*, but it assumes values are missing at random (MAR). Generalized estimating equations (GEE) require the more restrictive assumption that missing values are missing completely at random (MCAR). MAR and MCAR suggest that the missing data represent a random sample from all data that would have been available, and therefore, the results are not biased by their exclusion. Unfortunately, there is no way to test the assumption of MAR or MCAR.

With only about 5% of the data missing and no apparent patterns related to treatment or discontinuation, the missing value structure of Example 8.3 appears consistent with the MAR assumption. However, this is not usually the case in clinical studies. Because there is frequently missing data in clinical trials from early discontinuation of patients due to ineffectiveness or side effects, assumptions of MAR or MCAR are often violated in such data sets.

Estimates can sometimes be computed for missing values, and these can then be used in the analysis as if they were observed. The simplest estimate and one that is often used in clinical trials is the patient's observation from the previous time point. This has been referred to as the 'last-observation-carried-forward' (LOCF) technique, but it is not universally endorsed. Lachin (2000), for example, refers to this method as 'clearly ridiculous' in clinical trials that involve disease states that might progress or deteriorate during the study. Other estimates of missing values might be based on averages of adjacent values, or on row and column means, or based on regression techniques accounting for explanatory covariates. However, such estimation techniques also rely heavily on the MAR assumption to avoid bias.

If the *repeated measures* model assumptions are not satisfied and imputation techniques are not tenable in data sets plagued with missing values, one may deem the most appropriate analysis to be separate *ANOVA's* at each time point. Generally, if large amounts of missing data are expected, the *repeated measures ANOVA* should not even be considered as an analysis tool. However, if large amounts of missing data unexpectedly occur in a study for which you plan to use a *repeated measures analysis*, you might consider revising the hypothesis and conducting a new study. Some authors (e.g., Gillings and Koch, 1991) suggest that the credibility of an entire study might be in question if it unexpectedly contains a large number of missing values. In any case, the occurrence of missing data in a *repeated measures* setting calls for the application of alternative statistical methods to confirm the results of the method selected.

▶ **8.4.10** When there are no missing values, PROC MIXED, using the compound symmetric covariance structure (TYPE=CS), produces the same results as PROC GLM in the 'univariate' approach.

▶ **8.4.11** Interpretation difficulties using the *ANOVA* method for *repeated measures* data in the case of imbalance or missing data are magnified with the inclusion of numeric covariates as explanatory variables. However, GEE analyses are well-suited for use with covariates, but only with large data sets. The results of GEE analyses might not be reliable for smaller data sets. Generally, if there are no more than 3 or 4 explanatory variables (including 'Treatment Group'), a minimum sample size of 50 to 100 patients is desirable.

Estimates of the model parameters use a Likelihood Ratio method when the TYPE3 model option is used in PROC GENMOD, and p-values are based on a *chi-square test*. This method can be resource-intensive for very large data sets, in which case the WALD option can often be used more effectively. The p-values based on the *Wald* test are also asymptotic *chi-square tests*.

▶ **8.4.12** The covariance structure specified in PROC MIXED will model the variance assumptions at different time points and the patterns of correlations among the time points according to how you think measurements across time are related. The unstructured approach (TYPE=UN) makes no assumption at all about the relationship in the correlations among visits. Measurements taken closer together in time, however, often tend to be more highly correlated than measurements taken over lengthy periods of time. As seen previously, the compound symmetric structure (TYPE=CS) assumes the same correlation, say ρ ($0<\rho<1$), between each pair of time points without regard to how far apart they occur.

In the first-order autoregressive structure (TYPE= AR(1)), measurements taken at adjacent time points (e.g., consecutive visits) have the same correlation, such as ρ. The correlation of ρ^2 is assigned to measurements that are 2 visits apart; ρ^3, to measurements that are 3 visits apart, etc. The autoregressive moving average (TYPE=ARMA(1,1)) is similar, except the entries that involve powers of ρ are multiplied by a constant, γ ($0< \gamma<1$). The Toeplitz structure (TYPE=TOEP) is more general. It assigns a correlation of ρ_1 to measurements taken from consecutive visits; a different correlation, ρ_2, to measurements that are taken 2 visits apart; ρ_3, to measurements that are taken 3 visits apart, etc. Each of these (except the unstructured) assumes equal variances at all measurement times.

By using the RCORR option in the REPEATED statement in PROC MIXED, SAS will provide the estimated correlation matrix based on the type of structure assumed. The estimated correlation matrix for the unstructured type is shown in Output 8.5 for Example 8.3 (PROC MIXED) ❹. Notice that the estimated correlations shown in Output 8.4 for Example 8.3 (PROC GLM), "Partial Correlation Coefficients from the Error SSCP Matrix" ❹, are computed after excluding patients who have data missing.

> Note: Further details and examples of PROC MIXED in analyzing repeated measures data are available in "SAS System for Mixed Models" by Littell, Miliken, Stroup and Wolfinger, which was written under the SAS Books by Users program.

The GEE approach does not depend so heavily on the correct specification of the correlation structure. To illustrate this robustness, the significance of the interaction term of Example 8.3 is seen to be consistent for different correlations structures, as shown below for the exchangeable (or compound symmetric) (CS) working correlation structure and for a user-defined structure (USER()). The user-defined type is patterned after the estimated correlations shown in the SAS output for Example 8.3 (PROC MIXED) [41], where the correlations are high (e.g., 0.9) for adjacent time points then decrease and level off to 0.7 for time points farther apart. The interaction p-values of 0.0192 for the exchangeable and 0.0182 for the user-defined correlation structures are about the same as that obtained using the autoregressive structure (p=0.0164).

```
REPEATED SUBJECT=PAT / TYPE=CS;
```

```
          GEE Analysis Using PROC GENMOD
       Exchangeable (Compound Symmetric) Working Correlation (CS)

   Score Statistics For Type 3 GEE Analysis
                            Chi-
   Source              DF   Square    Pr > ChiSq

   TREAT               2     1.96      0.3745
   MONTH               5    45.41     <.0001
   TREAT*MONTH        10    21.28      0.0192
```

```
REPEATED SUBJECT=PAT /
TYPE=USER(1.0  0.9  0.8  0.7  0.7  0.7
          0.9  1.0  0.9  0.8  0.7  0.7
          0.8  0.9  1.0  0.9  0.8  0.7
          0.7  0.8  0.9  1.0  0.9  0.8
          0.7  0.7  0.8  0.9  1.0  0.9
          0.7  0.7  0.7  0.8  0.9  1.0);
```

```
          GEE Analysis Using PROC GENMOD
       User-Specified Working Correlation (USER())

        Score Statistics For Type 3 GEE Analysis
                              Chi-
        Source            DF  Square    Pr > ChiSq

        TREAT             2    2.05      0.3582
        MONTH             5   45.39     <.0001
        TREAT*MONTH      10   21.44      0.0182
```

▶ **8.4.14**   The term 'Time' has been used in this chapter to describe the study visit or time of measurement of the response variable during a trial. This is perhaps the most common *repeated measures* situation, especially for comparative drug studies. In general, however, the repeated factor need not refer to time at all.   The repeated factor could be a set of experimental conditions, each applied to the same set of patients in random order, such as subjecting each patient to each dose level of a test drug. The dose levels in this example represent the repeated measure, and the 'profiles' are the dose-response curves.

The *crossover* design (Chapter 9) is an example of this and can be analyzed with the *repeated measures ANOVA*. In the popular two-period *crossover*, the treatment (A or B) is the repeated factor, because both treatments A and B are given to each patient. The sequence group, representing the order in which patients receive the treatments (A-B or B-A), would represent the 'GROUP' effect. Patients are nested within sequence group, and the analysis would be carried out as in Example 8.1. A significant Treatment-by-Sequence group interaction would suggest a 'period effect', in which case, the analyst would perform separate analyses for each treatment period by using the *two-sample t-test*.

▶ **8.4.15**   This chapter focuses on response measurements assumed to be normally distributed. Non-normal data are also frequently collected in a *repeated measures* layout. Simple examples include studies in which the response measure is whether the patient is improving (binary response) or showing a categorical degree of improvement (e.g., 'none', 'some', 'complete') at each visit during the trial.

Analyses of non-normal data can often be handled by using categorical techniques. When the analysis includes additional factors or covariates, more sophisticated modeling using Weighted Least Squares (WLS) or Generalized Estimating Equations (GEE) can be employed. These techniques make use of the SAS procedures CATMOD and GENMOD, which can handle very complex designs.

> Note: Several different approaches to the analysis of repeated measures for categorical data, including WLS and GEE methodology, are illustrated in the excellent reference entitled, "Categorical Data Analysis Using the SAS System," Second Edition, by Stokes, Davis, and Koch, which was written under the SAS Books-by-Users program..

▶ **8.4.16**   Simple usage of the ODS statement to customize the SAS output is demonstrated in Examples 8.1, 8.2, and 8.3. Each section of the SAS output has an associated label and path name. ODS can be used to select or exclude specific sections of the output simply by identifying its name. Complete names can be determined from the SAS log by including the statement ODS TRACE ON as a statement within the SAS program.

Example 8.1 (Multivariate Approach) and Example 8.2 tell SAS to omit the printing of the correlation and covariance matrices, named PartialCorr and ErrorSSCP, by using an ODS EXCLUDE statement. Alternatively, you can use the ODS SELECT statement to include only specific parts of the output, as illustrated in Example 8.3. Obviously, these are very simple examples of using the powerful ODS features in SAS. Additional uses of the ODS EXCLUDE and ODS INCLUDE statements are used in other examples throughout this book.

The *Crossover Design*

9.1   Introduction

The *crossover design* is used to compare the mean responses of two or more treatments when each patient receives each treatment over successive time periods. Typically, patients are randomized to treatment sequence groups which determine the order of treatment administration.

While responses among treatments in a parallel study are considered independent, responses among treatments in a *crossover* study are correlated because they are measured on the same patient, much like the *repeated measures* setup discussed in Chapter 8. In fact, the *crossover* is a special case of a *repeated measures* design. Procedures for treatment comparisons must consider this correlation when analyzing data from a *crossover* design. In addition to treatment comparisons, the *crossover* analysis can also investigate period effects, sequence effects, and carryover effects.

Because the *crossover* study features within-patient control among treatment groups, fewer patients are generally required than with a parallel study. This advantage is often offset, however, by an increase in the length of the study. For example, when there are two treatments, the study will be at least twice as long as its parallel-design counterpart because treatments are studied in each of two successive periods. The addition of a wash-out period between treatments, which is usually required in a *crossover* study, tends to further lengthen the trial duration.

The *crossover* design is normally used in studies with short treatment periods, most frequently in pre-clinical and early-phase clinical studies, such as bioavailability, dose-ranging, bio-equivalence, and pharmacokinetic trials. If it's thought that the patient's condition will not be the same at the beginning of each treatment period, the *crossover* design should be avoided. Lengthier treatment periods provide increased opportunities for changing clinical conditions and premature termination. For the same reasons, *crossover* designs should limit the number of study periods as much as possible. The focus in this chapter is on the 2-period *crossover* design, although an example that uses 4 periods is also presented. Responses are assumed to be normally distributed.

9.2   Synopsis

For the two-way *crossover* design, each patient receives two treatments, A and B, in one of two sequences, that is, A followed by B (A-B) or B followed by A (B-A). Samples of n_1 and n_2 patients are randomly assigned to each of the two sequence groups, A-B and B-A, respectively (usually, $n_1 = n_2$). Response measurements (y_{ijk}) are taken for each patient following each treatment for a total of $N = 2n_1 + 2n_2$ measurements, where y_{ijk} is the measurement for the kth patient in the sequence group for which Treatment i (i$=1$ for Treatment A, i$=2$ for Treatment B) is given in Period j (j$=1, 2$). A sample layout is shown in Table 9.1.

TABLE 9.1. Crossover Layout

Sequence	Patient Number	Period 1	Period 2
		(Treatment A)	(Treatment B)
A-B	1	y_{111}	y_{221}
	3	y_{112}	y_{222}
	6	y_{113}	y_{223}
	7	y_{114}	y_{224}
	.	.	.
	.	.	.
	.	.	.
		(Treatment B)	(Treatment A)
B-A	2	y_{211}	y_{121}
	4	y_{212}	y_{122}
	5	y_{213}	y_{123}
	8	y_{214}	y_{124}
	.	.	.
	.	.	.
	.	.	.

The data are analyzed using *analysis of variance* methods with the following factors: Treatment Group, Period, Sequence, and Patient-within-Sequence. Computations proceed as shown in Chapters 6, 7, and 8 to obtain the ANOVA summary shown in Table 9.2.

TABLE 9.2. ANOVA Summary Table for a 2-Period Crossover

Source	df	SS	MS	F
Treatment (T)	1	SST	MST	$F_T = MST / MSE$
Period (P)	1	SSP	MSP	$F_P = MSP / MSE$
Sequence (S)	1	SSS	MSS	$F_S = MSS / MSP(S)$
Patient-within-Seqence (P(S))	n_1+n_2-2	SSP(S)	MSP(S)	
Error	n_1+n_2-2	SSE	MSE	
Total	N–1	TOT(SS)		

The Treatment sum of squares, SST, is proportional to the sum of squared deviations of each Treatment mean from the overall mean. Likewise, SSP is computed from the sum of squared deviations of each Period mean from the overall mean, etc. The mean squares (MS) are found by dividing the sums of squares (SS) by their respective degrees of freedom (df). Computations are shown in Example 9.1.

The hypothesis of equal treatment means is tested at a two-tailed significance level, α, by comparing the *F-test* statistic, F_T, with the critical F-value based on 1 upper and n_1+n_2-2 lower degrees of freedom, denoted by $F^1_{n_1+n_2-2}(\alpha)$. The test summary for no treatment effect is

> **null hypothesis**: H_0: $\mu_A = \mu_B$
> **alt. hypothesis**: H_A: $\mu_A \neq \mu_B$
>
> **test statistic**: $F_T = \dfrac{MST}{MSE}$
>
> **decision rule**: reject H_0 if $F_T > F^1_{n_1+n_2-2}(\alpha)$

The Period and Sequence effects can also be tested in a similar manner. As in the *repeated measures ANOVA* (Chapter 8), the test for Sequence effect uses the mean square for Patient-within-Sequence in the denominator because patients are nested within sequence groups. When the hypothesis of no Sequence Group effect is true, variation between sequence groups simply reflects patient-to-patient variation.

9.3   Examples

Example 9.1 -- Diaphoresis Following Cardiac Medication

A preliminary study was conducted on 16 normal subjects to examine the time to perspiration following administration of a single dose of a new cardiac medication with known diaphoretic effects. Subjects were asked to walk on a treadmill at the clinic following dosing with the new medication (A), and again on a separate clinic visit following placebo (B). A two-period crossover *design was used with 8 subjects randomized to each of the two sequence groups. Time in minutes until the appearance of perspiration beads on the forehead was recorded as shown in Table 9.3. Is there any difference in perspiration times?*

TABLE 9.3. Raw Data for Example 9.1

Sequence	Subject Number	Period 1	Period 2
		(A)	(B)
A-B	1	6	4
	3	8	7
	5	12	6
	6	7	8
	9	9	10
	10	6	4
	13	11	6
	15	8	8
		(B)	(A)
B-A	2	7	5
	4	6	9
	7	11	7
	8	7	4
	11	8	9
	12	4	5
	14	9	8
	16	13	9

Solution

Using the two-way *crossover ANOVA*, you want to compare mean perspiration times between treatment groups, controlling for treatment period and sequence (order) of administration. For a balanced design, the sum of squares for each of these sources can be computed in the same manner as demonstrated previously (Chapters 6, 7, 8). First, obtain the marginal means, as shown in Table 9.4.

TABLE 9.4. Summary of Marginal Means for Example 9.1

Sequence	Subject Number	Period 1	Period 2	Subject Means
		(A)	(B)	
A-B	1	6	4	5.0
	3	8	7	7.5
	5	12	6	9.0
	6	7	8	7.5
	9	9	10	9.5
	10	6	4	5.0
	13	11	6	8.5
	15	8	8	8.0
Sequence Means		8.375	6.625	7.5000
		(B)	(A)	
B-A	2	5	7	6.0
	4	9	6	7.5
	7	7	11	9.0
	8	4	7	5.5
	11	9	8	8.5
	12	5	4	4.5
	14	8	9	8.5
	16	9	13	11.0
Sequence Means		7.000	8.125	7.5625
Overall Means		7.6875	7.3750	7.53125

Treatment A Mean: 8.2500   Treatment B Mean: 6.8125

Now, you can compute the sum of squares as follows:

$$\text{SS(Treatment)} = (16 \cdot (8.2500 - 7.53125)^2) + (16 \cdot (6.8125 - 7.53125)^2)$$
$$= 16.53125$$

$$\text{SS(Period)} = (16 \cdot (7.6875 - 7.53125)^2) + (16 \cdot (7.3750 - 7.53125)^2)$$
$$= 0.78125$$

$$\text{SS(Sequence)} = (16 \cdot (7.5000 - 7.53125)^2) + (16 \cdot (7.5625 - 7.53125)^2)$$
$$= 0.03125$$

$$\text{TOTAL(SS)} = ((6 - 7.53125)^2 + (8 - 7.53125)^2 + \ldots + (13 - 7.53125)^2)$$
$$= 167.96875$$

SS(Patients-within-Sequence)

$$= ((5.0 - 7.5000)^2 + (7.5 - 7.5000)^2 + \ldots + (8.0 - 7.5000)^2 +$$
$$(6.0 - 7.5625)^2 + (7.5 - 7.5625)^2 + \ldots + (11.0 - 7.5625)^2)$$

$$= 103.4375$$

Because this is a balanced design, the error sum of squares can be found by subtraction,

$$\text{SS(Error)} \quad = \text{TOTAL(SS)} - (\text{SS(TRT)} + \text{SS(PD)} + \text{SS(SEQ)} + \text{SS(PAT(SEQ))})$$

$$= 167.96875 - (16.53125 + 0.78125 + 0.03125 + 103.4375)$$

$$= 47.1875$$

Completing the ANOVA table, you obtain

Table 9.5. ANOVA Summary for Example 9.1

Source	df	SS	MS	F
Treatment (T)	1	16.53125	16.53125	4.90
Period (P)	1	0.78125	0.78125	0.23
Sequence (S)	1	0.03125	0.03125	0.004
Patient-within Sequence (P(S))	14	103.4375	7.38839	
Error	14	47.1875	3.37054	
Total	31	167.96875		

The test summary for Treatment effect becomes

null hypothesis: H_0: $\mu_A = \mu_B$

alt. hypothesis: H_A: $\mu_A \neq \mu_B$

test statistic: $F_T = 4.90$

decision rule: reject H_0 if $F_T > F_{14}^{1}(0.05) = 4.60$

conclusion: Because $4.90 > 4.60$, you reject H_0 and conclude that the new medication and placebo have different diaphoretic profiles, based on a significance level of $\alpha = 0.05$.

SAS Analysis of Example 9.1

The SAS code for analyzing this data set and resulting output are shown below. All four sources of variation (Sequence Group, Treatment, Period, and Patient) must appear in the CLASS statement ❶ in PROC GLM. Note that the MODEL statement in PROC GLM is very similar to that of the *repeated measures ANOVA* (Chapter 8) ❷. The Sequence Group (SEQ) represents the two randomized groups, and patients are nested within Sequence Group. Therefore, a TEST statement is needed to conduct the appropriate *F-test* for the Sequence Group effect using the PAT(SEQ) as the error term ❸.

The SS3 option in the MODEL statement requests printing the SAS Type III results only. Because this data set is balanced, the Type I and III results would be identical. The *ANOVA* results shown in Output 9.1 ❹ agree with the manual calculations. The Treatment effect has a significant p-value of 0.0439 ❺, which indicates a departure from the null hypothesis of equal treatment means. Neither the Sequence effect (which tests for differences in the order of administration) nor the Period effect (which tests for differences between periods) are significant (p=0.9491 and 0.6376, respectively).

SAS Code for Example 9.1

```
DATA XOVER;
    INPUT PAT SEQ $ TRT $ PD Y @@;
    DATALINES;
 1 AB A 1   6    3 AB A 1  8    5 AB A 1 12    6 AB A 1  7
 9 AB A 1   9   10 AB A 1  6   13 AB A 1 11   15 AB A 1  8
 1 AB B 2   4    3 AB B 2  7    5 AB B 2  6    6 AB B 2  8
 9 AB B 2  10   10 AB B 2  4   13 AB B 2  6   15 AB B 2  8
 2 BA A 2   7    4 BA A 2  6    7 BA A 2 11    8 BA A 2  7
11 BA A 2   8   12 BA A 2  4   14 BA A 2  9   16 BA A 2 13
 2 BA B 1   5    4 BA B 1  9    7 BA B 1  7    8 BA B 1  4
11 BA B 1   9   12 BA B 1  5   14 BA B 1  8   16 BA B 1  9
;

PROC GLM DATA = XOVER;
    CLASS SEQ TRT PD PAT;                         ❶
    MODEL Y = SEQ PAT(SEQ) TRT PD / SS3;          ❷
        TEST H=SEQ  E=PAT(SEQ);                   ❸
    TITLE1 'Crossover Design';
    TITLE2 'Example 9.1: Diaphoresis Following Cardiac
            Medication';
RUN;
```

OUTPUT 9.1. SAS Output for Example 9.1

```
                          Crossover Design
           Example 9.1: Diaphoresis Following Cardiac Medication

                            The GLM Procedure

                        Class Level Information

        Class          Levels    Values

        SEQ               2      AB BA
        TRT               2      A B
        PD                2      1 2
        PAT              16      1 2 3 4 5 6 7 8 9 10 11 12 13 14 15 16

                    Number of observations    32


Dependent Variable: Y
                                  Sum of
        Source          DF       Squares    Mean Square   F Value   Pr > F

        Model           17    120.7812500     7.1047794     2.11    0.0824


        Error           14     47.1875000     3.3705357


        Corrected Total 31    167.9687500



                  R-Square      Coeff Var      Root MSE        Y Mean

                  0.719070      24.37712       1.835902       7.531250



        Source          DF    Type III SS   Mean Square   F Value   Pr > F
                                                ❹
        SEQ             1       0.0312500     0.0312500     0.01    0.9247
        PAT(SEQ)        14    103.4375000     7.3883929     2.19    0.0771
        TRT             1      16.5312500    16.5312500     4.90    0.0439 ❺
        PD              1       0.7812500     0.7812500     0.23    0.6376


        Tests of Hypotheses Using the Type III MS for PAT(SEQ) as an Error
        Term

        Source          DF    Type III SS   Mean Square   F Value   Pr > F

        SEQ             1      0.03125000    0.03125000     0.00    0.9491
```

The next example illustrates the analysis of a 4-period *crossover* design, including a test for carryover effect using SAS.

⁄⁄ **Example 9.2** -- Antibiotic Blood Levels Following Aerosol Inhalation

Normal subjects were enrolled in a pilot study to compare blood levels among 4 doses (A, B, C, and D) of an antibiotic using a new aerosol delivery formulation. The response measure is area-under-the-curve (AUC) up to 6 hours after dosing. A 4-period crossover design was used with a 3-day wash-out period between doses. Three subjects were randomized to each of four sequence groups, as shown in Table 9.6 along with the data (given as log-AUC's). Are there any differences in blood levels among the 4 doses?

TABLE 9.6. Raw Data for Example 9.2

Dosing Sequence	Subject Number	Period 1	Period 2	Period 3	Period 4
A-B-D-C	102	2.31	3.99	11.75	4.78
	106	3.95	2.07	7.00	4.20
	109	4.40	6.40	9.76	6.12
B-C-A-D	104	6.81	8.38	1.26	10.56
	105	9.05	6.85	4.79	4.86
	111	7.02	5.70	3.14	7.65
C-D-B-A	101	6.00	4.79	2.35	3.81
	108	5.25	10.42	5.68	4.48
	112	2.60	6.97	3.60	7.54
D-A-C-B	103	8.15	3.58	8.79	4.94
	107	12.73	5.31	4.67	5.84
	110	6.46	2.42	4.58	1.37

Solution

Treatment, Period, and Sequence effects are computed in the same way as presented for Example 9.1. Going directly to the SAS analysis of these data, a test for any treatment carryover effects is included. The carryover effect is somewhat entangled with the treatment effect. To separate them, you need to compute both the adjusted and unadjusted treatment effects and include a carry-over effect in the ANOVA model. In SAS, this can be done by obtaining both the Type I and Type III results from PROC GLM, as shown in the SAS analysis that follows.

SAS Analysis of Example 9.2

The data are input in data lines according to Sequence Group (SEQGRP) and Patient (PAT), as shown in the INHAL1 data set in the SAS code for Example 9.2. The Dose Group (DOSE) and Period (PER) variables are added in the data set INHAL2 ❻ using the OUTPUT statement in the DATA step. The final data set for analysis, INHAL, is created to include a character-valued variable for the carryover effect, CO ❼, whose values represent the dose group from the previous period. A value of 0 is assigned to CO for the first period.

Three additional carryover effects are included, one for each pairwise difference. Select Dose D as the 'reference' dose and define COA, COB, and COC as the difference in carryover effect between Doses A and D, B and D, and C and D, respectively. Thus, COA will take the value of +1 if Dose A was given in the previous period, –1 if Dose D was given in the previous period, and 0 otherwise. Similarly for COB and COC. The printout of the data set INHAL shows the values of each of these carryover effects ❽.

PROC GLM is used to analyze the data. Initially, the overall carryover effect, CO, is included in the crossover analysis (this is referred to as "Model 1"). The MODEL statement ❾ includes effects for Sequence Group (SEQGRP), Dose Group (DOSE), Period (PER), Patient-within-Sequence Group (PAT(SEQGRP)), and the overall carryover (CO).

The carryover effect has a sum of squares of 30.936 and a p-value of 0.0687 ❿, which deserves further analysis because of its marginal significance. You can run a second GLM model that includes the individual dose carryover effects (relative to Dose D) by including COA, COB, and COC in the MODEL statement (this is referred to as "Model 2") ⓫. This second GLM model separates the overall carryover effect sum of squares into the components due to each dose comparison. Note that the Type I sums of squares for COA, COB, and COC in Model 2 ⓬ add up to the sum of squares for CO in Model 1. The largest component of carryover is clearly due to Dose B, which has a significant p-value of 0.0267 ⓭.

The Dose Group effect adjusted for carryover is highly significant in both Models 1 ⓮ and 2 ⓯ (p=0.0001). No Sequence Group (p=0.6526) ⓰ or Period effects (p=0.7947) ⓱ are evident.

SAS Code for Example 9.2

```
DATA INHAL1;
    INPUT SEQGRP $ PAT AUC1 AUC2 AUC3 AUC4   @@;
    DATALINES;
ABDC 102   2.31   3.99 11.75   4.78
ABDC 106   3.95   2.07   7.00   4.20
ABDC 109   4.40   6.40   9.76   6.12
BCAD 104   6.81   8.38   1.26 10.56
BCAD 105   9.05   6.85   4.79   4.86
BCAD 111   7.02   5.70   3.14   7.65
CDBA 101   6.00   4.79   2.35   3.81
```

```
CDBA 108  5.25 10.42  5.68  4.48
CDBA 112  2.60  6.97  3.60  7.54
DACB 103  8.15  3.58  8.79  4.94
DACB 107 12.73  5.31  4.67  5.84
DACB 110  6.46  2.42  4.58  1.37
;

DATA INHAL2; SET INHAL1;
    DOSE = SUBSTR(SEQGRP,1,1); PER = 1; AUC = AUC1; OUTPUT;
    DOSE = SUBSTR(SEQGRP,2,1); PER = 2; AUC = AUC2; OUTPUT;    ❻
    DOSE = SUBSTR(SEQGRP,3,1); PER = 3; AUC = AUC3; OUTPUT;
    DOSE = SUBSTR(SEQGRP,4,1); PER = 4; AUC = AUC4; OUTPUT;
RUN;

PROC SORT DATA = INHAL2; BY PAT PER;
DATA INHAL; SET INHAL2;
    KEEP PAT SEQGRP DOSE PER AUC CO COA COB COC;
    CO = LAG(DOSE); IF PER = 1 THEN CO = '0';             ❼
    COA = 0; COB = 0; COC = 0;
    IF CO = 'A' THEN COA = 1;
    IF CO = 'B' THEN COB = 1;
    IF CO = 'C' THEN COC = 1;
    IF CO = 'D' THEN DO;
        COA = -1; COB = -1; COC = -1;
    END;
RUN;

PROC SORT DATA = INHAL; BY SEQGRP PER PAT;
PROC PRINT DATA = INHAL;
    TITLE1 'CrossOver Design';                            ❽
    TITLE2 'Example 9.2: Antibiotic Blood Levels Following
           Aerosol Inhalation' ;
RUN;

/* Model 1 */
PROC GLM DATA = INHAL;
    CLASS SEQGRP DOSE PER PAT CO;
    MODEL AUC = SEQGRP PAT(SEQGRP) DOSE PER CO;           ❾
        TEST H=SEQGRP  E=PAT(SEQGRP);
    TITLE3 'Model 1';
RUN;

/* Model 2 */
PROC GLM DATA = INHAL;
    CLASS SEQGRP DOSE PER PAT;
    MODEL AUC = SEQGRP PAT(SEQGRP) DOSE PER COA COB COC;   ⓫
        TEST H=SEQGRP  E=PAT(SEQGRP);
    TITLE3 'Model 2';
RUN;
```

OUTPUT 9.2. SAS Output for Example 9.2

```
                            CrossOver Design
        Example 9.2: Antibiotic Blood Levels Following Aerosol Inhalation


        Obs   PAT    SEQGRP    DOSE   PER    AUC    CO    COA    COB    COC

         1    102    ABDC       A      1     2.31    0     0      0      0
         2    106    ABDC       A      1     3.95    0     0      0      0
         3    109    ABDC       A      1     4.40    0     0      0      0
         4    102    ABDC       B      2     3.99    A     1      0      0
         5    106    ABDC       B      2     2.07    A     1      0      0
         6    109    ABDC       B      2     6.40    A     1      0      0
         7    102    ABDC       D      3    11.75    B     0      1      0
         8    106    ABDC       D      3     7.00    B     0      1      0
         9    109    ABDC       D      3     9.76    B     0      1      0
        10    102    ABDC       C      4     4.78    D    -1     -1     -1
        11    106    ABDC       C      4     4.20    D    -1     -1     -1
        12    109    ABDC       C      4     6.12    D    -1     -1     -1
        13    104    BCAD       B      1     6.81    0     0      0      0
        14    105    BCAD       B      1     9.05    0     0      0      0
        15    111    BCAD       B      1     7.02    0     0      0      0
        16    104    BCAD       C      2     8.38    B     0      1      0
        17    105    BCAD       C      2     6.85    B     0      1      0
        18    111    BCAD       C      2     5.70    B     0      1      0   ❽
        19    104    BCAD       A      3     1.26    C     0      0      1
        20    105    BCAD       A      3     4.79    C     0      0      1
        21    111    BCAD       A      3     3.14    C     0      0      1
        22    104    BCAD       D      4    10.56    A     1      0      0
        23    105    BCAD       D      4     4.86    A     1      0      0
        24    111    BCAD       D      4     7.65    A     1      0      0
        25    101    CDBA       C      1     6.00    0     0      0      0
        26    108    CDBA       C      1     5.25    0     0      0      0
        27    112    CDBA       C      1     2.60    0     0      0      0
        28    101    CDBA       D      2     4.79    C     0      0      1
        29    108    CDBA       D      2    10.42    C     0      0      1
        30    112    CDBA       D      2     6.97    C     0      0      1
        31    101    CDBA       B      3     2.35    D    -1     -1     -1
        32    108    CDBA       B      3     5.68    D    -1     -1     -1
        33    112    CDBA       B      3     3.60    D    -1     -1     -1
        34    101    CDBA       A      4     3.81    B     0      1      0
        35    108    CDBA       A      4     4.48    B     0      1      0
        36    112    CDBA       A      4     7.54    B     0      1      0
        37    103    DACB       D      1     8.15    0     0      0      0
        38    107    DACB       D      1    12.73    0     0      0      0
        39    110    DACB       D      1     6.46    0     0      0      0
        40    103    DACB       A      2     3.58    D    -1     -1     -1
        41    107    DACB       A      2     5.31    D    -1     -1     -1
        42    110    DACB       A      2     2.42    D    -1     -1     -1
        43    103    DACB       C      3     8.79    A     1      0      0
        44    107    DACB       C      3     4.67    A     1      0      0
        45    110    DACB       C      3     4.58    A     1      0      0
        46    103    DACB       B      4     4.94    C     0      0      1
        47    107    DACB       B      4     5.84    C     0      0      1
        48    110    DACB       B      4     1.37    C     0      0      1
```

OUTPUT 9.2. SAS Output for Example 9.2 (*continued*)

```
                              CrossOver Design
          Example 9.2: Antibiotic Blood Levels Following Aerosol Inhalation
                                   Model 1

                              The GLM Procedure

                         Class Level Information
        Class     Levels   Values

        SEQGRP       4     ABDC BCAD CDBA DACB

        DOSE         4     A B C D

        PER          4     1 2 3 4

        PAT         12     101 102 103 104 105 106 107 108 109 110 111 112

        CO           5     0 A B C D


                       Number of observations     48


Dependent Variable: AUC
                              Sum of
Source                DF      Squares      Mean Square  F Value  Pr > F

Model                 20    225.1866862    11.2593343    2.90    0.0053
Error                 27    104.8902450     3.8848239
Corrected Total       47    330.0769312

            R-Square      Coeff Var      Root MSE      AUC Mean

            0.682225      34.38658       1.970996      5.731875

Source          DF     Type I SS      Mean Square   F Value   Pr > F

SEQGRP           3     7.1111896      2.3703965      0.61     0.6142
PAT(SEQGRP)      8    48.6932667      6.0866583      1.57     0.1815
DOSE             3   134.4534729     44.8178243     11.54    <.0001
PER              3     3.9931229      1.3310410      0.34     0.7947
CO               3    30.9356342     10.3118781      2.65     0.0687


Source          DF    Type III SS    Mean Square   F Value   Pr > F

SEQGRP           3    10.3361626      3.4453875      0.89     0.4604
PAT(SEQGRP)      8    48.6932667      6.0866583      1.57     0.1815
DOSE             3   118.0792959     39.3597653     10.13     0.0001 ⑭
PER              2     0.0628167      0.0314083      0.01     0.9920
CO               3    30.9356342     10.3118781      2.65     0.0687 ❿


Tests of Hypotheses Using the Type III MS for PAT(SEQGRP) as an Error
Term

Source          DF    Type III SS    Mean Square   F Value   Pr > F

SEQGRP           3    10.33616258    3.44538753     0.57     0.6526
```

OUTPUT 9.2. SAS Output for Example 9.2 (*continued*)

```
                         CrossOver Design
       Example 9.2: Antibiotic Blood Levels Following Aerosol Inhalation
                             Model 2

                         The GLM Procedure

                       Class Level Information
       Class     Levels   Values

       SEQGRP       4      ABDC BCAD CDBA DACB
       DOSE         4      A B C D
       PER          4      1 2 3 4
       PAT         12      101 102 103 104 105 106 107 108 109 110 111 112

                       Number of observations     48
```

Dependent Variable: AUC

Source	DF	Sum of Squares	Mean Square	F Value	Pr > F
Model	20	225.1866862	11.2593343	2.90	0.0053
Error	27	104.8902450	3.8848239		
Corrected Total	47	330.0769312			

R-Square	Coeff Var	Root MSE	AUC Mean
0.682225	34.38658	1.970996	5.731875

Source	DF	Type I SS	Mean Square	F Value	Pr > F
SEQGRP	3	7.1111896	2.3703965	0.61	0.6142
PAT(SEQGRP)	8	48.6932667	6.0866583	1.57	0.1815
DOSE	3	134.4534729	44.8178243	11.54	<.0001
PER	3	3.9931229	1.3310410	0.34	0.7947
COA	1	0.0870204	0.0870204	0.02	0.8821
COB	1	21.3521113 ❶❷	21.3521113	5.50	0.0267 ❶❸
COC	1	9.4965025	9.4965025	2.44	0.1296

Source	DF	Type III SS	Mean Square	F Value	Pr > F
SEQGRP	3	10.3361626	3.4453875	0.89	0.4604
PAT(SEQGRP)	8	48.6932667	6.0866583	1.57	0.1815
DOSE	3	118.0792959	39.3597653	10.13	0.0001 ❶❺
PER	3	3.9931229	1.3310410	0.34	0.7947 ❶❼
COA	1	1.9374669	1.9374669	0.50	0.4861
COB	1	28.9850625	28.9850625	7.46	0.0110
COC	1	9.4965025	9.4965025	2.44	0.1296

Tests of Hypotheses Using the Type III MS for PAT(SEQGRP) as an Error Term

Source	DF	Type III SS	Mean Square	F Value	Pr > F
SEQGRP	3	10.33616258	3.44538753	0.57	0.6526 ❶❻

9.4 Details & Notes

▶ **9.4.1** Study resources might be wasted by conducting *crossover* studies that are likely to yield inconsistent treatment differences among periods. This scenario could arise from a carryover effect of certain treatments, improper wash-out periods between treatments, or the inability of patients to be restored to their original baseline conditions at the start of each period.

Designs balanced for residual effects should be used whenever possible with *crossover* studies. Such schemes have the property that each treatment is preceded by every other treatment the same number of times. The presence of treatment carryover effects can easily be investigated with these types of designs. The layout used in Example 9.2 is that of a 4-treatment design balanced for residuals. In this design, four sequence groups are used, and each treatment is preceded by each of the other treatments exactly once.

An example of a 3-treatment (A, B, and C), 3-period *crossover* design balanced for residuals is shown in Table 9.5. Six sequence groups are used, and each treatment is preceded by every other treatment exactly twice. Note that such balance would not be possible with only three sequence groups. In general, if k represents the number of treatments, the minimum number of sequence groups needed for complete residual balance is k, if k is even, and 2k, if k is odd.

TABLE 9.5. A 3-Period Crossover Design Balanced for Residuals

Sequence	Period 1	Period 2	Period 3
1	A	B	C
2	B	C	A
3	C	A	B
4	A	C	B
5	B	A	C
6	C	B	A

Study design features should also include an adequate wash-out duration between treatment periods. As previously mentioned, the length of the trial and the number of periods should also be limited to minimize changing clinical conditions of the patients during the study.

▶ **9.4.2** In a two-period *crossover design* under the assumption of no carryover effect (such as in Example 9.1), the Period effect is completely confounded with the Treatment-by-Sequence Group interaction. In other words, any difference between Sequence Groups in the Treatment comparisons are indistinguishable from Period differences. The results of Example 9.1 would be identical if the PD effect is replaced with the TRT*SEQ interaction in the MODEL statement in PROC GLM.

Similarly, a Treatment effect implies that response differences between Period 1 and Period 2 are in opposite directions for the two Sequence Groups, i.e., a Period-by-Sequence Group interaction. The Treatment (TRT) effect in the MODEL statement in PROC GLM used in Example 9.1 could be replaced with this interaction (PD*SEQ) with the same results. When the MODEL statement is written in this way, it is identical to the form discussed for the general *repeated measures ANOVA* of Chapter 8.

The preceding interactions cannot be used interchangeably with main effects in *crossovers* that involve more than two periods or those in which a carryover effect might exist.

▶ **9.4.3**   In the *crossover* analysis, the presence of a Treatment-by-Period interaction generally requires separate analyses within each period using, for example, the *two-sample t-test* (Chapter 5). In such a situation, many analysts accept only the results of the first period.

▶ **9.4.4**   Dropouts following the first period will create bias in the analysis of the *crossover* study. For example, in the two-way *crossover*, the 'within-patient control' advantage of the *crossover* is lost when a patient has data from the first period, but not from the second. Whether that patient is dropped from the analysis or the analysis is adjusted for the missing value (e.g., use of imputation), the results will likely have some unknown bias. If there are many dropouts, the primary analysis might use just the data from the first period. Because dropout rates usually increase with lengthier studies, this problem can be controlled by using a small number of short treatment periods whenever a *crossover* design is contemplated.

▶ **9.4.5**   In Example 9.2, the SAS Type I sums of squares for Dose Group (DOSE), Period (PER), and Sequence Group (SEQGRP) are unadjusted for carryover effects. These are the same SS's that would be obtained if the carryover terms (CO or COA, COB, COC) were omitted from the model (Model 2). Tests for a significant Dose Group effect would typically use the Type III sum of squares, which is adjusted for residuals. However, when a significant carryover effect is found, caution must be used in the interpretation of the Treatment effects (see Section 9.4.7).

▶ **9.4.6**   The term 'balanced residuals' implies that, if the carryover effect is the same for each treatment, these effects will be cancelled when looking at differences in treatment means, and thus, the true treatment difference is free of any carryover effects. Biased estimates of treatment differences will result if the residuals are not balanced across treatment groups.

▶ **9.4.7**   To check for different degrees of carryover among treatments, a preliminary test for carryover effects can be made in the manner demonstrated in Example 9.2. Such preliminary tests for model assumptions are often conducted at a significance level greater than 0.05, perhaps in the 0.10 to 0.20 range. If non-significant, the carryover effect can be dropped from the model.

The p-value for the overall carryover effect of 0.0687 in Example 9.2 is small enough to raise concern regarding carryover.

Significant carryover effects might provide useful information for designing future studies (e.g., using a longer observation period and/or a longer wash-out period).

▶ **9.4.8**   Although this chapter introduces the *crossover design* for normal response data, *crossover designs* can also be performed with non-normal responses, which include categorical and rank data. Using binary responses and non-parametric approaches to the analysis of non-normal responses in *crossovers* are discussed in Jones and Kenward (1989), and examples using SAS are included in Stokes, Davis, and Koch (2000).

CHAPTER 10

Linear Regression

10.1 Introduction

Regression analysis is used to analyze the relationship between a response, y, and a quantitative factor, x. Knowledge of this relationship can be important for predicting unmeasured responses from a known x-value.

Examples where regression analysis might be useful in clinical data analysis include the modeling of blood pressure response (y) on the dose of a new anti-hypertensive drug (x), cholesterol level (y) on patient's age (x), pain relief (y) on time after dosing with an anti-inflammatory treatment (x), or degree of wound healing (y) on the baseline surface area of a burn wound (x).

While a number of potential relationships between x and y might be considered, in this chapter, the focus is on linear relationships only. *Simple linear regression* methodology provides an estimate of the best-fitting line through a set of data points, (x_1,y_1), (x_2,y_2),..., (x_n,y_n). You can then determine the significance of the linear relationship or correlation, predict future responses, estimate mean responses for expected x-values, and make inferences regarding the slope of the regression line.

10.2 Synopsis

Given a number of observed values of a normally distributed response variable, $(y_1, y_2,..., y_n)$, the mean, $\overline{y}$, represents the best estimate of a future response. The idea behind regression analysis is to improve this estimate by using the value of some related factor, x. If x and y have a known linear relationship, the best estimate of y will be a linear function of the known value, x.

A linear relationship between a response, y, and an independent variable, x, can be expressed as

$$y = \alpha + \beta x + \varepsilon$$

where α is the intercept and β is the slope, as shown in Figure 10.1. Because the response is subject to random measurement error, y might differ in repeated sampling for the same value of x. The ε accounts for this random nature of the response y.

Figure 10.1. Simple Linear Regression of y on x

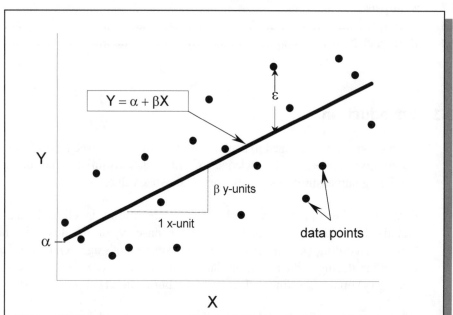

Typically, you have n pairs of coordinates, $((x_i, y_i)$, for i = 1, 2, ..., n), and assume that the y_i's are independent, normally distributed, and have the same variance, σ^2, for all x values. From these data, you estimate the model parameters α and β by **a** and **b**, respectively, in such a way that the resulting 'prediction equation'

$$\hat{y} = a + b x$$

is the 'best-fitting' line through the measured coordinates. In this sense, the prediction equation represents the best estimate of the unknown regression model.

You seek values for **a** and **b** such that the predicted response, $\hat{y}$, is as close as possible to the observed response, y, for all measured data points. One way to satisfy this requirement is to minimize the sum of squared differences between y and $\hat{y}$

$$SSE = \sum_{i=1}^{n}(y_i - \hat{y}_i)^2$$

This is known as the Least Squares criterion. SSE is the sum of squared errors or deviations between the actual and predicted responses.

Define the quantities S_{yy}, S_{xx}, and S_{xy} as follows:

$$S_{yy} = \sum_{i=1}^{n}(y_i - \overline{y})^2 = \sum_{i=1}^{n}y_i^2 - n \cdot (\overline{y})^2$$

$$S_{xx} = \sum_{i=1}^{n}(x_i - \overline{x})^2 = \sum_{i=1}^{n}x_i^2 - n \cdot (\overline{x})^2$$

and

$$S_{xy} = \sum_{i=1}^{n}(x_i - \overline{x})(y_i - \overline{y}) = \sum_{i=1}^{n}x_i \cdot y_i - (n \cdot \overline{x} \cdot \overline{y})$$

The 'best-fitting' line based on the Least Squares criterion is given by

$$\hat{y} = a + bx$$

where $b = S_{xy} / S_{xx}$

and $a = \overline{y} - b\,\overline{x}$

The best estimate of the variance, σ^2, is $s^2 = SSE/(n-2)$, where SSE can be calculated from the formula:

$$SSE = \frac{S_{xx} \cdot S_{yy} - S_{xy}^2}{S_{xx}}$$

based on n–2 degrees of freedom.

The main question posed by *simple linear regression* concerns the significance of the slope parameter. If the slope β is 0, then the value of x will not improve the prediction of y over the ordinary predictor, $\overline{y}$. A significant slope β, indicating a linear relationship between x and y, means that knowledge of the x-values will significantly improve your prediction ability.

The statistical test is based on a function of the slope estimate, b, which has the t-distribution when the null hypothesis of '0 slope' is true. The test summary is

null hypothesis: H_0: $\beta = 0$
alt. hypothesis: H_A: $\beta \neq 0$

test statistic: $t = \dfrac{b}{s / \sqrt{S_{xx}}}$

decision rule: reject H_0 if $|t| > t_{\alpha/2,\, n-2}$

If the slope is meaningful, you can estimate the mean response at a given value of x, for example x_0, with a 95% confidence interval by

$$\hat{y}_{x_0} \pm t_{0.025, n-2} \cdot s \cdot \sqrt{\frac{1}{n} + \frac{(x_0 - \overline{x})^2}{S_{xx}}}$$

where $\hat{y}_{x_0} = a + b\, x_0$

10.3 Examples

Example 10.1 -- Anti-Anginal Response vs. Disease History

Treadmill stress tests were administered to patients with angina pectoris before and 4 weeks after once-daily dosing with an experimental anti-anginal medication. The investigator wanted to know if the improvement in exercise duration is related to the patient's disease history. Disease duration since initial diagnosis (in years) and percent-improvement in treadmill walking times are shown in Table 10.1 for a study with 20 patients enrolled. Is there a significant linear relationship between improvement on medication and disease duration?

TABLE 10.1. Raw Data for Example 10.1

Patient Number	(x) Disease Duration (years)	(y) % Improvement	Patient Number	(x) Disease Duration (years)	(y) % Improvement
1	1	40	11	1	60
2	1	90	12	4	0
3	3	30	13	2	50
4	2	30	14	2	110
5	1	80	15	3	20
6	5	60	16	3	70
7	1	10	17	5	-30
8	4	-10	18	3	20
9	2	50	19	1	40
10	6	40	20	6	0

Solution

Using the formulas presented, compute

$$\sum x_i = 56 \qquad \sum y_i = 760 \qquad \sum x_i \cdot y_i = 1570$$

$$\sum x_i^2 = 212 \qquad \sum y_i^2 = 52,200 \qquad n = 20$$

so that

$$S_{xx} = 212 - \frac{56^2}{20} = 55.2$$

$$S_{yy} = 52,200 - \frac{760^2}{20} = 23,320$$

$$S_{xy} = 1570 - \frac{56 \times 760}{20} = -558$$

The estimated regression equation is found as follows:

$$b = \frac{-558}{55.2} = -10.109$$

and

$$a = \frac{760}{20} - (-10.109) \cdot \frac{56}{20} = 66.304$$

which yield

$$\hat{y} = 66.304 - 10.109\,x$$

In addition, you find

$$SSE = \frac{(55.2)(23{,}320) - (-558)^2}{55.2} = 17{,}679.35$$

and

$$s = \sqrt{\frac{17{,}679.35}{18}} = 31.34$$

The regression slope, which represents the average change in y for a one-unit change in x, is the best estimate of the rate of improvement in treadmill performance for each one-year increase in disease duration, i.e., -10.109% per year. The statistical significance is determined by the *t-test*, summarized as follows:

null hypothesis: $H_0: \beta = 0$

alt. hypothesis: $H_A: \beta \neq 0$

test statistic: $t = \dfrac{-10.109}{31.34 / \sqrt{55.2}} = -2.40$

decision rule: reject H_0 if $|t| > t_{0.025,18}$ $(=2.101)$

conclusion: Because $2.40 > 2.101$, you reject H_0 and conclude that treadmill improvement has a significant linear relationship to disease duration.

The mean improvement in treadmill exercise time for the average patient with a 5-year history of angina is computed as

$$\hat{y}_5 = 66.304 - 10.109(5) = 15.76\%$$

The 95% confidence interval for this mean is

$$15.76 \pm 2.101 \cdot (31.34) \cdot \sqrt{\frac{1}{20} + \frac{(5-2.8)^2}{55.2}}$$

$$= 15.76 \pm 2.101 \cdot (11.629)$$

$$= 15.76 \pm 24.43$$

or (−8.67% to 40.19%). Because this interval contains 0, you would be inclined to conclude that the average treated patient with a 5-year history of angina does not have significant improvement in exercise tolerance.

SAS Analysis of Example 10.1

The SAS code for analyzing the data set in this example is shown below, and the resulting output is shown in Output 10.1. A printout of the data set is first obtained by using PROC PRINT ❶, followed by the summary statistics for the x and y values using PROC MEANS ❷.

For this example, the regression analysis is performed using PROC GLM, although PROC REG can also be used. When PROC GLM is used without a CLASS statement, SAS assumes that the independent variables in the MODEL statement are quantitative and performs a regression analysis.

SAS Code for Example 10.1

```
DATA ANGINA;
    INPUT PAT X_DUR Y_IMPR @@;
    DATALINES;
 1 1   40    2 1   90    3 3  30    4 2  30
 5 1   80    6 5   60    7 1  10    8 4 -10
 9 2   50   10 6   40   11 1  60   12 4   0
13 2   50   14 2  110   15 3  20   16 3  70
17 5  -30   18 3   20   19 1  40   20 6   0
;
```

```
PROC SORT DATA = ANGINA; BY X_DUR Y_IMPR;
PROC PRINT DATA = ANGINA;                          ❶
    VAR PAT X_DUR Y_IMPR;
    TITLE1 'Linear Regression & Correlation';
    TITLE2 'Example 10.1: Improvement in Angina vs.
           Disease Duration';
RUN;

PROC MEANS MEAN STD N;                             ❷
    VAR X_DUR Y_IMPR;
RUN;

PROC GLM DATA = ANGINA;
    MODEL Y_IMPR = X_DUR / P CLM SS1;              ❺
RUN;
```

The regression estimates, **a** and **b**, are printed in the Estimate column in Output 10.3 ❸. Note the *t-test* for slope is –2.40 with a p-value of 0.0276 ❹, which confirms the analysis using the calculating formulas.

The P and CLM options specified in the MODEL statement ❺ request the predicted values based on the regression equation for each data point, along with 95% confidence intervals for the mean response at the corresponding x values. For x=5 (Observations 17 and 18), the predicted response (15.7608) has a corresponding 95% confidence interval of -8.67 to 40.19 ❻, which confirms the manual calculations.

OUTPUT 10.1. SAS Output for Example 10.1

```
              Linear Regression & Correlation
     Example 10.1: Improvement in Angina vs. Disease Duration

              Obs      PAT     X_DUR     Y_IMPR

               1        7        1         10
               2        1        1         40
               3       19        1         40
               4       11        1         60
               5        5        1         80
               6        2        1         90
               7        4        2         30
               8        9        2         50
               9       13        2         50              ❶
              10       14        2        110
              11       15        3         20
              12       18        3         20
              13        3        3         30
              14       16        3         70
              15        8        4        -10
              16       12        4          0
              17       17        5        -30
              18        6        5         60
              19       20        6          0
              20       10        6         40
```

OUTPUT 10.1. SAS Output for Example 10.1 (*continued*)

```
                 Linear Regression & Correlation
        Example 10.1: Improvement in Angina vs. Disease Duration

                       The MEANS Procedure

❷
        Variable            Mean        Std Dev     N
        -------------------------------------------------
        X_DUR           2.8000000      1.7044833    20
        Y_IMPR         38.0000000     35.0338182    20
        -------------------------------------------------
```

```
                        The GLM Procedure

                  Number of observations    20

     Dependent Variable: Y_IMPR

                           Sum of
     Source           DF   Squares     Mean Square  F Value  Pr > F

     Model             1  5640.65217   5640.65217     5.74   0.0276
     Error            18 17679.34783    982.18599
     Corrected Total  19 23320.00000


         R-Square     Coeff Var     Root MSE    Y_IMPR Mean
         0.241880 ❽    82.47328     31.33985     38.00000

     Source        DF     Type I SS    Mean Square   F Value   Pr > F

     X_DUR          1   5640.652174   5640.652174     5.74 ❼  0.0276


                                  Standard
     Parameter        Estimate      Error     t Value   Pr > |t|

     Intercept      66.30434783 ❸  13.73346931    4.83     0.0001
     X_DUR         -10.10869565      4.21820157   -2.40     0.0276 ❹
```

OUTPUT 10.1. SAS Output for Example 10.1 (*continued*)

```
                      Linear Regression & Correlation
            Example 10.1: Improvement in Angina vs. Disease Duration

                           The GLM Procedure


                                              95% Confidence Limits for
   Observation  Observed    Predicted     Residual      Mean      Predicted
                                                                    Value

        1       10.0000000  56.1956522  -46.1956522  34.4879982  77.9033062
        2       40.0000000  56.1956522 - 16.1956522  34.4879982  77.9033062
        3       40.0000000  56.1956522  -16.1956522  34.4879982  77.9033062
        4       60.0000000  56.1956522    3.8043478  34.4879982  77.9033062
        5       80.0000000  56.1956522   23.8043478  34.4879982  77.9033062
        6       90.0000000  56.1956522   33.8043478  34.4879982  77.9033062
        7       30.0000000  46.0869565  -16.0869565  29.7460282  62.4278848
        8       50.0000000  46.0869565    3.9130435  29.7460282  62.4278848
        9       50.0000000  46.0869565    3.9130435  29.7460282  62.4278848
       10      110.0000000  46.0869565   63.9130435  29.7460282  62.4278848
       11       20.0000000  35.9782609  -15.9782609  21.1491101  50.8074117
       12       20.0000000  35.9782609  -15.9782609  21.1491101  50.8074117
       13       30.0000000  35.9782609   -5.9782609  21.1491101  50.8074117
       14       70.0000000  35.9782609   34.0217391  21.1491101  50.8074117
       15      -10.0000000  25.8695652  -35.8695652   7.7076388  44.0314916
       16        0.0000000  25.8695652  -25.8695652   7.7076388  44.0314916
       17      -30.0000000  15.7608696  -45.7608696  -8.6702890  40.1920281 ❻
       18       60.0000000  15.7608696   44.2391304  -8.6702890  40.1920281
       19        0.0000000   5.6521739   -5.6521739 -26.3006276  37.6049755
       20       40.0000000   5.6521739   34.3478261 -26.3006276  37.6049755


            Sum of Residuals                          -0.00000
            Sum of Squared Residuals               17679.34783
            Sum of Squared Residuals - Error SS        0.00000
            PRESS Statistic                        22187.33121
            First Order Autocorrelation               -0.05364
            Durbin-Watson D                            1.91983   ❾
```

Multiple Linear Regression

Simple linear regression refers to a single response variable, y, modeled on a single predictor variable, x. Sometimes, several quantitative factors (x_1, x_2, x_3, ...) are thought to affect a response, y. These predictors can be used simultaneously in a *multiple linear regression* equation of the form

$$y = b_0 + b_1 x_1 + b_2 x_2 + ... + b_k x_k$$

assuming k factors. Like the estimate b of β in the simple linear model, b_i estimates the unknown parameter, β_i, and is determined by the amount of contribution x_i makes to the prediction of y (for i = 1,2,...,k). Interpretation and estimation of the β_i's is the same as in the *simple linear regression* case. β_i represents the expected increase in response, y, for a 1-unit increase in x_i (when all other x's are held constant). These β_i's are estimated by using the Least Squares method. The REG procedure in SAS is used to illustrate this analysis, as shown in Example 10.2.

✐ **Example 10.2** -- Symptomatic Recovery in Pediatric Dehydration

A study was conducted to determine the degree of recovery that takes place 90 minutes following treatment of 36 children diagnosed at the clinic with moderate to severe dehydration. Upon diagnosis and study entry, patients were treated with an electrolytic solution at various dose levels (0, 0.5, 1.0, 1.5, 2.0, 2.5, 3.0 mEq/l) in a frozen, flavored, ice popsicle. The degree of rehydration was determined by using a subjective scale based on physical examination and parental input. These scores were converted to a 0 to 100 point scale, representing the percent of recovery. The child's age and weight were also recorded. Is recovery related to electrolyte dose based on the data shown in Table 10.2?

Solution

The regression procedure (PROC REG) in SAS is used to perform a *multiple linear regression* analysis, regressing the percent recovery at 90 minutes (y) on the concomitant variables Dose Level (X_1), Age (X_2), and Weight (X_3). Although, PROC GLM can also be used for this analysis, PROC REG has diagnostic and model building advantages for regression analysis when there are no class variables. In addition, multiple MODEL statements can be used with PROC REG.

In this example, the model is written

$$y = \beta_0 + \beta_1 x_1 + \beta_2 x_2 + \beta_3 x_3 + \varepsilon$$

where x_1 = dose (mEq/l), x_2 = patient's age (years), and x_3 = patient's weight (lbs.) are the independent or 'explanatory' variables. The parameters are β_0, which represents the overall average response, and β_i, which represents the average increase in the degree of recovery (y) for a one-unit increase in x_i (i = 1, 2, 3). The objective is to investigate the effect of Dose Level on response and how age and weight might influence that effect.

TABLE 10.2. Raw Data for Example 10.2

Patient Number	Degree of Recovery (%) (Y)	Dose (mEq/l) (X_1)	Age (yrs) (X_2)	Weight (lbs) (X_3)
1	77	0.0	4	28
2	65	1.5	5	35
3	75	2.5	8	55
4	63	1.0	9	76
5	75	0.5	5	31
6	82	2.0	5	27
7	70	1.0	6	35
8	90	2.5	6	47
9	49	0.0	9	59
10	72	3.0	8	50
11	67	2.0	7	50
12	100	2.5	7	46
13	75	1.5	4	33
14	58	3.0	8	59
15	58	1.5	6	40
16	55	0.0	8	58
17	80	1.0	7	55
18	55	2.0	10	76
19	44	0.5	9	66
20	62	1.0	6	43
21	60	1.0	6	48
22	75	2.5	7	50
23	77	1.5	5	29
24	80	2.5	11	64
25	68	3.0	9	61
26	71	2.5	10	71
27	90	1.5	4	26
28	80	2.0	3	27
29	70	0.0	9	56
30	58	2.5	8	57
31	88	1.0	3	22
32	68	0.5	5	37
33	60	0.5	6	44
34	90	3.0	5	45
35	79	1.5	8	53
36	90	2.0	4	29

SAS Analysis of Example 10.2

The SAS code and output for analyzing the data set in this example are shown on the following pages. A printout of the data set is first obtained using PROC PRINT ❿. The CORR option in PROC REG requests the inclusion of the correlation coefficients between each pair of variables in the output ⓫. Notice that Age and Weight are highly correlated (r=0.9367), and that the degree of recovery at 90 minutes after treatment (y) is positively correlated with dose and negatively correlated with Age and Weight.

The F-value 9.03 ⓬ for the MODEL statement is a global test of the hypothesis,

$$H_0: \beta_1 = \beta_2 = \beta_3 = 0$$
vs.
$$H_a: \beta_1 = 0, \text{ or } \beta_2 = 0, \text{ or } \beta_3 = 0$$

This is highly significant (p=0.0002) indicating that the response is linearly related to at least one of the independent variables.

The prediction model can be written from the parameter estimates ⓭ as

$$\hat{y} = 85.48 + (6.17 \times \text{Dose}) + (0.28 \times \text{Age}) - (0.54 \times \text{Weight})$$

The β_i's can be tested individually for equality to 0 using the *t-test*, as shown in Example 10.1. SAS prints these tests with the corresponding p-values as shown in Output 10.2 ⓮. Dose Level is significant (p = 0.0016), while Age (p=0.9043) and Weight (p=0.1032) are not, based on this model.

One method to check the 'goodness-of-fit' of a regression model is by its coefficient of determination, R^2. You see an R^2 of 0.4584 ⓯, which indicates that about 46% of the variability of the measured responses can be accounted for by the explanatory variables, Dose Level, Age, and Weight. Sometimes there can be other (unmeasured) explanatory variables that might increase R^2 by their inclusion in the model which leads to a better fit, or the relationship might be a non-linear one. Many times, much of the unexplained variation is simply due to measurement error or the random nature of the responses that cannot be measured.

Multiple MODEL statements can be used in PROC REG. These are labeled consecutively in the SAS output (MODEL1, MODEL2, etc.) according to the order specified in the PROC REG syntax. The second MODEL statement (see SAS code for Example 10.2) requests a *simple linear regression* and uses Dose Level as the only explanatory variable. The output shows a significant linear relationship between Dose and response (p = 0.0313) when Age and Weight are not included. However, the R^2 has been reduced to only 12.9% ⓰, which indicates a relatively poor fit compared to the full model, despite the lack of significance found for Age and Weight in MODEL1.

This finding, combined with the high correlation between Age and Weight, suggests the possibility of collinearity, a condition in which two or more independent variables, both of which measure similar underlying effects, are included in the regression model. By using redundant model information, the parameter estimates (b_i's) might be inappropriate and/or the variance of these estimates might be inflated, which results in fewer significant findings.

Results for two additional models are shown. Age and Weight are separately included with Dose Level in MODEL3 **⓱** and MODEL4 **⓲**, respectively. A coefficient of determination of $R^2 = 41.1\%$ **⓳** is obtained by using Dose Level and Age, and an $R^2 = 45.8\%$ **⓴** is found with Dose Level and Weight. These results indicate that if Age or Weight is used in the model, including the other does not help much.

The final model used is MODEL4 because it has the highest R^2. With this model, Weight is a highly significant explanatory variable ($p<0.0001$).

SAS Code for Example 10.2

```
DATA DEHYD;
    INPUT PAT Y DOSE AGE WT @@;
    DATALINES;
  1   77 0.0   4 28    2   65 1.5   5 35    3   75 2.5   8 55
  4   63 1.0   9 76    5   75 0.5   5 31    6   82 2.0   5 27
  7   70 1.0   6 35    8   90 2.5   6 47    9   49 0.0   9 59
 10   72 3.0   8 50   11   67 2.0   7 50   12  100 2.5   7 46
 13   75 1.5   4 33   14   58 3.0   8 59   15   58 1.5   6 40
 16   55 0.0   8 58   17   80 1.0   7 55   18   55 2.0  10 76
 19   44 0.5   9 66   20   62 1.0   6 43   21   60 1.0   6 48
 22   75 2.5   7 50   23   77 1.5   5 29   24   80 2.5  11 64
 25   68 3.0   9 61   26   71 2.5  10 71   27   90 1.5   4 26
 28   80 2.0   3 27   29   70 0.0   9 56   30   58 2.5   8 57
 31   88 1.0   3 22   32   68 0.5   5 37   33   60 0.5   6 44
 34   90 3.0   5 45   35   79 1.5   8 53   36   90 2.0   4 29
;

PROC PRINT DATA = DEHYD;                                    ❿
    VAR PAT Y DOSE AGE WT;
    TITLE1 'Multiple Linear Regression';
    TITLE2 'Example 10.2: Recovery in Pediatric
       Dehydration';
RUN;

PROC REG CORR DATA = DEHYD;                                 ⓫
    MODEL Y = DOSE AGE WT / SS1 SS2 VIF COLLINOINT;
    MODEL Y = DOSE        ;
    MODEL Y = DOSE AGE    ;                                 ⓱
    MODEL Y = DOSE WT     ;                                 ⓲
RUN;
```

OUTPUT 10.2. SAS Output for Example 10.2

```
              Multiple Linear Regression
     Example 10.2: Recovery in Pediatric Dehydration

     Obs    PAT     Y     DOSE     AGE     WT

      1      1     77     0.0      4      28
      2      2     65     1.5      5      35
      3      3     75     2.5      8      55
      4      4     63     1.0      9      76
      5      5     75     0.5      5      31
      6      6     82     2.0      5      27
      7      7     70     1.0      6      35
      8      8     90     2.5      6      47
      9      9     49     0.0      9      59
     10     10     72     3.0      8      50
     11     11     67     2.0      7      50
     12     12    100     2.5      7      46
     13     13     75     1.5      4      33
     14     14     58     3.0      8      59
     15     15     58     1.5      6      40
     16     16     55     0.0      8      58
     17     17     80     1.0      7      55
     18     18     55     2.0     10      76
     19     19     44     0.5      9      66
     20     20     62     1.0      6      43
     21     21     60     1.0      6      48
     22     22     75     2.5      7      50
     23     23     77     1.5      5      29
     24     24     80     2.5     11      64
     25     25     68     3.0      9      61
     26     26     71     2.5     10      71
     27     27     90     1.5      4      26
     28     28     80     2.0      3      27
     29     29     70     0.0      9      56
     30     30     58     2.5      8      57
     31     31     88     1.0      3      22
     32     32     68     0.5      5      37
     33     33     60     0.5      6      44
     34     34     90     3.0      5      45
     35     35     79     1.5      8      53
     36     36     90     2.0      4      29
```

❿

OUTPUT 10.2. SAS Output for Example 10.2 (*continued*)

```
                      Multiple Linear Regression
              Example 10.2: Recovery in Pediatric Dehydration

                          The REG Procedure

                            Correlation                    ⑪

     Variable         DOSE            AGE          WT              Y

     DOSE           1.0000         0.1625       0.1640         0.3595
     AGE            0.1625         1.0000       0.9367        -0.4652
     WT             0.1640         0.9367       1.0000        -0.5068
     Y              0.3595        -0.4652      -0.5068         1.0000


                          The REG Procedure
                           Model: MODEL1
                         Dependent Variable: Y

                        Analysis of Variance

                              Sum of         Mean
     Source          DF       Squares        Square      F Value    Pr > F

     Model            3     2667.66870     889.22290       9.03 ⑫   0.0002
     Error           32     3151.22019      98.47563
     Corrected Total 35     5818.88889


          Root MSE              9.92349    R-Square     0.4584    ⑮
          Dependent Mean       71.55556    Adj R-Sq     0.4077
          Coeff Var            13.86823


                          Parameter Estimates

                       Parameter    Standard
     Variable    DF    Estimate       Error    t Value    Pr>|t|   Type I SS
                         ⑬                        ⑭
     Intercept    1    85.47636      5.96528      14.33   <.0001      184327
     DOSE         1     6.16969      1.79081       3.45   0.0016   752.15170
     AGE          1     0.27695      2.28474       0.12   0.9043   638.51013
     WT           1    -0.54278      0.32362      -1.68   0.1032   277.00687

                          Parameter Estimates

                                               Variance
          Variable    DF    Type II SS        Inflation

          Intercept    1        20219                0
          DOSE         1   1168.84352          1.02833
          AGE          1      1.44701          8.16330
          WT           1    277.00687          8.16745
```

OUTPUT 10.2. SAS Output for Example 10.2 (*continued*)

```
                        Multiple Linear Regression
                Example 10.2: Recovery in Pediatric Dehydration

                            The REG Procedure
                            Model: MODEL1


                Collinearity Diagnostics(intercept adjusted)    ㉑


                          Condition   -----Proportion of Variation---
        Number   Eigenvalue    Index       DOSE        AGE       WT

           1      1.99054    1.00000     0.02518    0.02918    0.02918
           2      0.94617    1.45044     0.97480    0.00337    0.00330
           3      0.06329    5.60804   0.00002134   0.96745    0.96752




                            Model: MODEL2
                        Dependent Variable: Y

                        Analysis of Variance

                              Sum of        Mean
        Source         DF     Squares      Square    F Value   Pr > F

        Model           1    752.15170   752.15170     5.05    0.0313
        Error          34   5066.73719   149.02168
        Corrected Total 35  5818.88889


             Root MSE            12.20744   R-Square     0.1293   ⑯
             Dependent Mean      71.55556   Adj R-Sq     0.1037
             Coeff Var           17.06009


                        Parameter Estimates

                        Parameter    Standard
        Variable    DF   Estimate      Error    t Value   Pr > |t|

        Intercept    1   63.89576     3.97040    16.09     <.0001
        DOSE         1    4.88058     2.17242     2.25     0.0313
```

OUTPUT 10.2. SAS Output for Example 10.2 (*continued*)

```
                          Multiple Linear Regression
                 Example 10.2: Recovery in Pediatric Dehydration

                            The REG Procedure
                              Model: MODEL3
                           Dependent Variable: Y                        ⑰

                            Analysis of Variance

                               Sum of        Mean
      Source          DF       Squares      Square     F Value   Pr > F

      Model            2     2390.66183   1195.33092    11.51    0.0002
      Error           33     3428.22706    103.88567
      Corrected Total 35     5818.88889


           Root MSE            10.19243    R-Square     0.4108   ⑲
           Dependent Mean      71.55556    Adj R-Sq     0.3751
           Coeff Var           14.24408


                           Parameter Estimates

                         Parameter      Standard
      Variable     DF     Estimate       Error      t Value   Pr > |t|

      Intercept     1     84.07228      6.06631      13.86     <.0001
      DOSE          1      6.06709      1.83827       3.30     0.0023
      AGE           1     -3.30580      0.83240      -3.97     0.0004




                              Model: MODEL4
                           Dependent Variable: Y
                                                                       ⑱
                            Analysis of Variance

                               Sum of        Mean
      Source          DF       Squares      Square     F Value   Pr > F

      Model            2     2666.22169   1333.11084    13.95    <.0001
      Error           33     3152.66720     95.53537
      Corrected Total 35     5818.88889


           Root MSE             9.77422    R-Square     0.4582   ⑳
           Dependent Mean      71.55556    Adj R-Sq     0.4254
           Coeff Var           13.65962


                           Parameter Estimates

                         Parameter      Standard
      Variable     DF     Estimate       Error      t Value   Pr > |t|

      Intercept     1     85.59416      5.79705      14.77     <.0001
      DOSE          1      6.17526      1.76329       3.50     0.0013
      WT            1     -0.50610      0.11307      -4.48     <.0001
```

10.4   Details & Notes

▶ **10.4.1.**   In *simple linear regression*, the hypothesis of 'zero regression slope' is equivalent to the hypothesis that the covariate is not an important predictor of response. The covariate, x, can be viewed as an ANOVA model factor with 1 degree of freedom with the following ANOVA summary:

ANOVA

SOURCE	df	SS	MS	F
X	1	SSX	MSX	$F_x = MSX/MSE$
Error	n–2	SSE	MSE	
Total	n–1	TOT(SS)		

The SSX and MSX can be computed as

$$SSX = MSX = \frac{S_{xy}^2}{S_{xx}}$$

The F-value for the null hypothesis that the covariate is unimportant is $F = MSX / MSE$, with 1 upper and n–2 lower degrees of freedom. Algebraically, this is equivalent to the square of the *t-test* for the 'zero slope' hypothesis because

$$F = \frac{MSX}{MSE} = \frac{\left(\dfrac{S_{xy}^2}{S_{xx}}\right)}{s^2} = \frac{\left(\dfrac{S_{xy}}{S_{xx}}\right)^2}{s^2/S_{xx}} = \left(\frac{b}{s/\sqrt{S_{xx}}}\right)^2 = t^2$$

The F-value for the covariate effect in Example 10.1 is seen in Output 10.1 to be 5.74 ❼, which is the square of the t-value (–2.40).

An ANOVA table can be prepared in a similar manner for each model effect, x_i, in a *multiple linear regression* analysis. There is 1 degree of freedom for each new parameter (β_i), so that the error degrees of freedom decrease by 1 for each explanatory variable.

▶ **10.4.2.**   Another equivalent method of making inferences about the covariate effect in *simple linear regression* is with the correlation coefficient. A positive regression slope indicates a positive correlation, i.e., y increases as x increases. A negative slope indicates a negative correlation, i.e., y decreases as x increases. The Pearson-product-moment correlation coefficient is often used as a measure of the degree of linear correlation between two variables, x and y. The correlation coefficient, ρ, is a unitless measure between −1 and +1. A correlation of +1 indicates a perfect positive correlation, a correlation of −1 indicates a perfect negative correlation, and a 0 indicates no linear correlation. The population parameter, ρ, is estimated by the sample correlation coefficient, r

$$r = \frac{S_{xy}}{\sqrt{S_{xx} \cdot S_{yy}}}$$

A *t-test* for significant linear correlation is

---

null hypothesis: H_0: $\rho = 0$
alt. hypothesis: H_A: $\rho \neq 0$

test statistic: $t = \dfrac{r \cdot \sqrt{n-2}}{\sqrt{1-r^2}}$

decision rule: reject H_0 if $|t| > t_{\alpha/2, n-2}$

Expressing the slope b, the standard deviation s, and the correlation coefficient r, in terms of S_{xx}, S_{yy}, and S_{xy}, it is easy to show that the *t-test* based on the correlation is identical to the *t-test* based on the slope. Notice the equivalency of the hypotheses, H_0: $\beta = 0$ and H_0: $\rho = 0$.

The correlation coefficient for Example 10.1 is

$$r = -558 \ / \ (55.2 \ (23{,}320))^{1/2} = -0.492$$

The t-statistic for significant correlation is

$$t = \frac{(-0.492) \cdot \sqrt{18}}{\sqrt{1 - (-0.492)^2}} = -2.4$$

which is the same t-value computed from the slope estimate b. The SAS output for Example 10.1 prints r^2 ($-0.492^2 = 0.242$) ❽ (R-Square), which is a measure of goodness-of-fit.

▶ **10.4.3.**   The coefficient of determination for a *multiple linear regression* model, R^2, represents the reduction in error variability by using the explanatory variables as predictors of y over just using the mean, $\overline{y}$. Thus, you can write

$$R^2 = (TSS - SSE) \ / \ TSS$$

where TSS is the total sum of squares. In this case, the SSE is a measure of error variation associated with the 'full' model, which includes all explanatory variables, and TSS is a measure of error variation associated with the 'reduced' model, which includes none of the explanatory variables. The difference is the 'model' sum of squares. In Output 10.2 for MODEL1, the R-Square value 0.4584 **⓯** can be found as Model SS / Total SS = 2667.67 / 5818.89.

Similarly, you can compute 'partial' correlation coefficients (r_j) between the response (y) and any independent variable (x_j) adjusted for all other variables in the model. The coefficient of determination associated with x_j is r_j^2, a measure of the reduction in variability accounted for by including x_j in the model. This can be found by using the partial sum of squares, labeled Type II SS in Output 10.2, which represent the sums of squares associated with x_j adjusted for all other independent variables in the model.

If SSE represents the error sum of squares based on the 'full' model, which includes k explanatory variables, and SSE(j) is the error sum of squares based on the set of k–1 variables, which excludes x_j, then the reduction in variability due to x_j is the Type II sum of squares for x_j. Thus, SSE(j) = Type II SSX_j + SSE, and the partial coefficient of determination can be computed as

$$r_j^2 = (SSE(j) - SSE) / SSE(j)$$

The SS1 and SS2 options in the initial MODEL statement (MODEL1) in Example 10.2 request the SAS Type I and II sums of squares. For Dose Level (DOSE), the Type II SS is 1168.8, so SSE(1) = 1168.8 + 3151.2 = 4320.0 and $r_1^2 = (1168.8 / 4320.0) = 0.271$.

The SAS Type I SS, sometimes called the sequential sum of squares, represent the sum of squares adjusted only for the factors preceding it in the model specification. Consequently, the sequence in which they are specified in the MODEL statement is important.

▶ **10.4.4.** When using PROC GLM, the Types I and III sums of squares are printed by default. In the SAS Code for Example 10.1 only Type I is requested by using SS1 in the MODEL statement because Type III usually pertains to *ANOVA* rather than regression analysis. In the *simple linear regression* case, SS Types I, II, and III are identical.

▶ **10.4.5.** A significant correlation implies a significant linear relationship between x and y but does not imply causality. Conversely, a non-significant correlation does not imply that there is no causal (or other) relationship between x and y. There might, in fact, be a quadratic or parabolic relationship, or some other relationship between x and y resulting in no *linear* correlation.

It is always a good idea to plot the data to obtain a visual impression of any relationship. Quadratic, cubic, and higher-order regression analyses can be performed quite easily by including the appropriate variables in the MODEL statement when using PROC GLM or PROC REG in SAS. For example, a quadratic model for Example 10.1 can be specified by using the following SAS statements after defining the new variable X_DUR2 = X_DUR**2 in the DATA step:

```
PROC GLM DATA = ANGINA;
    MODEL Y_IMPR = X_DUR X_DUR2;
```

▶ **10.4.6.** When estimating a mean response for a specified value of x, say x_0, the confidence interval will be smallest when x_0 is closest to the mean, $\bar{x}$, because the confidence interval width is a monotonically increasing function of $(x_0 - \bar{x})^2$. Such intervals can be computed for multiple x_0 values and plotted along with the regression equation to form confidence bands. Figure 10.2 shows the confidence bands for Example 10.1.

Figure 10.2. 95% Confidence Bands for Example 10.1

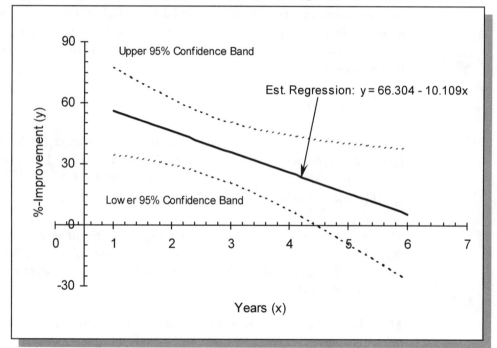

▶ **10.4.7.** The P and CLM options can be used in SAS with *multiple linear regression* models to obtain predicted values of the response variable and 95% confidence intervals, in the same way as illustrated in the *simple linear regression* case (Example 10.1).

▶ **10.4.8.** The prediction equation can be used to estimate the response, y, for any value of the predictor, x, within the experimental region. The experimental region consists of the range of x-values from the data used to compute the regression estimates. Predicting a response, y, for a value of x outside the experimental region is called 'extrapolation'. Extrapolation to the point x_e should not be used unless it can be safely assumed that x and y have the same linear relationship outside the experimental region at point x_e. Because, often, this assumption might not be met, extrapolation should be avoided if there is any uncertainty about this assumption.

▶ **10.4.9.** One of the assumptions needed to perform regression analysis is a constant error variance over the experimental region. To investigate the validity of this assumption, you can look for a constant, horizontal pattern in the plot of the residuals (i.e., the difference between the observed and predicted values) against the x-values. If the residuals appear to increase or decrease with x, the assumption of variance homogeneity might be violated. If that is the case, you might use a transformation of the data to attempt to stabilize the variance. Popular variance-stabilizing transformations include the natural logarithm, square root, and arcsine transformation (see Appendix F).

▶ **10.4.10.** Another assumption of the regression procedures is that of independent observations. If x represents time, and the responses, y, represent measurements on the same experimental unit (e.g., patient) at various time points, the assumption of independence is violated. In such cases, use of a *repeated measures ANOVA* might be more appropriate (see Chapter 8).

A correlation over time is referred to as 'autocorrelation' in time-series analysis. SAS uses the *Durbin-Watson test* to check for autocorrelation. A value close to 2, such as 1.92 ❾ in Output 10.1, indicates no significant autocorrelation. When using PROC REG, the *Durbin-Watson test* can be requested by using the DW option in the MODEL statement to check for autocorrelation.

▶ **10.4.11.** For a particular value of x, say x_p, a 95% 'prediction interval' for the predicted response of a future observation is given by

$$\hat{y}_{x_p} \pm t_{0.025,n-2} \cdot s \sqrt{1 + \frac{1}{n} + \frac{(x_p - \overline{x})^2}{S_{xx}}}$$

where $\hat{y}_{x_p} = a + b\, x_p$

Prediction bands can be established around the prediction equation in a way that is similar to that described for confidence bands.

▶ **10.4.12.** Diagnostics available for detecting collinearity in *multiple linear regression* models that contain a large number of independent variables include the variance inflation factor (VIF) and eigenvalue analysis of the model factors. These analyses are performed in SAS by using the VIF and

COLLINOINT options in the MODEL statement in PROC REG. Very large relative values of VIF might suggest collinearity. The eigenvalue analysis is a method used in a statistical technique called *principal component analysis*, often encountered in the social sciences. The basic idea is that very small values of the eigenvalues might suggest collinearity, especially if the 'condition index' (also printed in the SAS output) is large, e.g., >30.

> Note: For further reading, an entire chapter is devoted to a discussion of principal component analysis in "*A Step-by-Step Approach to Using the SAS System for Univariate and Multivariate Statistics*" by Hatcher and Stepanski, which was written under the SAS Books byUsers program.

In Example 10.2, the VIF (as shown in the Parameter Estimates section in Model 1 of Output 10.2), is 8.16 for both Age and Weight. These are relatively large values compared with the VIF for Dose Level (1.0), consistent with collinearity. The third eigenvalue in the Collinearity Diagnostics output[21] is very small, and although the condition index is not close to exceeding 30, you see that weightings for Age and Weight are large (0.967) compared with Dose. This points to evidence of a linear dependence between these two independent variables. These observations support the suspicion of collinearity between Age and Weight, and suggest that the model should avoid including both of these factors simultaneously.

▶ **10.4.13.** PROC REG is very useful for 'model-building'. The process of fitting various models and checking the R^2 (as shown in Example 10.2) is similar to one of the model building procedures that uses the stepwise option in PROC REG (see SAS Help and Documentation) to help determine the best fitting model to describe the response. Stepwise regression techniques can be very useful in fitting a model to existing data. Great caution must be used in making inferences, however, whenever the model is data-generated.

▶ **10.4.14.** Regression analysis has limited use in comparative clinical trials because the 'Treatment Group' effect is almost always a class variable. When classification variables, such as Treatment effect, are included in the same model as numeric explanatory variables, you use an analytic procedure known as *analysis of covariance* (*ANCOVA*), which is the subject of the next chapter. The concepts of regression analysis are introduced in this chapter to provide the necessary background for applying *ANCOVA* methods, which have greater use in the clinical setting.

PROC REG in SAS is very efficient for performing regression analysis and selecting appropriate models, but it cannot be used for *ANCOVA*. PROC GLM, although lacking some of the regression diagnostics available in PROC REG, can be used for regression, in addition to *ANOVA* and *ANCOVA*

> Note: For more details about regression analysis using PROC REG in SAS, see "*SAS System for Regression, Second Edition*", by Freund and Littell, which was written under the SAS Books by Users program.

Analysis of Covariance

11.1 Introduction

Analysis of covariance (*ANCOVA*) provides a method for comparing response means among two or more groups adjusted for a quantitative concomitant variable, or 'covariate', thought to influence the response. The attention here is confined to cases in which the response, y, might be linearly related to the covariate, x. *ANCOVA* combines regression and *ANOVA* methods by fitting simple linear regression models within each group and comparing regressions among groups.

ANCOVA methods represent one of the most widely used statistical methods in clinical trials. Examples where *ANCOVA* might be applied include:

- comparing cholesterol levels (y) between a treated group and a reference group adjusted for age (x, in years)

- comparing scar healing (y) between conventional and laser surgery adjusted for excision size (x, in mm)

- comparing exercise tolerance (y) in 3 dose levels of a treatment used for angina patients adjusted for smoking habits (x, in cigarettes/day).

ANCOVA can often increase the precision of comparisons of the group means by including the covariate, x, as a source of variation, thereby decreasing the estimated error variance. *ANCOVA* is especially useful when the values of the covariate differ among the groups. When this occurs and the response is linearly related to the covariate, covariance adjustments can lead to markedly different conclusions than those obtained using the unadjusted *ANOVA* methods.

11.2 Synopsis

Suppose you have k groups with n_i independent x-y points in Group i ($i = 1, 2, ..., k$), as shown in Table 11.1.

TABLE 11.1. ANCOVA Layout

GROUP 1		GROUP 2		...	GROUP k	
x	**y**	**x**	**y**		**x**	**y**
x_{11}	y_{11}	x_{21}	y_{21}	...	x_{k1}	y_{k1}
x_{12}	y_{12}	x_{22}	y_{22}	...	x_{k2}	y_{k2}
x_{13}	y_{13}	x_{23}	y_{23}	...	x_{k3}	y_{k3}
...	...	...	...	...	...	...
x_{1n_1}	y_{1n_1}	x_{2n_2}	y_{2n_2}	...	x_{kn_k}	y_{kn_k}

As with *ANOVA*, *ANCOVA* assumes independent groups with a normally distributed response measure, y, and variance homogeneity. In addition, you assume that the regression slopes are the same for each group, i.e., $\beta_1 = \beta_2 = ... = \beta_k = \beta$. The mean response within each group depends on the covariate, which results in a model for the ith group mean as

$$\mu_i = \alpha_i + \beta x$$

For each group, you can compute $\bar{x}$, $\bar{y}$, S_{xx}, S_{yy}, and S_{xy} using the formulas given in Chapter 10. Let $\bar{x}_i$, $\bar{y}_i$, $S_{xx(i)}$, $S_{yy(i)}$, and $S_{xy(i)}$ represent these quantities, respectively, for Group i ($i = 1, 2, ..., k$). Also, compute S_{xx}, S_{yy}, and S_{xy} for all groups combined (ignoring group). The estimated regression line for Group i is

$$\hat{y} = a_i + b x$$

where a_i and b are the Least Squares estimates computed as

$$b = \frac{\sum_i S_{xy(i)}}{\sum_i S_{xx(i)}}$$

and

$$a_i = \bar{y}_i - b \bar{x}$$

With $N = n_1 + n_2 + \ldots + n_k$, the ANOVA table summarizing the significance of the sources of variation is shown in Table 11.2.

TABLE 11.2. ANOVA Summary Table for a Simple ANCOVA Model

SOURCE	df	SS	MS	F
GROUP	k–1	SSG	MSG	$F_G = MSG/MSE$
X (covariate)	1	SSX	MSX	$F_X = MSX/MSE$
Error	N–k–1	SSE	MSE	
Total	N–1	TOT(SS)		

The sums of squares (SS) can be found from the following computing formulas:

$$TOT(SS) = S_{yy}$$

$$SSE = \frac{\left(\sum_i S_{xx(i)}\right) \cdot \left(\sum_i S_{yy(i)}\right) - \left(\sum_i S_{xy(i)}\right)^2}{\left(\sum_i S_{xx(i)}\right)}$$

$$SSG = \frac{S_{xx} \cdot S_{yy} - S_{xy}^2}{S_{xx}} - SSE$$

$$SSX = \sum_i S_{yy(i)} - SSE$$

Notice that when k=1 (one group), SSG = 0 and the computing formulas are identical to those used for *linear regression* in Chapter 10.

The mean squares (MS) are the sum of squares (SS) divided by the degrees of freedom (df). Of primary interest is the comparison of the group means adjusted to a common value of the covariate, e.g., x_0. Letting μ_{i0} represent the mean of Group i for $x = x_0$, the test can be summarized as follows:

---

null hypothesis: H_0: $\mu_{10} = \mu_{20} = ... = \mu_{k0}$

alt. hypothesis: H_A: NOT H_0

test statistic: $F_G = MSG / MSE$

rejection region: reject H_0 if $F_G > F_{N-k-1}^{k-1}(\alpha)$

Notice that the hypothesis is equivalent to the equality of intercepts among groups,

$$H_0: \alpha_1 = \alpha_2 = ... = \alpha_k$$

and the test does not depend on the value of x_0.

This test might result in improved precision for the group means comparisons over *one-way ANOVA* methods if the slope, β, differs from 0. To determine whether the covariate has a significant effect on the response, use the F_X ratio to test for 0 regression slope using the following test summary:

---

null hypothesis: H_0: $\beta = 0$

alt. hypothesis: H_A: $\beta \neq 0$

test statistic: $F_X = MSX / MSE$

rejection region: reject H_0 if $F_x > F_{N-k-1}^{1}(\alpha)$

11.3 Examples

Example 11.1 -- Triglyceride Changes Adjusted for Glycemic Control

The new cholesterol-lowering supplement, Fibralo, was studied in a double-blind study against the marketed reference supplement, Gemfibrozil, in 34 non-insulin dependent diabetic (NIDDM) patients. One of the study's objectives was to compare the mean decrease in triglyceride levels between groups. The degree of glycemic control, measured by hemoglobin A_{1c} levels (HbA$_{1c}$), was thought to be an important factor in response to the treatment. This covariate was measured at the start of the study and is shown in Table 11.3, with the percent changes in triglycerides from pre-treatment to the end of the 10-week trial. Is there a difference in mean responses between supplements?

TABLE 11.3. Raw Data for Example 11.1

FIBRALO GROUP			GEMFIBROZIL GROUP		
Patient Number	HbA$_{1c}$ ng/ml (X)	Triglyceride % Change (Y)	Patient Number	HbA$_{1c}$ ng/ml (X)	Triglyceride % Change (Y)
2	7.0	5	1	5.1	10
4	6.0	10	3	6.0	15
7	7.1	-5	5	7.2	-15
8	8.6	-20	6	6.4	5
11	6.3	0	9	5.5	10
13	7.5	-15	10	6.0	-15
16	6.6	10	12	5.6	-5
17	7.4	-10	14	5.5	-10
19	5.3	20	15	6.7	-20
21	6.5	-15	18	8.6	-40
23	6.2	5	20	6.4	-5
24	7.8	0	22	6.0	-10
27	8.5	-40	25	9.3	-40
28	9.2	-25	26	8.5	-20
30	5.0	25	29	7.9	-35
33	7.0	-10	31	7.4	0
			32	5.0	0
			34	6.5	-10

Solution

To apply *ANCOVA* using HbA_{1c} as a covariate, first obtain some summary results from the data as shown in Table 11.4.

TABLE 11.4. Summary Results for Example 11.1

	Fibralo (Group 1)	Gemfibrozil (Group 2)	Combined
Σx	112.00	119.60	231.60
Σx^2	804.14	821.64	1625.78
Σy	-65.00	-185.00	-250.00
Σy^2	4575.00	6475.00	11050.00
Σxy	-708.50	-1506.50	-2215.00
$\overline{x}$	7.0000	6.6444	6.8118
$\overline{y}$	-4.0625	-10.2778	-7.3529
N	16	18	34

Using the formulas in Chapter 10, you compute for the *Fibralo* group (i=1):

$$S_{xx(1)} = 804.14 - (112)^2 / 16 = 20.140$$

$$S_{yy(1)} = 4575.00 - (-65)^2 / 16 = 4310.938$$

$$S_{xy(1)} = -708.50 - (112)(-65) / 16 = -253.500$$

Similarly, computing for the *Gemfibrozil* group (i=2), you obtain:

$$S_{xx(2)} = 26.964$$

$$S_{yy(2)} = 4573.611$$

$$S_{xy(2)} = -277.278$$

Finally, for the combined data (ignoring groups), compute

$$S_{xx} = 48.175$$

$$S_{yy} = 9211.765$$

$$S_{xy} = -512.059$$

The sums of squares can now be obtained as

$$TOT(SS) = 9211.8$$

$$SSE = \frac{(20.140 + 26.964)(4310.938 + 4573.611) - (-253.500 - 277.278)^2}{(20.140 + 26.964)}$$

$$= 2903.6$$

$$SSG = \frac{(48.175)(9211.765) - (-512.059)^2}{48.175} - 2903.6 = 865.4$$

$$SSX = (4310.938 + 4573.611) - 2903.6 = 5980.9.$$

and the ANOVA summary table can be completed as shown in Table 11.5.

TABLE 11.5. ANCOVA Summary for Example 11.1

SOURCE	df	SS	MS	F
Treatment	1	865.4	865.4	9.2 *
X (HbA$_{1c}$)	1	5980.9	5980.9	63.8 *
Error	31	2903.6	93.7	
Total	33	9211.8		

* Significant ($p < 0.05$); critical F-value = 4.16

The F-statistics are formed as the ratios of effect mean squares (MS) to the MSE (93.7). Each F-statistic is compared with the critical F-value with 1 upper and 31 lower degrees of freedom. The critical F-value for $\alpha = 0.05$ is 4.16.

The significant covariate effect (F=63.8) indicates that the triglyceride response has a significant linear relationship with HbA_{1c}. The significant F-value for Treatment indicates that the mean triglyceride response adjusted for glycemic control differs between treatment groups.

Application of the *one-way ANOVA* (Chapter 6) to compare treatment group means (ignoring the covariate) results in the following:

TABLE 11.6. ANOVA for Example 11.1 Ignoring Covariate

SOURCE	df	SS	MS	F
Treatment	1	327.22	327.22	1.18
Error	32	8884.55	277.64	
Total	33	9211.76		

The rejection region for the Treatment effect based on a significance level of α=0.05 includes F-values greater than 4.15, the critical F-value with 1 upper and 32 lower degrees of freedom With an F-value of only 1.18, you cannot reject the hypothesis of equal means. Therefore, you must conclude that no difference in mean response betweeen treatment groups is evident based on this test.

One reason the *ANCOVA* produces a significant treatment group difference but the *ANOVA* does not is a large reduction in MSE, (from 277.6 to 93.7). This results in greater precision of the treatment group comparison.

Another reason for this difference is the increase in the difference between means by using the adjusted values, as shown below. You estimate the common slope, β, as

$$b = ((-253.500) + (-277.278)) / (20.140 + 26.964)$$

$$= -11.268$$

and the intercepts (a_i's) as

$$a_1 = (-4.0625) - (-11.268)(7.0000) = 74.81$$

$$a_2 = (-10.2778) - (-11.268)(6.6444) = 64.59$$

which yield the estimated regression equations:

$$\textit{Fibralo Group:} \qquad \hat{y} = 74.81 - 11.268\,x$$

$$\textit{Gemfibrozil:} \qquad \hat{y} = 64.59 - 11.268\,x$$

The adjusted mean responses for each group are the values of the estimated regression equations evaluated at the overall mean of the covariate, $\bar{x} = 6.8118$, as follows:

Fibralo: $\qquad 74.81 - 11.268\,(6.8118) = -1.9$

Gemfibrozil: $\qquad 64.59 - 11.268\,(6.8118) = -12.2$

These means differ considerably from the unadjusted means already computed (Table 11.4). Table 11.7 summarizes the unadjusted and adjusted means by treatment groups.

TABLE 11.7. Means by Treatment Group for Example 11.1

Mean Response	Fibralo Group	Gemfibrozil Group	p-value
Unadjusted	−4.1%	−10.3%	0.2858
Adjusted	−1.9%	−12.2%	0.0048 *

* Significant (p < 0.05) (p-values from SAS output)

Triglycerides decrease by a mean of 11.27% for every 1 ng/ml increase in HbA_{1c}, and this rate of change is seen to be significant. Notice that (Table 11.4) the mean HbA_{1c} level is slightly higher in the *Fibralo* group compared with the *Gemfibrozil* group (7.00 v. 6.64). The unadjusted mean responses are those that lie on the regression lines that correspond to the mean of the covariate for each group, as shown in Figure 11.1. Comparing the mean responses of the two groups at the same value of the covariate (x = 6.81) requires using a smaller x value for the *Fibralo* group (which results in a smaller triglyceride decrease), and a larger x value for the *Gemfibrozil* group (which results in a larger triglyceride decrease). The end result is a larger difference in response means based on the adjusted values compared with the unadjusted values.

FIGURE 11.1. ANCOVA-Adjusted Means for Example 11.1

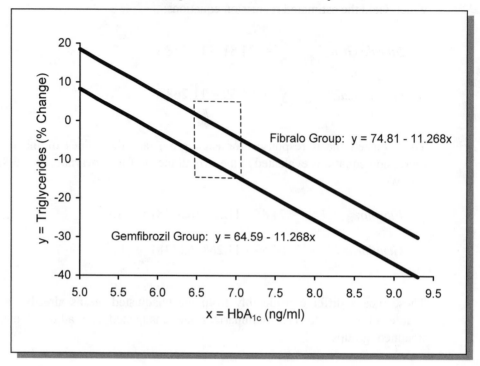

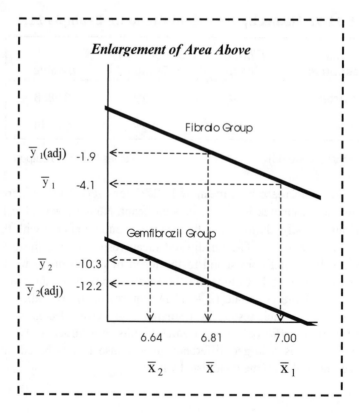

SAS Analysis of Example 11.1

The SAS code for performing this analysis is shown below followed by the SAS output (Output 11.1). The PRINT, PLOT, and MEANS procedures are used to provide a data listing ❶, a scatterplot of the data ❷, and basic summary statistics ❸.

PROC GLM is used to conduct the *ANCOVA*, using the Treatment (TRT) effect as a class variable and HGBA1C as a numeric covariate. The sums of squares, mean squares, and *F-tests* ❹ all corroborate the manual calculations.

The SOLUTION option in the MODEL statement ❺ in PROC GLM obtains the estimates for the regression equations. The slope estimate, b, is –11.268 ❻. The intercept estimates are found by adding each treatment group effect to the intercept estimate:

$$a_1 = 64.59 + 10.22 = 74.81$$

and

$$a_2 = 64.59 + 0.00 = 64.59 \quad ❼$$

The LSMEANS statement instructs SAS to print out the adjusted mean responses❽ at the common covariate mean, $\overline{x}$, as demonstrated in the manual calculations.

The data set is also analyzed using the *one-way ANOVA*, ignoring the covariate ❾. These results, as discussed previously, show a non-significant treatment effect (p = 0.2858).

SAS Code for Example 11.1

```
DATA TRI;
    INPUT TRT $ PAT HGBA1C TRICHG @@;
    DATALINES;
FIB  2 7.0    5   FIB  4 6.0   10   FIB  7 7.1   -5
FIB  8 8.6 -20    FIB 11 6.3    0   FIB 13 7.5  -15
FIB 16 6.6   10   FIB 17 7.4  -10   FIB 19 5.3   20
FIB 21 6.5  -15   FIB 23 6.2    5   FIB 24 7.8    0
FIB 27 8.5  -40   FIB 28 9.2  -25   FIB 30 5.0   25
FIB 33 7.0  -10   GEM  1 5.1   10   GEM  3 6.0   15
GEM  5 7.2  -15   GEM  6 6.4    5   GEM  9 5.5   10
GEM 10 6.0  -15   GEM 12 5.6   -5   GEM 14 5.5  -10
GEM 15 6.7  -20   GEM 18 8.6  -40   GEM 20 6.4   -5
GEM 22 6.0  -10   GEM 25 9.3  -40   GEM 26 8.5  -20
GEM 29 7.9  -35   GEM 31 7.4    0   GEM 32 5.0    0
GEM 34 6.5  -10
;

PROC SORT DATA = TRI;
    BY TRT HGBA1C TRICHG;
```

```
/* Print data set */
PROC PRINT DATA = TRI;                                      ❶
    VAR TRT PAT HGBA1C TRICHG;
    TITLE1 'Analysis of Covariance';
    TITLE2 'Example 11.1: Triglyceride Changes Adjusted for
        Glycemic Control';
RUN;

/* Plot data, by group */
PROC PLOT VPERCENT=45 DATA = TRI;                           ❷
    PLOT TRICHG*HGBA1C = TRT;
RUN;

/* Obtain summary statistics for each group */
PROC MEANS MEAN STD N DATA = TRI;                           ❸
    BY TRT;
    VAR HGBA1C TRICHG;
RUN;

/* Use glycemic control as covariate */
PROC GLM DATA = TRI;
    CLASS TRT;
    MODEL TRICHG = TRT HGBA1C / SOLUTION;                   ❺
        LSMEANS TRT/PDIFF STDERR;                           ❽
RUN;

/* Compare groups with ANOVA, ignoring the covariate */
PROC GLM DATA = TRI;                                        ❾
    CLASS TRT;
    MODEL TRICHG = TRT / SS3;
RUN;
```

OUTPUT 11.1 SAS Output for Example 11.1

```
                    Analysis of Covariance
Example 11.1: Triglyceride Changes Adjusted for Glycemic Control

            Obs    TRT    PAT    HGBA1C    TRICHG

             1     FIB    30     5.0        25
             2     FIB    19     5.3        20
             3     FIB     4     6.0        10
             4     FIB    23     6.2         5
             5     FIB    11     6.3         0
             6     FIB    21     6.5       -15
             7     FIB    16     6.6        10
             8     FIB    33     7.0       -10
             9     FIB     2     7.0         5
            10     FIB     7     7.1        -5
            11     FIB    17     7.4       -10
            12     FIB    13     7.5       -15
            13     FIB    24     7.8         0
            14     FIB    27     8.5       -40      ❶
            15     FIB     8     8.6       -20
```

OUTPUT 11.1 SAS Output for Example 11.1 (*continued*)

16	FIB	28	9.2	-25
17	GEM	32	5.0	0
18	GEM	1	5.1	10
19	GEM	14	5.5	-10
20	GEM	9	5.5	10
21	GEM	12	5.6	-5
22	GEM	10	6.0	-15
23	GEM	22	6.0	-10
24	GEM	3	6.0	15
25	GEM	20	6.4	-5
26	GEM	6	6.4	5
27	GEM	34	6.5	-10
28	GEM	15	6.7	-20
29	GEM	5	7.2	-15
30	GEM	31	7.4	0
31	GEM	29	7.9	-35
32	GEM	26	8.5	-20
33	GEM	18	8.6	-40
34	GEM	25	9.3	-40

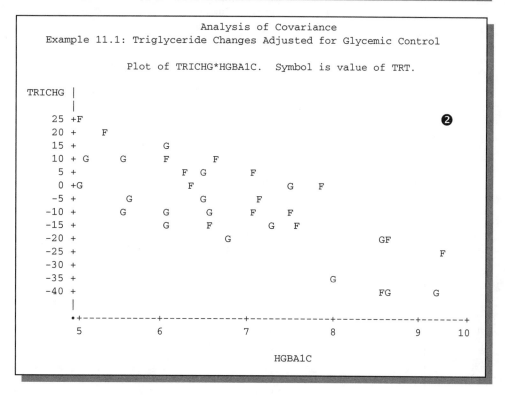

```
                         Analysis of Covariance
           Example 11.1: Triglyceride Changes Adjusted for Glycemic Control

                  Plot of TRICHG*HGBA1C.   Symbol is value of TRT.

TRICHG |
       |
   25  +F                                                        ❷
   20  +      F
   15  +                 G
   10  + G       G          F           F
    5  +                  F   G           F
    0  +G                    F               G     F
   -5  +      G                 G           F
  -10  +      G       G          G      F     F
  -15  +              G       F           G    F
  -20  +                    G                        GF
  -25  +                                                    F
  -30  +
  -35  +                                     G
  -40  +                                          FG       G
       |
       •+-------------+-------------+-------------+-------------+-------+
        5             6             7             8             9      10

                                  HGBA1C
```

OUTPUT 11.1 SAS Output for Example 11.1 (*continued*)

```
                         The MEANS Procedure

------------------------------ TRT=FIB ------------------------------

              Variable          Mean        Std Dev      N
              --------------------------------------------------
              HGBA1C        7.0000000      1.1587349     16
              TRICHG       -4.0625000     16.9527530     16
              --------------------------------------------------
                                                               ❸

---------------------- ----- TRT=GEM ------------------------------

              Variable          Mean        Std Dev      N
              --------------------------------------------------
              HGBA1C        6.6444444      1.2594220     18
              TRICHG      -10.2777778     16.4023153     18
              --------------------------------------------------
```

```
                        Analysis of Covariance
       Example 11.1: Triglyceride Changes Adjusted for Glycemic Control

                          The GLM Procedure

                       Class Level Information

                 Class          Levels     Values

                 TRT               2        FIB GEM

                    Number of observations     34


Dependent Variable: TRICHG
                          Sum of
Source            DF      Squares     Mean Square   F Value   Pr > F

Model              2     8.075283    3154.037642     33.67   <.0001   ❹
Error             31  2903.689422      93.667401
Corrected Tot     33  9211.764706


              R-Square     Coeff Var     Root MSE     TRICHG Mean

              0.684785     -131.6234     9.678192      -7.352941


Source            DF    Type I SS     Mean Square   F Value   Pr > F

TRT                1    327.216095     327.216095      3.49   0.0711
HGBA1C             1   5980.859189    5980.859189     63.85   <.0001

Source            DF    Type III SS   Mean Square   F Value   Pr > F   ❹

TRT                1    865.363546     865.363546      9.24   0.0048
HGBA1C             1   5980.859189    5980.859189     63.85   <.0001
```

OUTPUT 11.1 SAS Output for Example 11.1 (*continued*)

```
                              Standard
     Parameter         Estimate         Error    t Value   Pr > |t|

     Intercept       64.59251309 B    9.64331471     6.70    <.0001
     TRT    FIB  ❼   10.22171475 B    3.36293670 ⓳  3.04     0.0048
     TRT    GEM        0.00000000 B        .           .        .
     HGBA1C          -11.26810398 ❻   1.41014344    -7.99 ❿   <.0001
```

NOTE: The X'X matrix has been found to be singular, and a
generalized inverse was used to solve the normal equations. Terms
whose estimates are followed by the letter 'B' are not uniquely
estimable.

```
                        Least Squares Means

                                                    H0:LSMean1=
                    TRICHG      Standard   H0:LSMEAN=0    LSMean2
     TRT            LSMEAN        Error      Pr > |t|    Pr > |t|

     FIB         -1.9414451    2.4340646 ⓫    0.4312      0.0048
     GEM        -12.1631599 ❽  2.2933414      <.0001
```

```
                        Analysis of Covariance
     Example 11.1: Triglyceride Changes Adjusted for Glycemic Control

                          The GLM Procedure

                        Class Level Information

                  Class       Levels    Values

                  TRT            2       FIB GEM

                     Number of observations    34


Dependent Variable: TRICHG
                           Sum of
     Source         DF     Squares    Mean Square   F Value   Pr > F

     Model           1   327.216095    327.216095     1.18    0.2858
     Error          32  8884.548611    277.642144
     Corrected Tot  33  9211.764706                                 ❾


             R-Square    Coeff Var     Root MSE    TRICHG Mean

             0.035522    -226.6113     16.66260     -7.352941


     Source         DF   Type III SS  Mean Square   F Value   Pr > F

     TRT             1   327.2160948   327.2160948     1.18    0.2858
```

The next example illustrates *ANCOVA* using multiple numeric covariates with multiple classification factors.

Example 11.2 -- ANCOVA in Multi-Center Hypertension Study

The experimental anti-hypertensive agent, GB2995, was studied in 4 study centers to compare 12 weeks of treatment using GB2995 as the sole therapy vs. using GB2995 in combination with a stable dose of a marketed calcium-channel blocker when given to patients with moderate to severe hypertension. The primary analysis focuses on a comparison of the mean decreases in diastolic blood pressure between the two treatment groups, adjusted for the patient's age and severity of hypertension at study entry. (Baseline severity is the average diastolic blood pressure obtained on three pre-study visits). Do the data in Table 11.8 show any difference in response between the two treatment groups?

TABLE 11.8. Raw Data for Example 11.2

Sole Therapy				Combination Therapy			
Patient Number*	AGE (yrs.)	Baseline DIA BP (mm Hg)	DIA BP Change (mm Hg)	Patient Number*	AGE (yrs.)	Baseline DIA BP (mm Hg)	DIA BP Change (mm Hg)
101	55	102	-6	102	68	112	-10
103	68	115	-10	105	64	105	-4
104	45	97	-2	107	48	107	-9
106	69	107	-5	108	60	107	-5
109	54	115	-7	201	44	109	-7
202	58	99	-4	205	53	99	0
203	62	119	-11	207	48	107	-9
204	51	107	-9	209	65	106	-3
206	47	96	0	210	79	108	-6
208	61	98	-6	213	45	110	-9
211	40	110	5	215	44	93	0
212	36	103	-3	218	62	99	-5
214	58	109	10	220	59	119	-14
216	64	119	-12	221	50	104	-6
217	55	104	4	222	61	107	-14
219	54	97	-5	224	36	95	3
223	39	95	-8	225	34	95	-9
301	49	115	-3	303	49	115	-8
302	46	105	4	305	57	115	7
304	59	116	-10	306	58	116	-20
307	42	108	-5	309	43	108	-7
308	65	101	-7	310	66	101	-5

*First digit indicates study center

Sole Therapy					Combination Therapy			
Patient Number*	AGE (yrs.)	Baseline DIA BP (mm Hg)	DIA BP Change (mm Hg)		Patient Number*	AGE (yrs.)	Baseline DIA BP (mm Hg)	DIA BP Change (mm Hg)
311	68	102	-5		312	55	102	-9
313	57	110	-8		314	70	110	-16
402	73	119	-12		315	52	104	-8
404	48	99	-7		401	42	119	-15
406	53	117	0		403	49	109	-6
407	46	96	4		405	53	117	4
409	60	118	-15		408	55	96	6
412	66	104	-3		410	65	98	-8
414	59	115	-4		411	75	108	-7
415	41	109	3		413	59	104	-10
418	53	116	-10		416	60	115	-16
421	57	100	-8		417	53	109	3
424	52	103	0		419	43	96	-14
425	41	95	9		420	77	100	-5
					422	55	103	-8
					423	66	115	-14
					426	38	105	-3

*First digit indicates study center

SAS Analysis of Example 11.2

The SAS code and output for this example are shown on the following pages. The PRINT and MEANS procedures provide a (partial) data listing ⑫ and summary statistics by treatment group ⑬. Combination treatment (COMB) shows an unadjusted mean decrease in diastolic blood pressure of 6.82 mm Hg, compared with a decrease of 4.06 mm Hg for sole therapy (SOLE).

PROC GLM is used to conduct an *ANCOVA* using Treatment Group (TRT) and Study Center (CENTER) as variables in the CLASS statement ⑭. Age (AGE) and baseline diastolic blood pressure (BPDIA0) are used as numeric covariates by including them in the MODEL statement but omitting them from the CLASS statement. The MODEL statement corresponds to a main effects model that ignores any interactions. The linear model used in this analysis can be written as

$$y_{ij} = \alpha + \tau_i + \beta_j + \gamma_1 x_1 + \gamma_1 x_2 + \varepsilon$$

where y_{ij} is the response measurement (change in diastolic blood pressure) for Treatment i (i=1 or 2) and Center j (j=1, 2, 3, or 4), α is the overall mean response, τ_i is the effect of Treatment i, β_j is the effect of Center j, x_1 is age (in years), x_2 is baseline diastolic blood pressure (in mm Hg), γ_k is the increase in response associated with a one-unit change in x_k (k=1 or 2), and ε represents the random error component.

This analysis assumes that if the response is linearly related to the covariates, then that same linear relationship exists within each subgroup formed by combinations of levels of the class variables. This assumption can be tested by including interactions such as TRT*AGE or TRT*BPDIA0 in the model (see Section 11.4.7). A preliminary test for a Treatment-by-Center interaction can also be made before proceeding with this model.

The output shows a mean square error (MSE) of 32.9 based on 68 degrees of freedom, and indicates a significant overall model effect (p=0.0072) ⓯, which means that not all factors included in the model are unrelated to the response.

The SAS Type III sums of squares indicate a significant treatment (TRT) effect (p=0.0435) ⓰. No evidence of differences is seen among Centers (p= 0.9403), while the baseline severity (BPDIA0) is a significant covariate (p=0.0070). The Type III results for each factor are adjusted for the inclusion of all other factors in the model. The Type I results are only adjusted for the factors preceding it in the MODEL statement. Note that the Age covariate is significant (p=0.0175) when it is not adjusted for baseline diastolic blood pressure (Type I SS), but Age is not significant (p=0.0979) after adjusting for BPDIA0 (Type III results).

The adjusted mean responses (Least Squares Means), –6.93 mm Hg for combination treatment and –4.19 mm Hg for sole therapy ⓱, are slightly greater than the unadjusted means, –6.82 and –4.06, respectively.

The SOLUTION option used in the MODEL statement estimates the model parameters shown in the Estimate column in Output 11.2 ⓲. For example, the estimated response for combination therapy in Center 1 can be found by using the equation

$$\hat{y} = 30.8866 - 2.7401 - 0.9642 - (0.1150*AGE) - (0.2640*BPDIA0)$$

or

$$\hat{y} = 27.1823 - 0.115*AGE - 0.264*BPDIA0$$

An estimate of the mean response for patients who receive combination therapy in Center 1 can be found by substituting the overall mean age (54.8133 yrs.) and the overall mean baseline diastolic blood pressure (106.4933 mm Hg) into this equation, as follows:

$$\overline{y} = 27.1823 - 0.115*(54.8133) - 0.264*(106.4933) = -7.23$$

Similarly, estimated response equations and means for the other combinations of Treatment and Center are shown in Table 11.9.

TABLE 11.9. Adjusted Mean Responses by Treatment Group and Center for Example 11.2

TRT	CENTER	Estimated Response Equation	Mean Response at Average Value of Covariates
COMB	1	$\hat{y} = 27.1823 - 0.115*AGE - 0.264*BPDIA0$	-7.23
	2	$\hat{y} = 27.4964 - 0.115*AGE - 0.264*BPDIA0$	-6.92
	3	$\hat{y} = 27.1154 - 0.115*AGE - 0.264*BPDIA0$	-7.30
	4	$\hat{y} = 28.1465 - 0.115*AGE - 0.264*BPDIA0$	-6.27
SOLE	1	$\hat{y} = 29.9224 - 0.115*AGE - 0.264*BPDIA0$	-4.49
	2	$\hat{y} = 30.2365 - 0.115*AGE - 0.264*BPDIA0$	-4.18
	3	$\hat{y} = 29.8555 - 0.115*AGE - 0.264*BPDIA0$	-4.56
	4	$\hat{y} = 30.8866 - 0.115*AGE - 0.264*BPDIA0$	-3.53

The adjusted treatment means (LS-means) can be verified by averaging the estimates of the within-center means over all centers for that treatment:

$$\overline{y}_{comb} = (-7.234 - 6.920 - 7.301 - 6.270) / 4 = -6.93$$

$$\overline{y}_{sole} = (-4.494 - 4.180 - 4.561 - 3.520) / 4 = -4.19$$

SAS Code for Example 11.2

```
DATA BP;
    INPUT TRT $ PAT AGE BPDIA0 BPDIACH @@;
    CENTER = INT(PAT/100);
    DATALINES;
SOLE 101 55 102  -6   SOLE 103 68 115 -10
SOLE 104 45  97  -2   SOLE 106 69 107  -5
SOLE 109 54 115  -7   SOLE 202 58  99  -4

      ... (more data lines)  ...

COMB 422 55 103  -8   COMB 423 66 115 -14
COMB 426 38 105  -3
;

PROC PRINT DATA = BP;
    TITLE1 'Analysis of Covariance';
    TITLE2 'Example 11.2: ANCOVA in Multi-Center Hypertension
          Study';
RUN;
```

⑫

```
PROC SORT DATA = BP;
    BY TRT CENTER;

PROC MEANS MEAN STD N MIN MAX DATA = BP;              ⓭
    BY TRT;
    VAR AGE BPDIA0 BPDIACH;
RUN;

PROC GLM DATA = BP;
   CLASS TRT CENTER;                                  ⓮
   MODEL BPDIACH = TRT CENTER AGE BPDIA0 / SOLUTION;
      LSMEANS TRT / STDERR PDIFF;
   TITLE3 'GLM Model Including Effects: TRT, CENTER, AGE, BPDIA0';
RUN;
```

OUTPUT 11.2. SAS Output for Example 11.2

```
                        Analysis of Covariance
            Example 11.2: ANCOVA in Multi-Center Hypertension Study

        Obs    TRT    PAT    AGE    BPDIA0    BPDIACH    CENTER

         1     SOLE   101    55      102        -6          1
         2     SOLE   103    68      115       -10          1
         3     SOLE   104    45       97        -2          1
         4     SOLE   106    69      107        -5          1
         5     SOLE   109    54      115        -7          1
         6     SOLE   202    58       99        -4          2
         7     SOLE   203    62      119       -11          2
         8     SOLE   204    51      107        -9          2
         9     SOLE   206    47       96         0          2
        10     SOLE   208    61       98        -6          2
        11     SOLE   211    40      110         5          2
        12     SOLE   212    36      103        -3          2
        13     SOLE   214    58      109        10          2      ⓬
        14     SOLE   216    64      119       -12          2
        15     SOLE   217    55      104         4          2
         .
         .
         .
        70     COMB   417    53      109         3          4
        71     COMB   419    43       96       -14          4
        72     COMB   420    77      100        -5          4
        73     COMB   422    55      103        -8          4
        74     COMB   423    66      115       -14          4
        75     COMB   426    38      105        -3          4
```

OUTPUT 11.2. SAS Output for Example 11.2 (*continued*)

```
                         The MEANS Procedure

------------------------- TRT=COMB ----------------------------

Variable          Mean       Std Dev     N       Minimum        Maximum
-------------------------------------------------------------------------
AGE          55.3846154   11.0706235    39    34.0000000    79.0000000
BPDIA0      106.3333333    7.0012530    39    93.0000000   119.0000000
BPDIACH      -6.8205128    6.2318021    39   -20.0000000     7.0000000
-------------------------------------------------------------------------
```
❸

```
------------------------- TRT=SOLE ----------------------------

Variable          Mean       Std Dev     N       Minimum        Maximum
-------------------------------------------------------------------------
AGE          54.1944444    9.4923110    36    36.0000000    73.0000000
BPDIA0      106.6666667    7.9677923    36    95.0000000   119.0000000
BPDIACH      -4.0555556    5.9997354    36   -15.0000000    10.0000000
-------------------------------------------------------------------------
```

```
                     Analysis of Covariance
          Example 11.2: ANCOVA in Multi-Center Hypertension Study
          GLM Model Including Effects: TRT, CENTER, AGE, BPDIA0

                        The GLM Procedure

                     Class Level Information
                Class        Levels    Values
                TRT             2       COMB SOLE
                CENTER          4       1 2 3 4

                 Number of observations      75


Dependent Variable: BPDIACH

                            Sum of
Source              DF      Squares     Mean Square   F Value   Pr > F

Model                6     641.585250    106.930875     3.25    0.0072  ❺
Error               68    2237.161416     32.899433
Corrected Total     74    2878.746667

          R-Square     Coeff Var     Root MSE     BPDIACH Mean
          0.222870     -104.4139     5.735803       -5.493333
```

OUTPUT 11.2. SAS Output for Example 11.2 (*continued*)

Source	DF	Type I SS	Mean Square	F Value	Pr > F
TRT	1	143.1141880	143.1141880	4.35	0.0408
CENTER	3	49.0195734	16.3398578	0.50	0.6858
AGE	1	195.3204109	195.3204109	5.94	0.0175
BPDIA0	1	254.1310779	254.1310779	7.72	0.0070

Source	DF	Type III SS	Mean Square	F Value	Pr > F	
TRT	1	139.2345407	139.2345407	4.23	0.0435	⑯
CENTER	3	13.1006818	4.3668939	0.13	0.9403	
AGE	1	92.6596679	92.6596679	2.82	0.0979	
BPDIA0	1	254.1310779	254.1310779	7.72	0.0070	

Parameter		Estimate ⑱		Standard Error	t Value	Pr > |t|
Intercept		30.88660621	B	10.04435860	3.08	0.0030
TRT	COMB	-2.74007804	B	1.33193688	-2.06	0.0435
TRT	SOLE	0.00000000	B	.	.	.
CENTER	1	-0.96419474	B	2.23622128	-0.43	0.6677
CENTER	2	-0.65014780	B	1.63467283	-0.40	0.6921
CENTER		-1.03110593	B	1.86433408	-0.55	0.5820
CENTER		0.00000000	B	.	.	.
AGE		-0.11500993		0.06853055	-1.68	0.0979
BPDIA0		-0.26398254		0.09498183	-2.78	0.0070

NOTE: The X'X matrix has been found to be singular, and a generalized inverse was used to solve the normal equations. Terms whose estimates are followed by the letter 'B' are not uniquely estimable.

                        Analysis of Covariance
          Example 11.2: ANCOVA in Multi-Center Hypertension Study
            GLM Model Including Effects: TRT, CENTER, AGE, BPDIA0

                       Least Squares Means

TRT	BPDIACH LSMEAN		Standard Error	H0:LSMEAN=0 Pr > |t|	H0:LSMean1= LSMean2 Pr > |t|
COMB	-6.93129242	⑰	0.98013179	<.0001	0.0435
SOLE	-4.19121438		0.99307483	<.0001	

11.4 Details & Notes

▶ **11.4.1.** The standard error of the slope estimate, **b**, is given by

$$s_b = \sqrt{\frac{MSE}{\sum_i S_{xx(i)}}}$$

Because "*a significant covariate effect*" means the same as "*a non-zero slope*", an alternate but equivalent test to the *F-test* for the covariate effect is the *t-test* as follows:

null hypothesis: H_0: $\beta = 0$
alt. hypothesis: H_A: $\beta \neq 0$

test statistic: $t = \dfrac{b}{s_b}$

decision rule: reject H_0 if $|t| > t_{\alpha/2}$

In Example 11.1, you have MSE = 93.67, so that

$$s_b = \sqrt{\frac{93.67}{20.140 + 26.964}} = 1.410$$

The t-statistic is computed as

$$t = (-11.27) / 1.41 = -7.99$$

based on 31 degrees of freedom, as shown in Output 11.1 **❿**. Notice that the square of the t-statistic is the F-statistic, $(-7.99)^2 = 63.8$, based on 1 upper and 31 lower degrees of freedom.

▶ **11.4.2.**   Differences in adjusted response means are the same regardless of the value of the covariate, x, because the slopes are assumed to be equal among groups. In Example 11.1, the estimated difference in adjusted response means at x_0 is

$$(74.81 - 11.27x_0) - (64.59 - 11.27x_0) = 10.22$$

regardless of what value x_0 takes. This is not the case if the slopes differ among groups.

If the assumption of equal slopes within each group is not valid, the *ANCOVA* methods described in this chapter cannot be used. One method of testing for equal slopes is to use an 'interaction' factor between GROUP and X in the MODEL statement in SAS, e.g.,

```
MODEL Y = GROUP X GROUP*X;
```

A significant interaction effect (GROUP*X) implies that the differences among group levels change for different X values, i.e., different slopes. *ANCOVA* should not be used if a preliminary test results in significantly different slopes among groups.

▶ **11.4.3.**   A 95% confidence interval for the adjusted mean response in Group i (i = 1, 2, ..., k) is given by

$$(a_i + b\,\overline{x}) \pm t_{0.025,N-k-1} \cdot s \cdot \sqrt{\frac{1}{n_i} + \frac{(\overline{x}_i - \overline{x})^2}{S_{xx}}}$$

where $s = \sqrt{MSE}$ from the ANOVA table.

In Example 11.1, 95% confidence intervals for the adjusted mean responses for each treatment group are

Fibralo Group

$$(74.81 - (11.268 \cdot 6.8118)) \pm 2.04 \cdot \sqrt{93.67} \cdot \sqrt{\frac{1}{16} + \frac{(7.0000 - 6.8118)^2}{48.175}} =$$

-1.95 ± 4.96 or   (−6.91 to 3.01)

Gemfibrozil Group:

$$(64.59 - (11.268 \cdot 6.8118)) \pm 2.04 \cdot \sqrt{93.67} \cdot \sqrt{\frac{1}{18} + \frac{(6.6444 - 6.8118)^2}{48.175}} =$$

-12.17 ± 4.68 or $(-16.85$ to $-7.49)$

Notice that the confidence interval widths (4.96 and 4.68) can be easily computed as $t \times$ SEM where t is the critical t-value, 2.04, and SEM is the standard error of the LS-mean shown in Output 11.1 ⓫

▶ **11.4.4.**   A 95% confidence interval for the difference in adjusted mean responses between two groups, say Group u and Group v, is given by

$$(a_u - a_v) \pm t_{0.025, N-k-1} \cdot s \cdot \sqrt{\frac{1}{n_u} + \frac{1}{n_v} + \frac{(\overline{x}_u - \overline{x}_v)^2}{S_{xx}}}$$

In Example 11.1, a 95% confidence interval for the difference in adjusted means between the *Fibralo* and *Gemfibrozil* groups is

$$(74.81 - 64.59) \pm 2.04 \cdot \sqrt{93.7} \cdot \sqrt{\frac{1}{16} + \frac{1}{18} + \frac{(7.0000 - 6.6444)^2}{48.175}} =$$

$10.22 \pm 2.04 \cdot (3.3629) = 10.22 \pm 6.86$ or $(3.36$ to $17.08)$

Notice that the standard error (3.3629) used in this calculation can be obtained from the SAS output for TRT effect (see Output 11.1 ⓳).

▶ **11.4.5.**   The standard errors of the adjusted group means and mean differences are smallest when $\overline{x}_i = \overline{x}$ for all i (= 1, 2, ..., k). In this case, the standard error is the same as that of the unadjusted case (see Chapter 6).

▶ **11.4.6.**   As shown in Output 11.1, the adjusted *F-tests* in SAS are found with the Type III sums of squares. SAS prints these by default, in addition to the Type I sums of squares. The Type I results depend on the order in which the factors are specified in the MODEL statement (see Appendix D). When the Treatment effect is specified before the covariate in the MODEL statement in PROC GLM, the Type I sum of squares represents the unadjusted sum of squares for Treatment (ignoring the covariate), which could alternatively be found by using the *one-way ANOVA* with Treatment as the only effect.

Notice that the Type I SS for TRT in Output 11.1, using the *ANCOVA* model is the same as the SS for TRT in the *one-way ANOVA* results. While the same sum of squares are obtained, the corresponding *F-test* is not the same *F-test* because the covariate-adjusted MSE is used as a divisor.

> Note: Although the examples in this section use PROC GLM in SAS, PROC MIXED can also be used for *ANCOVA* methods. The book, "*SAS System for Mixed Models*" by Littell, Milliken, Stroup, and Wolfinger, provides a good discussion of the use of PROC MIXED with *ANCOVA*. This book was written under the SAS Books By Users program.

▶ **11.4.7.**   In Example 11.2, various other models could have been selected for the analysis. Output 11.3 shows the *ANCOVA* results produced by models which correspond to the following GLM MODEL statements.

```
(1)     MODEL BPDIACH = TRT / SS3 ;
(2)     MODEL BPDIACH = TRT CENTER / SS3;
(3)     MODEL BPDIACH = TRT BPDIA0 / SS3;
(4)     MODEL BPDIACH = TRT AGE / SS3;
(5)     MODEL BPDIACH = TRT AGE BPDIA0 / SS3;
(6)     MODEL BPDIACH = TRT CENTER BPDIA0 / SS3;
(7)     MODEL BPDIACH = TRT CENTER AGE / SS3;
```

The SAS Type III results for each model factor are produced in the output for each of the above models by using the `ods select ModelANOVA`; statement.

Using a *one-way ANOVA* (Chapter 6) or, equivalently, the *two-sample t-test* (Chapter 5) to compare treatment groups, ignoring all other study factors, results in only marginal significance (p=0.0545) of the Treatment effect (Model (1) above). Using a *two-way ANOVA* (Chapter 7) by including Treatment Group and Center without the covariates results in a similar p-value for Treatment (p=0.0547) (Model (2) above).

You see that Age is a significant covariate when used as a sole numeric covariate (Models (4) and (7) above), but Age is no longer significant when baseline diastolic blood pressure is also included (Model (5) above). There might be some collinearity issues causing this outcome, which can be investigated using the methods discussed for Example 10.2 (Chapter 10). The significance of the Treatment Group effect increases when BPDIA0 is used as a covariate without Age, with p-values of 0.0331–0.0343 (Models (3) and (6) above).

Output 11.3. SAS Output for Example 11.2 Using Alternative Models

```
(1)
Source          DF      Type III SS     Mean Square     F Value     Pr > F

TRT              1      143.1141880     143.1141880       3.82      0.0545
-----------------------------------------------------------------------
(2)
Source          DF      Type III SS     Mean Square     F Value     Pr > F

TRT              1      146.5980349     146.5980349       3.82      0.0547
CENTER           3       49.0195734      16.3398578       0.43      0.7352
-----------------------------------------------------------------------
(3)
Source          DF      Type III SS     Mean Square     F Value     Pr > F

TRT              1      153.8692890     153.8692890       4.72      0.0331
BPDIA0           1      388.0563898     388.0563898      11.90      0.0009
-----------------------------------------------------------------------
(4)
Source          DF      Type III SS     Mean Square     F Value     Pr > F

TRT              1      122.7314895     122.7314895       3.51      0.0649
AGE              1      220.8161121     220.8161121       6.32      0.0142
-----------------------------------------------------------------------
(5)
Source    DF    Type III SS      Mean Square      F Value    Pr > F

TRT        1    137.3094860     137.3094860        4.33      0.0410
AGE        1     97.3139906      97.3139906        3.07      0.0840
BPDIA0     1    264.5542683     264.5542683        8.35      0.0051
-----------------------------------------------------------------------
(6)
Source          DF      Type III SS     Mean Square     F Value     Pr > F

TRT              1      157.4152735     157.4152735       4.66      0.0343
CENTER           3       17.7550045       5.9183348       0.18      0.9128
BPDIA0           1      356.7918209     356.7918209      10.57      0.0018
-----------------------------------------------------------------------
(7)
Source          DF      Type III SS     Mean Square     F Value     Pr > F

TRT              1      124.5076559     124.5076559       3.45      0.0676
CENTER           3       23.5238722       7.8412907       0.22      0.8842
AGE              1      195.3204109     195.3204109       5.41      0.0230
```

These analyses indicate the importance of giving adequate consideration when establishing an appropriate statistical model at the design stage. As discussed in Chapter 1, bias can be introduced at the analysis stage if statistical methods are not pre-planned. This includes specification of appropriate statistical models. In a pivotal study, appropriate covariates should be specified in the primary model only if indicated, such as by earlier phase studies. Inclusion of pertinent covariates provides an automatic adjustment for differences in covariate means between treatment groups and can markedly increase the power for detecting treatment differences. However, inclusion of inappropriate covariates might lead to factor dilution, collinearity problems, and unnecessary reduction in error degrees of freedom, which, in turn, could result in loss of power or even inappropriate p-values.

▶ **11.4.8.**   When *ANCOVA* is used for model-building or exploratory analysis rather than as a primary analysis, the coefficient of determination (R-square) can be used as a relative measure of goodness-of-fit, as illustrated in Example 10.2. Some stepwise procedures rely on R^2 values for inclusion or exclusion of covariates (see SAS Help and Documentation for PROC GLM).

CHAPTER 12

The *Wilcoxon Signed-Rank Test*

12.1 Introduction

The *Wilcoxon signed-rank test* is a non-parametric analog of the *one-sample t-test* (Chapter 4). The *signed-rank test* can be used to make inferences about a population mean or median without requiring the assumption of normally distributed data. As its name implies, the *Wilcoxon signed-rank test* is based on the ranks of the data.

One of the most common applications of the *signed-rank test* in clinical trials is to compare responses between correlated or paired data, such as testing for significant pre- to post-study changes of a non-normally distributed evaluation measurement. The layout is the same as that for the *paired-difference t-test* (Chapter 4).

12.2 Synopsis

Given a sample, y_1, y_2, ..., y_n, of n non-zero differences or changes (zeroes are ignored), let R_i represent the rank of $|y_i|$ (when ranked lowest to highest). Let $R^{(+)}$ represent the sum of the ranks associated with the positive values of the y_i's, and let $R^{(-)}$ represent the sum of the ranks associated with the negative values of the y_i's. The test statistic is based on the smaller of $R^{(+)}$ and $R^{(-)}$. The hypothesis of 'no mean difference' is rejected if this statistic is larger than the critical value found in a special set of tables.

To avoid the requirement of special table values, you can use an approximation to this test based on the t-distribution, as shown next.

Let

$$S = (R^{(+)} - R^{(-)}) / 2$$

and

$$V = (n(n + 1)(2n + 1)) / 24$$

The approximate test can be summarized as

null hypothesis:	H_0: $\theta = 0$
alt. hypothesis:	H_A: $\theta \neq 0$
test statistic:	$T = \dfrac{S \cdot \sqrt{n-1}}{\sqrt{n \cdot V - S^2}}$
decision rule:	reject H_0 if $|T| > t_{\alpha/2, n-1}$

θ represents the unknown population mean, median, or other location parameter. When H_0 is true, T has an approximate Student-t distribution with $n-1$ degrees of freedom. Widely available t-tables can be used to determine the rejection region.

When there are tied data values, the averaged rank is assigned to the corresponding R_i values. A small adjustment to V for tied data values is appropriate, as follows: suppose there are **g** groups of tied data values. For the jth group, compute $c_j = m(m-1)(m+1)$, where m is the number of tied data values for that group. The correction factor of $C = c_1 + c_2 + ... + c_g$ is used to adjust V, as follows:

$$V = (n (n + 1) (2n + 1) - C / 2) / 24$$

12.3 Examples

Example 12.1 – Rose-Bengal Staining in KCS

A study enrolling 24 patients diagnosed with keratitis sicca (KCS) was conducted to determine the effect of a new ocular wetting agent, Oker-Rinse, for improving ocular dryness based on Rose-Bengal staining scores. Patients were instructed to use Oker-Rinse in one eye and Hypotears®, as a control, in the other eye 4 times a day for 3 weeks. Rose-Bengal staining scores were measured as 0, 1, 2, 3, or 4 in each of four areas of the eye: cornea, limbus, lateral conjunctiva, and medial conjunctiva. Higher scores represent a greater number of devitalized cells, a condition associated with KCS. The overall scores for each eye (see Table 12.1) were obtained by adding the scores over the four areas. Is there evidence of a difference between the two test preparations in the overall Rose-Bengal staining scores?

TABLE 12.1. Raw Data for Example 12.1

Patient Number	Hypotears	Oker-Rinse	Patient Number	Hypotears	Oker-Rinse
1	15	8	13	8	10
2	10	3	14	10	2
3	6	7	15	11	4
4	5	13	16	13	7
5	10	2	17	6	1
6	15	12	18	6	11
7	7	14	19	9	3
8	5	8	20	5	5
9	8	13	21	10	2
10	12	3	22	9	8
11	4	9	23	11	5
12	13	3	24	8	8

Solution

Because each patient receives both treatments, you have a matched-pairs setup. The analysis is performed on the differences in Rose-Bengal scores between the treatment groups. The data can be plotted to reveal that the differences have a bimodal distribution (two peaks), which is not consistent with an assumption of normality. Indeed, a formal test for normality (see SAS results later) indicates a significant departure from this assumption. Therefore, use of the *Wilcoxon signed-rank test* is preferable to using the *paired-difference t-test*.

You want to test the hypothesis that θ, the 'average' difference in Rose-Bengal scores between the treatment groups, is 0. The differences in scores and ranks of their absolute values are shown in Table 12.2.

The average rankings for tied differences are used. For example, a difference of ±1 occurs twice (Patients 3 and 22) so the average of the ranks 1 and 2 (= 1.5) is used. Notice that the 0 differences are omitted from the rankings, leaving $n = 22$, not 24.

TABLE 12.2. Ranks of the Data for Example 12.1

Patient Number	Difference	Rank	Patient Number	Difference	Rank
1	7	14.5	13	-2	3
2	7	14.5	14	8	18.5
3	-1	1.5	15	7	14.5
4	-8	18.5	16	6	11
5	8	18.5	17	5	7.5
6	3	4.5	18	-5	7.5
7	-7	14.5	19	6	11
8	-3	4.5	20	0	--
9	-5	7.5	21	8	18.5
10	9	21	22	1	1.5
11	-5	7.5	23	6	11
12	10	22	24	0	--

Compute

$$R^{(+)} = (14.5 + 14.5 + 18.5 + 4.5 + 21 + 22 + 18.5 +$$
$$14.5 + 11 + 7.5 + 11 + 18.5 + 1.5 + 11)$$
$$= 188.5$$

and

$$R^{(-)} = (1.5 + 18.5 + 14.5 + 4.5 + 7.5 + 7.5 + 3 + 7.5)$$
$$= 64.5$$

so that

$$S = (188.5 - 64.5)/2 = 62.0$$

To apply the correction factor for ties, you record 6 groups of ties with the frequencies (m's): 2, 2, 4, 3, 4, and 4, (see Table 12.3). Thus, $c_1 = 2\,(1)\,(3) = 6$, $c_2 = 6$, $c_3 = 4\,(3)\,(5) = 60$, $c_4 = 3\,(2)\,(4) = 24$, $c_5 = 60$, and $c_6 = 60$, yielding $C = 216$.

TABLE 12.3. Calculation of Correction for Ties for Example 12.1

Tie Group (i)	|Difference|	Number of Ties (m)	$c_i = m(m-1)(m+1)$
1	1	2	6
2	3	2	6
3	5	4	60
4	6	3	24
5	7	4	60
6	8	4	60
			C=216

Finally,

$$V = (n(n+1)(2n+1) - C/2)/24$$

$$= (22(23)(45) - 108)/24 = 944.25$$

The test is summarized as follows:

null hypothesis:	H_0: $\theta = 0$
alt. hypothesis:	H_A: $\theta \neq 0$

$$T = \frac{S \cdot \sqrt{n-1}}{\sqrt{n \cdot V - S^2}}$$

test statistic:

$$= \frac{62 \cdot \sqrt{21}}{\sqrt{(22 \cdot 944.25) - 62^2}} = 2.184$$

decision rule: reject H_0 if $|T| > t_{0.025,21} = 2.080$

conclusion: Because $2.184 > 2.080$, reject H_0, and conclude that there is a significant difference in Rose-Bengal scores between treatments.

SAS Analysis of Example 12.1

In the test summary just presented, the SAS function PROBT can be used to obtain the p-value associated with a t-statistic of 2.184 based on 21 degrees of freedom, namely, p = 0.0405 (found by using the SAS expression 2*(1–PROBT(2.184, 21))).

The SAS code and output for executing this analysis are shown on the next pages. The *Wilcoxon signed-rank test* can be performed in SAS using PROC UNIVARIATE. The NORMAL option ❶ is used to provide a test for normality based on the *Shapiro-Wilk test*. This test is rejected with a p-value of 0.0322 ❷, which indicates that the data cannot be assumed to have come from a normal distribution. This result makes the paired-difference *one-sample t-test* (Chapter 4) inappropriate for this analysis.

In Output 12.1, the signed-rank statistic is confirmed to be 62 ❸ with a p-value of 0.0405 ❹.

SAS uses the t-approximation to the *Wilcoxon signed-rank test* if n is greater than 20. For $n \leq 20$, SAS computes the exact probability.

SAS Code for Example 12.1

```
DATA KCS;
    INPUT PAT HYPOTEAR OKERINSE @@;
    DIFF = HYPOTEAR - OKERINSE;
    DATALINES;
 1 15  8     2 10  3      3  6  7      4  5 13
 5 10  2     6 15 12      7  7 14      8  5  8
 9  8 13    10 12  3     11  4  9     12 13  3
13  8 10    14 10  2     15 11  4     16 13  7
17  6  1    18  6 11     19  9  3     20  5  5
21 10  2    22  9  8     23 11  5     24  8  8
;


PROC UNIVARIATE NORMAL DATA = KCS;              ❶
    VAR DIFF;
    TITLE1 'The Wilcoxon-Signed-Rank Test';
    TITLE2 'Example 12.1:  Rose Bengal Staining in KCS';
RUN;
```

OUTPUT 12.1. SAS Output for Example 12.1

```
                  The Wilcoxon-Signed-Rank Test
             Example 12.1:  Rose Bengal Staining in KCS

                    The UNIVARIATE Procedure
                        Variable:  DIFF

                            Moments

N                        24    Sum Weights               24
Mean               2.29166667  Sum Observations          55
Std Deviation      5.66821164  Variance            32.1286232
Skewness           -0.4011393  Kurtosis            -1.2859334
Uncorrected SS           865   Corrected SS        738.958333
Coeff Variation    247.340144  Std Error Mean       1.15701886


                    Basic Statistical Measures

         Location                        Variability

     Mean      2.29167     Std Deviation         5.66821
     Median    4.00000     Variance             32.12862
     Mode     -5.00000     Range                18.00000
                           Interquartile Range   9.50000

NOTE: The mode displayed is the smallest of 4 modes with a count of
      3.
```

OUTPUT 12.1 SAS Output for Example 12.1 (*continued*)

```
                  The Wilcoxon-Signed-Rank Test
             Example 12.1:  Rose Bengal Staining in KCS

                    The UNIVARIATE Procedure
                       Variable: DIFF

                  Tests for Location: Mu0=0

        Test            -Statistic-      -----p Value------

        Student's t     t 1.980665    Pr > |t|    0.0597
        Sign            M        3    Pr >= |M|   0.2863
        Signed Rank     S       62    Pr >= |S|   0.0405
                                 ❸                      ❹


                    Tests for Normality

      Test                --Statistic---      -----p Value------

      Shapiro-Wilk        W    0.908189    Pr < W      0.0322    ❷
      Kolmogorov-Smirnov  D    0.201853    Pr > D      0.0125
      Cramer-von Mises    W-Sq 0.145333    Pr > W-Sq   0.0248
      Anderson-Darling    A-Sq 0.859468    Pr > A-Sq   0.0235


                    Quantiles (Definition 5)

                     Quantile     Estimate

                     100% Max        10.0
                     99%             10.0
                     95%              9.0
                     90%              8.0
                     75% Q3           7.0
                     50% Median       4.0
                     25% Q1          -2.5
                     10%             -5.0
                     5%              -7.0
                     1%              -8.0
                     0% Min          -8.0


                    Extreme Observations

              ----Lowest----          ----Highest---

              Value      Obs          Value      Obs

                -8         4            8          5
                -7         7            8         14
                -5        18            8         21
                -5        11            9         10
                -5         9           10         12
```

12.4   Details & Notes

▶ **12.4.1.**   The *Wilcoxon signed-rank test* is considered a non-parametric test because it makes no assumptions regarding the distribution of the population from which the data are collected. This appears to be a tremendous advantage over the *t-test*, so why not use the *signed-rank test* in all situations?

First, the *t-test* has been shown to be a more powerful test in detecting true differences when the data *are* normally distributed. Because the normal distribution occurs quite often in nature, the *t-test* is the method of choice for a wide range of applications. Secondly, analysts often feel more comfortable reporting a *t-test* whenever it is appropriate, especially to a non-statistician, because many clinical research professionals have become familiar with the terminology. One reason the *t-test* has enjoyed popular usage is its robustness under deviations to the underlying assumptions. Finally, the *Wilcoxon signed-rank test* does require the assumption of a symmetrical underlying distribution. When the data are highly skewed or otherwise non-symmetrical, an alternative to the *signed-rank test*, such as the *sign test* (discussed in Chapter 15), can be used.

▶ **12.4.2.**   Let $W_i = R_i$ if $y_i > 0$ and $W_i = -R_i$ if $y_i < 0$. It can be shown that the T statistic discussed is equivalent to performing a *one-sample t-test* (Chapter 4) on the W_i's, that is, the ranked data adjusted by the appropriate sign. This is sometimes referred to as performing a *t-test* on the 'rank-transformed' data.

▶ **12.4.3.**   An alternative approximation to the *signed-rank test* for large samples is the *Z-test*. The test statistic is taken to be $S' =$ smaller of $(R^{(+)}, R^{(-)})$. S' has mean and variance:

$$\mu_{S'} = \frac{n \cdot (n+1)}{4}$$

and

$$\sigma^2_{S'} = \frac{n \cdot (n+1) \cdot (2n+1)}{24}$$

Under H_0,

$$Z = \frac{S' - \mu_{S'}}{\sigma_{S'}}$$

has an approximate normal distribution with mean 0 and variance 1. The *Z–test* statistic is compared with the tabled value of $Z_{\alpha/2}$ for a *two-tailed test* (= 1.96 for $\alpha = 0.05$).

To illustrate this approximation for Example 12.1, compute

$$S' = 64.5$$

$$\mu_{S'} = \frac{22 \cdot 23}{4} = 126.5$$

and

$$\sigma_{S'} = \sqrt{\frac{22 \cdot 23 \cdot 45}{24}} = 30.8$$

so that

$$Z = (64.5 - 126.5)\,/\,30.8 = -2.013.$$

At $p = 0.05$, you reject H_0 because $2.013 > 1.96$. The SAS function PROBNORM can be used to obtain the actual p-value of 0.044.

▶ **12.4.4.** The *one-sample t-test* is often used with larger samples, regardless of the distribution of the data, because the *Central Limit Theorem* states that the sample mean $\bar{y}$ is normally distributed for large n, no matter what distribution the underlying data have (see Chapter 1). Usually, for $n > 30$, we can safely use the *one-sample t-test* (Chapter 4), and ignore distributional assumptions, providing the distribution is symmetric. The *Wilcoxon signed-rank test* and the *t-test* become closer as n gets larger. For non-symmetrical distributions, the mean, median, and other measures of central tendency might have widely disparate values. The *t-test* should be used only if the mean is the appropriate measure of central tendency for the population being studied.

▶ **12.4.5.** The method shown here is for a *two-tailed test*. For a *one-tailed test*, the same methods that are shown in Chapter 4 for the *one-sample t-test* can be used. If SAS is used, the p-value associated with the *signed-rank test* can be halved for an approximate *one-tailed test*.

The *Wilcoxon Rank-Sum Test*

13.1 Introduction

The *Wilcoxon rank-sum test* is a non-parametric analog of the *two-sample t-test* (Chapter 5). It is based on ranks of the data, and is used to compare location parameters, such as the mean or median, between two independent populations without the assumption of normally distributed data.

Although the *Wilcoxon rank-sum test* was developed for use with continuous numeric data, the test is also applied to the analysis of ordered categorical data. In clinical data analysis, this test is often useful, for example, for comparing patient global assessments or severity ratings between two treatment groups.

13.2 Synopsis

The data are collected as two independent samples of size n_1 and n_2, denoted by $y_{11}, y_{12}, ..., y_{1n_1}$ and $y_{21}, y_{22}, ..., y_{2n_2}$. The data are ranked, from lowest to highest, over the combined samples, and the test statistic is based on the sum of ranks for the first group.

Let r_{1j} = rank of y_{1j} (j = 1, 2, ..., n_1) and r_{2j} = rank of y_{2j} (j = 1, 2, ..., n_2), and compute

$$R_1 = \sum_{j=1}^{n_1} r_{1j}$$

and

$$R_2 = \sum_{j=1}^{n_2} r_{2j}$$

The hypothesis of equal means would be supported by similar average ranks between the two groups, i.e., if R_1/n_1 is close to R_2/n_2. R_1 is compared to a critical value obtained from a special set of tables based on *Wilcoxon rank-sum* exact probabilities to determine the appropriate rejection region. Such tables can be found in many intermediate statistical books or non-parametric statistical references.

Lack of availability of these tables might somewhat limit the usefulness of this test. However, the requirement for special tables can often be circumvented by using a normal approximation for larger samples. It has been shown that the normal approximation for the *rank-sum test* is excellent for samples as small as 8 per group.

With $N = n_1 + n_2$, the sum of the ranks $(1 + 2 + ... + N)$ can be expressed as $N \cdot (N+1)/2$. When the hypothesis of equality is true (H_0), you would expect the proportion of this sum from Sample 1 to be about n_1/N and the proportion from Sample 2 to be about n_2/N. That is, the expected value of R_1 under H_0 is

$$\mu_{R_1} = \left(\frac{n_1}{N}\right) \cdot \left(\frac{N(N+1)}{2}\right) = \frac{n_1 \cdot (N+1)}{2}$$

Additionally, the variance of R_1 can be computed as

$$\sigma^2_{R_1} = \frac{n_1 \cdot n_2}{12}(N+1)$$

If there are tied data values, the average rank is assigned to the corresponding r_{ij} values. Suppose there are g groups of tied data values. For the kth group, compute $c_k = m(m^2-1)$, where m is the number of tied values for that group. You can make a small adjustment to the variance by using the correction factor $C = c_1 + c_2 + ... + c_g$, as follows:

$$\sigma^2_{R_1} = \frac{n_1 \cdot n_2}{12}\left(N+1 - \frac{C}{N(N-1)}\right)$$

The test statistic, using a 0.5 continuity correction, is based on an approximate normal distribution, summarized as follows:

---

null hypothesis: H_0: $\theta_1 = \theta_2$

alt. hypothesis: H_A: $\theta_1 \neq \theta_2$

test statistic:
$$Z = \frac{|R_1 - \mu_{R1}| - 0.5}{\sigma_{R1}}$$

decision rule: reject H_0 if $|Z| > Z_{\alpha/2}$

---

where θ_1 and θ_2 represent the mean, median, or other location parameters for the two populations.

13.3 Examples

✎ **Example 13.1** -- Global Evaluations of *Seroxatene* in Back Pain

In previous studies of the new anti-depressant, Seroxatene, researchers noticed that patients with low back pain experienced a decrease in radicular pain after 6 to 8 weeks of daily treatment. A new study was conducted in 28 patients to determine whether this phenomenon is a drug-related response or coincidental. Patients with MRI-confirmed disk herniation and symptomatic leg pain were enrolled and randomly assigned to receive Seroxatene or a placebo for 8 weeks. At the end of the study, patients were asked to provide a global rating of their pain, relative to baseline, on a coded improvement scale as follows:

-------- Deterioration -------				--------- Improvement -------		
Marked	Moderate	Slight	No Change	Slight	Moderate	Marked
-3	-2	-1	0	+1	+2	+3

The data are shown in Table 13.1. Is there evidence that Seroxatene has any effect on radicular back pain?

TABLE 13.1. Raw Data for Example 13.1

------ Seroxatene Group -------				-------- Placebo Group ---------			
Patient Number	**Score**	**Patient Number**	**Score**	**Patient Number**	**Score**	**Patient Number**	**Score**
2	0	16	-1	1	3	15	0
3	2	17	2	4	-1	18	-1
5	3	20	-3	7	2	19	-3
6	3	21	3	9	3	23	-2
8	-2	22	3	11	-2	25	1
10	1	24	0	13	1	28	0
12	3	26	2				
14	3	27	-1				

Solution

With a situation involving a two-sample comparison of means, you might first consider the *two-sample t-test* or the *Wilcoxon rank-sum test*. Because the data consist of ordered categorical responses, the assumption of normality is dubious, so you can apply the *rank-sum test*.

Tied data values are identified as shown in Table 13.2.

TABLE 13.2. Calculation of Correction for Ties in Example 13.1

Response (y)	Number of Ties (m)	Ranks	Average Rank	$c_k = m(m^2-1)$
-3	2	1, 2	1.5	6
-2	3	3, 4, 5	4	24
-1	4	6, 7, 8, 9	7.5	60
0	4	10, 11, 12, 13	11.5	60
+1	3	14, 15, 16	15	24
+2	4	17, 18, 19, 20	18.5	60
+3	8	21, 22, 23, 24, 25, 26, 27, 28	24.5	504
				C = 738

With $n_1 = 16$, $n_2 = 12$, and $N = 28$, the ranked values (r's) of the responses (y's) are shown in Table 13.3.

TABLE 13.3. Ranks of the Data for Example 13.1

----- Seroxatene Group -----				------- Placebo Group -------			
Patient Number	Score Rank	Patient Number	Score Rank	Patient Number	Score Rank	Patient Number	Score Rank
2	11.5	16	7.5	1	24.5	15	11.5
3	18.5	17	18.5	4	7.5	18	7.5
5	24.5	20	1.5	7	18.5	19	1.5
6	24.5	21	24.5	9	24.5	23	4
8	4	22	24.5	11	4	25	15
10	15	24	11.5	13	15	28	11.5
12	24.5	26	18.5				
14	24.5	27	7.5				

Compute

$$R_1 = 11.5 + 18.5 + 24.5 + \ldots + 7.5 = 261$$

and

$$R_2 = 24.5 + 7.5 + 18.5 + \ldots + 11.5 = 145$$

As a check, note that $R_1 + R_2 = N(N+1)/2 = 406$. You further compute

$$\mu_{R_1} = \frac{16 \cdot (29)}{2} = 232$$

and

$$\sigma^2_{R_1} = \frac{(16)(12)}{12} \cdot \left(29 - \frac{738}{(28)(27)}\right) = 448.38$$

The test summary, based on a normal approximation at a significance level of $\alpha = 0.05$, becomes

null hypothesis: H_0: $\theta_1 = \theta_2$
alt. hypothesis: H_A: $\theta_1 \neq \theta_2$

test statistic: $$Z = \frac{|R_1 - \mu_{R1}| - 0.5}{\sigma_{R1}}$$

$$= \frac{(261 - 232) - 0.5}{\sqrt{448.38}} = 1.346$$

decision rule: reject H_0 if $|Z| > 1.96$

conclusion: Because 1.346 is not > 1.96, you do not reject H_0, and conclude that there is insufficient evidence of a difference between *Seroxatene* and placebo in global back pain evaluations.

Interpolation of normal probabilities tabulated in Appendix A.1 results in a two-tailed p-value of 0.178 for the Z-statistic of 1.346. The p-value can also be found by using the SAS function PROBNORM. In SAS, the two-tailed p-value for a Z-value of 1.346 is $(1 - \text{PROBNORM}(1.346)) = 0.1783$.

SAS Analysis of Example 13.1

The *Wilcoxon rank-sum test* is performed in SAS by using PROC NPAR1WAY with the WILCOXON option, as shown in the SAS code on the next page. The sum of ranks for either group can be used to compute the test statistic. The manual calculations use $R_1 = 261$, while SAS uses $R_2 = 145$ ❶. When the smaller value is used, the result is a negative Z-value ❷. In either case, for a *two-tailed test*, $|Z| = 1.346$ with a p-value of 0.1783 ❸.

The output from PROC NPAR1WAY also gives the results of the analysis using the *Kruskal-Wallis* chi-square approximation ❹ (Chapter 14).

SAS Code for Example 13.1

```
DATA RNKSM;
    INPUT TRT $ PAT SCORE @@;
    DATALINES;
SER  2  0    SER  3  2    SER  5  3    SER  6  3
SER  8 -2    SER 10  1    SER 12  3    SER 14  3
SER 16 -1    SER 17  2    SER 20 -3    SER 21  3
SER 22  3    SER 24  0    SER 26  2    SER 27 -1
PBO  1  3    PBO  4 -1    PBO  7  2    PBO  9  3
PBO 11 -2    PBO 13  1    PBO 15  0    PBO 18 -1
PBO 19 -3    PBO 23 -2    PBO 25  1    PBO 28  0
;

PROC NPAR1WAY WILCOXON DATA = RNKSM;
    CLASS TRT; VAR SCORE;
    TITLE1 'The Wilcoxon Rank-Sum Test';
    TITLE2 'Example 13.1:  Seroxatene in Back Pain';
RUN;
```

OUTPUT 13.1. SAS Output for Example 13.1

```
                 The Wilcoxon Rank-Sum Test
            Example 13.1:  Seroxatene in Back Pain


                 The NPAR1WAY Procedure


        Wilcoxon Scores (Rank Sums) for Variable SCORE
                  Classified by Variable TRT


         Sum of       Expected       Std Dev         Mean
TRT       N          Scores       Under H0      Under H0       Score
-------------------------------------------------------------------
SER      16          261.0          232.0      21.175008    16.312500
PBO      12          145.0          174.0      21.175008    12.083333


          Average scores were used for ties.


              Wilcoxon Two-Sample Test

         Statistic            145.0000           ❶


         Normal Approximation
         Z                     -1.3459           ❷
         One-Sided Pr <  Z      0.0892
         Two-Sided Pr > |Z|     0.1783           ❸

         t Approximation
         One-Sided Pr <  Z      0.0948
         Two-Sided Pr > |Z|     0.1895

     Z includes a continuity correction of 0.5.


              Kruskal-Wallis Test                ❹

         Chi-Square             1.8756
         DF                          1
         Pr > Chi-Square        0.1708
```

13.4 Details & Notes

▶ **13.4.1.** The term 'mean' is used loosely in this chapter to refer to the appropriate location parameter. Because the mean is not always the best measure of a distribution's center, the location parameter can refer to some other measure, such as one of the measures of central tendency described in Chapter 1 (Table 1.3).

▶ **13.4.2.** For symmetric distributions, the population mean and median are the same. For skewed distributions with long tails to the right, the median is usually smaller than the mean and considered a better measure of the distributional 'center' or location. The geometric mean is also smaller than the arithmetic mean and is often used as a location parameter for exponentially distributed data. The *Wilcoxon rank-sum test* tests for a location or positional shift in distributions without the need to identify the best measure of central tendency. Thus, the parameter θ is simply a symbol generically denoting a distribution's location.

▶ **13.4.3.** Although you need not make assumptions regarding the actual distributions of the data, the *Wilcoxon rank-sum test* does assume that the two population distributions have the same shape and differ only by a possible shift in location. Thus, you assume the same dispersion, which is analogous to the assumption of variance homogeneity required of the *two-sample t-test*. Unlike the *Wilcoxon signed-rank test*, you need not assume the data come from a symmetric distribution.

▶ **13.4.4.** The test statistic, R_1, has a symmetric distribution about its mean, $n_1(N+1)/2$. Because of this symmetry, the one-tailed p-value is easily obtained by halving the two-tailed p-value.

▶ **13.4.5.** The *Mann-Whitney U-test* is another non-parametric test for comparing location parameters based on two independent samples. Mathematically, it can be shown that the *Mann-Whitney test* is equivalent to the *Wilcoxon rank-sum test*.

▶ **13.4.6.** Notice that the approximate test statistic, Z, can be computed from R_2 instead of R_1. When using R_2, the mean and standard deviation (μ_R, σ_R) are computed by reversing n_1 and n_2 in the formulas given.

▶ **13.4.7.** Another approximation to the *Wilcoxon rank-sum test* is the use of the *two-sample t-test* on the ranked data. In SAS, use PROC RANK to rank the pooled data from the two samples, then use PROC TTEST. A comparison between using the SAS procedures with the standard *Wilcoxon rank-sum test* is discussed by Conover and Iman (1981).

▶ **13.4.8.** The assumption of normality can be tested by using PROC UNIVARIATE in SAS. If this is rejected, the *Wilcoxon rank-sum test* is preferable to the *two-sample t-test*.

Tests such as the *Kolmogorov-Smirnov test*, available by specifying the EDF option in PROC NPAR1WAY in SAS, can be used to compare the equality of two distributions. Significance indicates a difference in location, variability, or distributional 'shapes' between the two populations.

The *Kruskal-Wallis Test*

14.1 Introduction

The *Kruskal-Wallis test* is a non-parametric analogue of the *one-way ANOVA* (Chapter 6). It is used to compare population location parameters (mean, median, etc.) among two or more groups based on independent samples. Unlike an *ANOVA*, the assumption of normally distributed responses is not necessary. The *Kruskal-Wallis test* is an extension of the *Wilcoxon rank-sum test* (Chapter 13) for more than two groups, just as a *one-way ANOVA* is an extension of the *two-sample t-test*.

The *Kruskal-Wallis test* is based on the ranks of the data. This test is often useful in clinical trials for comparing responses among three or more dose groups or treatment groups using samples of non-normally distributed response data.

14.2 Synopsis

The data are collected as k (≥ 2) independent samples of size $n_1, n_2, \ldots n_k$, as shown in Table 14.1.

TABLE 14.1. Layout for the Kruskal-Wallis Test

Group 1	Group 2	...	Group k
y_{11}	y_{21}		y_{k1}
y_{12}	y_{22}		y_{k2}
...	...		...
y_{1n_1}	y_{2n_2}		y_{kn_k}

You want to test the hypothesis of equal mean responses among groups (H_0). The data are ranked, from lowest to highest, over the combined samples, and the test statistic is a function of the ranks and sample sizes.

For i = 1, 2, ..., k and j = 1, 2, ..., n_i, let r_{ij} = rank of y_{ij} over the k combined samples. For each group (i = 1, 2, ..., k), compute

$$R_i = \sum_{j=1}^{n_i} r_{ij}$$

The average rank of all $N = n_1 + n_2 + \ldots + n_k$ observations is $\bar{R} = (N+1)/2$. Therefore, when the null hypothesis is true, the average rank for each group, namely $\bar{R}_i = (R_i / n_i)$, should be close to this value and the sum-of-squared deviations

$$\sum_{i=1}^{k} n_i (\bar{R}_i - \bar{R})^2$$

should be small.

This form is recognizable as the familiar 'between-group' sum of squares used in the *analysis of variance* (Chapters 6 and 7), after replacing the observed values with their ranks. The *Kruskal-Wallis test* statistic is a function of this sum of squares, which simplifies algebraically to the quantity

$$h^* = \frac{12}{N(N+1)} \cdot \left(\sum_{i=1}^{k} \frac{R_i^2}{n_i} \right) - 3(N+1)$$

When H_0 is true, h^* has an approximate *chi-square* distribution with k–1 degrees of freedom.

As with other ranking procedures, when you have tied data values, the average rank of the tied values is assigned to the corresponding r_{ij} values. Suppose there are g categories of tied values. For the Lth such category, compute $c_L = m(m^2-1)$, where m is the number of tied values for that category. A small adjustment can be made to the test statistic by using the correction factor $C = c_1 + c_2 + \ldots + c_g$. With θ representing the population location parameter, the test is summarized as shown next.

null hypothesis: $H_0: \theta_1 = \theta_2 = \dots = \theta_k$

alt. hypothesis: $H_A: \theta_i \neq \theta_j$ for at least one pair (i,j)

test statistic:
$$h = \frac{h^*}{\left(1 - \dfrac{C}{N(N^2 - 1)}\right)}$$

decision rule: reject H_0 if $h > \chi^2_{k-1}(\alpha)$

$\chi^2_{k-1}(\alpha)$ represents the critical chi-square value based on k–1 degrees of freedom and a significance level of α. Critical chi-square values can be found in tables of the chi-square distribution or by using the PROBCHI function in SAS.

14.3 Examples

Example 14.1 -- Psoriasis Evaluation in Three Groups

A study comparing a low dose (0.1%) and a high dose (0.2%) of a new, non-steroidal, anti-psoriasis medication was conducted using a parallel design, including a placebo group as control. Thirty-two patients were studied for 4 weeks of daily treatment. The primary efficacy response measure was the degree of psoriatic lesion reduction at study termination, rated on an ordinal scale, as follows:

Coded Response Category	Reduction in Lesion Size	Coded Response Category	Reduction in Lesion Size
1	< 0%	5	26-50%
2	0%	6	51-75%
3	1-10%	7	76-99%
4	11-25%	8	100%

Based on the data shown in Table 14.2, is there any difference in response among the three groups?

TABLE 14.2. Raw Data for Example 14.1

0.1% Solution		0.2% Solution		Placebo	
Patient Number	Category Code	Patient Number	Category Code	Patient Number	Category Code
1	5	3	5	2	5
6	4	5	8	4	3
9	1	7	2	8	7
12	7	10	8	11	1
15	4	14	7	13	2
19	3	18	4	16	4
20	6	22	5	17	2
23	7	26	4	21	1
27	8	28	6	24	4
32	7	31	4	25	5
				29	4
				30	5

Solution

This data set has an ordinal scale response with unequally spaced intervals. If you use a *one-way ANOVA*, the results might depend on the coding scheme used. Because the codes of 1 to 8 are arbitrary, the *Kruskal-Wallis test* is appropriate; the results do not depend on the magnitude of the coded values, only their ranks.

The data can be summarized in a frequency table format that includes the ranks, as shown in Table 14.3.

TABLE 14.3. Calculation of Ranks and Correction for Ties in Example 14.1

Response Category	Code	-- Frequencies -- 0.1%	0.2%	Placebo	Ranks	Average Rank	Total Frequency (m)	$c = m(m^2-1)$
<0%	1	1	0	2	1-3	2	3	24
0%	2	0	1	2	4-6	5	3	24
1-10%	3	1	0	1	7-8	7.5	2	6
11-25%	4	2	3	3	9-16	12.5	8	504
26-50%	5	1	2	3	17-22	19.5	6	210
51-75%	6	1	1	0	23-24	23.5	2	6
76-99%	7	3	1	1	25-29	27	5	120
100%	8	1	2	0	30-32	31	3	24
		10	10	12			32	C = 918

The table of ranks and the rank sums for each group are shown in Table 14.4.

TABLE 14.4. Ranks of the Data in Example 14.1

0.1% Solution		0.2% Solution		Placebo	
Patient Number	**Category Rank**	**Patient Number**	**Category Rank**	**Patient Number**	**Category Rank**
1	19.5	3	19.5	2	19.5
6	12.5	5	31	4	7.5
9	2	7	5	8	27
12	27	10	31	11	2
15	12.5	14	27	13	5
19	7.5	18	12.5	16	12.5
20	23.5	22	19.5	17	5
23	27	26	12.5	21	2
27	31	28	23.5	24	12.5
32	27	31	12.5	25	19.5
				29	12.5
				30	19.5
$R_1 = 189.5$ $(n_1 = 10)$		$R_2 = 194.0$ $(n_2 = 10)$		$R_3 = 144.5$ $(n_3 = 12)$	

Compute the unadjusted test statistic as

$$h^* = \frac{12}{32(33)} \cdot \left(\frac{189.5^2}{10} + \frac{194.0^2}{10} + \frac{144.5^2}{12} \right) - 3(33) = 4.348$$

and the test is summarized as follows:

null hypothesis: H_0: $\theta_1 = \theta_2 = \theta_3$

alt. hypothesis: H_A: not H_0

test statistic:
$$h = \frac{4.348}{\left(1 - \frac{918}{32 \cdot (32^2 - 1)} \right)} = \frac{4.348}{0.972} = 4.473$$

decision rule: reject H_0 if $h > \chi_2^2(0.05) = 5.991$

conclusion: Because 4.473 is not > 5.991, there is insufficient evidence to reject H_0. You conclude that the data fail to reveal a statistical difference in psoriatic lesion reduction among the groups.

SAS Analysis of Example 14.1

In the preceding test summary, the PROBCHI function in SAS can be used to obtain the p-value associated with the test statistic 4.473 based on 2 degrees of freedom namely, $p = 0.1068$ (=$1 - PROBCHI(4.473,2)$).

The *Kruskal-Wallis test* can be performed in SAS by using PROC NPAR1WAY with the WILCOXON option, as shown in the SAS code for Example 14.1. SAS will automatically perform the *Wilcoxon rank-sum test* (Chapter 13) if there are only two groups and the *Kruskal-Wallis test* if there are more than two groups, as determined by the number of levels in the class variable. In this example, there are three treatment levels in the DOSE variable, which is used in the CLASS statement ❶.

The output shows the rank sums for each group ❷ and the chi-square statistic ❸, which corroborate the manual calculations demonstrated. The p-value ❹ is also printed out by SAS.

SAS Code for Example 14.1

```
DATA PSOR;
    INPUT DOSE $ PAT SCORE @@;
    DATALINES;
0.1  1   5    0.1  6   4    0.1  9   1    0.1 12   7
0.1 15   4    0.1 19   3    0.1 20   6    0.1 23   7
0.1 27   8    0.1 32   7    0.2  3   5    0.2  5   8
0.2  7   2    0.2 10   8    0.2 14   7    0.2 18   4
0.2 22   5    0.2 26   4    0.2 28   6    0.2 31   4
PBO  2   5    PBO  4   3    PBO  8   7    PBO 11   1
PBO 13   2    PBO 16   4    PBO 17   2    PBO 21   1
PBO 24   4    PBO 25   5    PBO 29   4    PBO 30   5
;

PROC NPAR1WAY WILCOXON DATA = PSOR;
    CLASS DOSE;                                      ❶
    VAR SCORE;
    TITLE1 'The Kruskal-Wallis Test';
    TITLE2 'Example 14.1: Psoriasis Evaluation in Three
        Groups';
RUN;
```

OUTPUT 14.1. SAS Output for Example 14.1

```
                    The Kruskal-Wallis Test
            Example 14.1:  Psoriasis Evaluation in Three Groups

                    The NPAR1WAY Procedure

          Wilcoxon Scores (Rank Sums) for Variable SCORE
                  Classified by Variable DOSE

                  Sum of      Expected       Std Dev        Mean
      DOSE    N   Scores ❷    Under H0      Under H0        Score
      ---------------------------------------------------------------
      0.1    10   189.50       165.0        24.249418     18.950000
      0.2    10   194.00       165.0        24.249418     19.400000
      PBO    12   144.50       198.0        25.327691     12.041667

          Average scores were used for ties.

                  Kruskal-Wallis Test

              Chi-Square        4.4737       ❸
              DF                     2
              Pr > Chi-Square   0.1068       ❹
```

14.4 Details & Notes

▶ **14.4.1.**   When k=2, the *Kruskal-Wallis* chi-square value has 1 degree of freedom This test is identical to the normal approximation used for the *Wilcoxon rank-sum test* (Chapter 13). As noted in previous sections, a chi-square with 1 degree of freedom can be represented by the square of a standardized normal random variable (see Appendix B). For k=2, the h-statistic is the square of the *Wilcoxon rank-sum Z-test* (without the continuity correction).

▶ **14.4.2.**   The effect of adjusting for tied ranks is to slightly increase the value of the test statistic, h. Therefore, omission of this adjustment results in a more conservative test.

▶ **14.4.3.**   For small n_i's (< 5), the chi-square approximation might not be appropriate. Special tables for the exact distribution of h are available in many non-parametric statistics books. These tables can be used to obtain the appropriate rejection region for small samples. (For example, *Nonparametric Statistical Methods* by Hollander and Wolfe (1973) provides tables of the critical values for the *Kruskal-Wallis test*, the *Wilcoxon rank-sum test,* and the *Wilcoxon signed-rank test.*)

Exact tests are also available in SAS by using the EXACT statement in PROC NPAR1WAY (see SAS documentation). Exact tests should be used in special cases when the distribution of the test statistic (h) is not well approximated with the chi-square, such as tests involving very small sample sizes or many ties.

▶ **14.4.4.** When the distribution of the response data is unknown and cannot be assumed to be normal, the median (rather than the mean) is frequently used as a measure of location or central tendency. The median is computed as the middle value (for an odd number of observations) or the average of the two middle values (for an even number of observations). Approximate 95% confidence intervals for the median can be constructed using non-parametric methods developed by Hodges and Lehmann (see Hollander and Wolfe, 1973).

▶ **14.4.5.** Another approximate test based on the ranks uses a *one-way ANOVA* on the ranked data. This method is often used instead of the *Kruskal-Wallis test* because similar results can be expected. Use the following SAS statements to rank the data for Example 14.1, then perform the ANOVA.

```
PROC RANK DATA = PSOR OUT = RNK;
    VAR SCORE;
    RANKS RNKSCORE;
RUN;

PROC GLM DATA = RNK;
    CLASS DOSE;
    MODEL RNKSCORE = DOSE / SS3;
RUN;
```

The output (Output 14.2) shows the ANOVA results using the ranked data, which gives the p-value 0.1044 ❺ (compared with 0.1068 for the chi-square method).

▶ **14.4.6.** When the *Kruskal-Wallis test* is significant, pairwise comparisons can be carried out with the *Wilcoxon rank-sum test* for each pair of groups. However, the multiplicity problem affecting the overall error rate must be considered for larger values of k. For example, the adjusted p-value method, such as a *Bonferroni* or Holm's method using PROC MULTTEST in SAS, can be performed as described in Appendix E. Other techniques for handling multiple comparisons when using non-parametric tests are discussed in Hollander and Wolfe (1973).

OUTPUT 14.2. Analysis of Example 14.1 Using a One-Way ANOVA on the Ranks

```
                    The Kruskal-Wallis Test
        Example 14.1:  Psoriasis Evaluation in Three Groups

                      The GLM Procedure

                    Class Level Information

              Class        Levels     Values
              DOSE            3        0.1 0.2 PBO

               Number of observations    32

          Dependent Variable: RNKSCORE    Rank for Variable SCORE

                          Sum of
    Source           DF     Squares    Mean Square   F Value   Pr > F

    Model             2   382.645833   191.322917     2.45     0.1044
    Error            29  2268.854167    78.236351
    Corrected Total  31  2651.500000


         R-Square      Coeff Var     Root MSE     RNKSCORE Mean

         0.144313      53.60686      8.845131       16.50000

    Source           DF    Type III SS   Mean Square   F Value   Pr > F

    DOSE              2   382.6458333   191.3229167     2.45     0.1044
```
❺

▶ **14.4.7.** When the k levels of the Group factor can be ordered, you might want to test for association between response and increasing levels of Group. The dose-response study is an example. If the primary question is whether increasing response is related to larger doses, the *Jonckheere-Terpstra test* for ordered alternatives can be used. This is a non-parametric test that shares the same null hypothesis with the *Kruskal-Wallis test*, but the alternative is more specific:

$$H_A: \theta_1 \leq \theta_2 \leq \ldots \leq \theta_k$$

with at least one strict inequality (<).

The *Jonckheere-Terpstra test* can be performed by specifying the JT option in the TABLES statement when using PROC FREQ in SAS. The SAS statements for this test using Example 14.1 are shown in the program that follows. (Notice that you first create a new variable, DOS, so that the dose levels are in ascending order.)

```
DATA JTTEST; SET PSOR;
    IF DOSE = 'PBO' THEN DOS = 0;
    ELSE DOS = DOSE;
RUN;

PROC FREQ DATA = JTTEST;
    TABLES DOS*SCORE / JT;
RUN;
```

This test results in a p-value of 0.056 (compared with 0.107 for the *Kruskal-Wallis test*), which illustrates the increased power when using this test for the more targeted alternative. The *Jonckheere-Terpstra test* uses a chi-square approximation for large samples. Exact tests are available (see Hollander and Wolfe, 1973), and these tests can be performed by using the EXACT statement in PROC FREQ in SAS.

► **14.4.8.**   As illustrated in 14.4.5, using *ANOVA* methods based on the rank-transformed data is a common way to analyze data when the parametric assumptions might not be fulfilled. This approach can also be used for a two-way layout by first ranking the observations from lowest to highest across all treatment groups within each block, then using the usual *two-way ANOVA* methods (Chapter 7) on these ranks to test for significant treatment effects. Such a technique is often substituted for *Friedman's test*, which is the non-parametric analog of the *two-way ANOVA*. This approach assumes multiple observations per cell ($n_{ij} > 1$). Other types of layouts can be analyzed using similar ranking methods (see Conover and Iman, 1981).

The *Binomial Test*

15.1 Introduction

The *binomial test* is used to make inferences about a proportion or response rate based on a series of independent observations, each resulting in one of two possible mutually exclusive outcomes. The outcomes can be: response to treatment or no response, cure or no cure, survival or death, or in general, *event* or *non-event*. These observations are 'binomial' outcomes if the chance of observing the *event* of interest is the same for each observation.

In clinical trials, a common use of the *binomial test* is for estimating a response rate, p, using the number of patients (X) who respond to an investigative treatment out of a total of n studied. Special cases of the *binomial test* include two commonly used tests in clinical data analysis, *McNemar's test* (Chapter 18) and the *sign test* (discussed later in this chapter).

15.2 Synopsis

The experiment consists of observing n independent observations, each with one of two possible outcomes: *event* or *non-event*. For each observation, the probability of the *event* is denoted by p ($0 < p < 1$).

The total number of *events* in n observations, X, follows the binomial probability distribution (Chapter 1). Intuitively, the sample proportion, X/n, would be a good estimate of the unknown population proportion, p. Statistically, it is the best estimate.

The general formula for a binomial probability is:

$$\Pr(X{=}x) \; = \; \frac{n!}{x!(n-x)!} \; \cdot \; p^x(1-p)^{n-x}$$

where x can take integer values 0, 1, 2, ..., n.

> The symbol '!' is read 'factorial' and indicates multiplication by successively smaller integer values down to 1, i.e., $a! = (a)\cdot(a\text{-}1)\cdot(a\text{-}2) \ldots (3)\cdot(2)\cdot(1)$.
>
> (For example, $5! = 5 \times 4 \times 3 \times 2 \times 1 = 120$).

You want to determine whether the population proportion, p, differs from a hypothesized value, p_0. If the unknown proportion, p, equals p_0, then the estimated proportion, X/n, should be close to p_0, i.e., X should be close to $n \cdot p_0$. When p differs from p_0, X might be much larger or smaller than $n \cdot p_0$. Therefore, you reject the null hypothesis if X is 'too large' or 'too small'.

The test summary is:

> **null hypothesis**: H_0: $p = p_0$
> **alt. hypothesis**: H_A: $p \neq p_0$
>
> **test statistic**:   X = the number of *events* in n observations
>
> **decision rule**:   reject H_0 if $X \leq X_L$ or $X \geq X_U$, where X_L and X_U are chosen to satisfy $\Pr(X_L < X < X_U) \geq 1-\alpha$

Tables of binomial probabilities found in most introductory statistical texts or the SAS function PROBBNML can be used to determine X_L and X_U. This method is demonstrated in Example 15.1. Another option, using a normal approximation, is discussed following Example 15.1.

15.3 Examples

✍ **Example 15.1** -- Genital Wart Cure Rate

A company markets a therapeutic product for genital warts with a known cure rate of 40% in the general population. In a study of 25 patients with genital warts treated with this product, patients were also given high doses of vitamin C. As shown in Table 15.1, 14 patients were cured. Is this consistent with the cure rate in the general population?

TABLE 15.1. Raw Data for Example 15.1

Patient Number	Cured ?	Patient Number	Cured ?	Patient Number	Cured ?	Patient Number	Cured ?
1	YES	8	YES	15	YES	22	YES
2	NO	9	NO	16	NO	23	NO
3	YES	10	NO	17	NO	24	YES
4	NO	11	YES	18	YES	25	YES
5	YES	12	NO	19	YES		
6	YES	13	YES	20	NO		
7	NO	14	NO	21	YES		

Solution

Let p represent the probability of a cure in any randomly selected patient with genital warts and treated with Vitamin C concomitantly with the company's product. You want to know if this unknown rate differs from the established rate of $p_0 = 0.4$. Thus,

null hypothesis: H_0: $p = 0.4$

alt. hypothesis: H_A: $p \neq 0.4$

test statistic: $X = 14$ (the number cured out of the $n = 25$ patients treated)

decision rule: reject H_0 if $X \leq 4$ or $X \geq 15$

conclusion: Do not reject the null hypothesis. Because 14 does not lie in the rejection region, you conclude that there is insufficient evidence from this study to indicate that concomitant Vitamin C treatment has an effect on the product's cure rate.

The decision rule is established by finding a range of X values such that the probability of X being outside that range when the null hypothesis is true is approximately equal to the significance level. With a nominal significance level of $\alpha = 0.05$, the limits of the rejection region, 4 and 15, can be found from a table of binomial probabilities, satisfying $Pr(X \leq 4) + Pr(X \geq 15) \leq 0.05$. The PROBBNML function in SAS can also be used (see Section 15.4.4). The actual significance level is 0.044.

Normal Approximation

For large values of n and non-extreme values of p, a binomial response, X, can be approximated by a normal distribution with mean $n \cdot p$ and variance $n \cdot p \cdot (1-p)$. The approximation improves as n gets larger or as p gets closer to 0.5. Based on this statistical principle, another way to establish the rejection region for $\alpha = 0.05$ and large n is by computing

$$X_L = (n \cdot p_0) - 1.96(n \cdot p_0 \cdot (1 - p_0))^{\frac{1}{2}}$$

and

$$X_U = (n \cdot p_0) + 1.96(n \cdot p_0 \cdot (1 - p_0))^{\frac{1}{2}}$$

Applying these formulas to Example 15.1, you obtain

$$X_L = (25 \cdot 0.4) - 1.96(25(0.4)(0.6))^{\frac{1}{2}} = 5.2$$

and

$$X_U = (25 \cdot 0.4) + 1.96(25(0.4)(0.6))^{\frac{1}{2}} = 14.8$$

Because X can only take integer values, the rejection region becomes $X \leq 5$ and $X \geq 15$. Because of the small sample size, this approximation produces a slightly larger lower rejection region and yields an actual significance level of 0.064 (based on exact binomial probabilities).

A more common form of the normal approximation to the binomial test uses as the test statistic the actual estimate of p, namely $\hat{p} = X/n$. Under the assumption of approximate normality, the test summary becomes:

null hypothesis: H_0: $p = p_0$

alt. hypothesis: H_A: $p \neq p_0$

test statistic:
$$Z = \frac{|\hat{p} - p_0| - \frac{1}{2n}}{\sqrt{\frac{p_0 \cdot (1 - p_0)}{n}}}$$

decision rule: reject H_0 if $|Z| > Z_{\alpha/2}$

Because the binomial distribution is a discrete distribution (i.e., takes integer values), while the normal distribution is continuous, the $1/(2n)$ in the numerator of the test statistic is used as a 'continuity correction' to improve the approximation. When H_0 is true, Z has an approximate standard normal distribution. For the commonly used value of $\alpha = 0.05$, $Z_{0.025} = 1.96$.

In Example 15.1, the test statistic based on the normal approximation is

$$Z = \frac{\left| \frac{14}{25} - 0.4 \right| - \frac{1}{50}}{\sqrt{\frac{0.4 \cdot 0.6}{25}}} = \frac{0.140}{0.098} = 1.429$$

Because 1.429 is less than 1.96, the null hypothesis is not rejected.

15.4   Details & Notes

▶ **15.4.1.**   The normal approximation to the binomial distribution is a result of the *Central Limit Theorem* (Chapter 1). Let y_i represent a binomial response for Patient i (i = 1, 2, ..., n) with numeric values of 0 ('*non-event*') and 1 ('*event*'). Note that X, the number of '*events*' in n trials, is simply the sum of the y_i's. The probability of '*event*', p, is simply the population mean of the distribution from which the y_i's have been selected. That distribution is the binomial distribution with mean, p, and variance, $p \cdot (1-p)$. Therefore, $\hat{p} = X/n = \bar{y}$ has an approximate normal distribution with mean p and variance $p \cdot (1-p)/n$ for large n, according to the *Central Limit Theorem*. The *Z-test* statistic shown above uses p_0, the hypothesized value of the unknown parameter p because the test is conducted assuming H_0 is true.

▶ **15.4.2.**   The normal approximation to the binomial is generally a good approximation if

$$(n \cdot p) - 2\sqrt{n \cdot p \cdot (1-p)} \geq 0$$

and

$$(n \cdot p) + 2\sqrt{n \cdot p \cdot (1-p)} \leq n$$

or equivalently, if

$$n \geq 4 \times \max((p/(1-p)), ((1-p)/p))$$

The minimum sample size, n, satisfying this inequality is shown in Table 15.2 for various values of p. Larger n's are required for response probabilities (p) closer to 0 or 1.

TABLE 15.2. Minimum n Required by Normal Approximation as a Function of p

p	n
0.5	4
0.4 or 0.6	6
0.3 or 0.7	10
0.2 or 0.8	16
0.1 or 0.9	36

▶ **15.4.3.**   An approximate 95% confidence interval for estimating the proportion, p, is given by

$$\hat{p} \pm 1.96 \cdot \sqrt{\frac{\hat{p} \cdot (1-\hat{p})}{n}}$$

where $\hat{p} = X/n$.

With $X/n = 14/25 = 0.56$ in Example 15.1, a 95% confidence interval for p is

$$0.56 \pm 1.96 \, ((0.56 \times 0.44)/25)^{1/2} =$$

$$0.56 \pm 0.19 = (0.37 - 0.75)$$

▶ **15.4.4.** The SAS function PROBBNML can be used to obtain binomial probabilities for specified p and n. The actual significance level 0.044 in Example 15.1 is found by using the SAS statement PROBBNML(0.4,25,4) + (1 − PROBBNML(0.4,25,14)).

The PROBNORM function in SAS can be used with the normal approximation to obtain p-values. The approximate p-value for Example 15.1 with a *Z-test* statistic of 1.429 is found in SAS as p=2*(1 − PROBNORM(1.429)) = 0.136.

▶ **15.4.5.** When $p_0 = 0.5$, the *binomial test* is sometimes called the *sign test*. A common application of the *sign test* is in testing for pre- to post-treatment changes, given information only about whether a measurement increases or decreases following treatment. The number of increases is a binomial random variable with $p = 0.5$ when the null hypothesis of no pre- to post-treatment changes is true. The UNIVARIATE procedure in SAS can be used to conduct the *sign test* (Chapter 18).

▶ **15.4.6.** Because Example 15.1 tests for a difference from the hypothesized value in either direction, a *two-tailed test* is used. A *one-tailed test* would be used when you want to test whether the population proportion, p, is strictly *greater than* or strictly *less than* the threshold level, p_0. Use the rejection region according to the alternative hypothesis as follows:

Type of Test	Alternative Hypothesis	Corresponding Rejection Region
two-tailed	H_A: $p \neq p_o$	reject H_0 if $Z > Z_{\alpha/2}$ or $Z < -Z_{\alpha/2}$
one-tailed (right)	H_A: $p > p_0$	reject H_0 if $Z > Z_\alpha$
one-tailed (left)	H_A: $p < p_0$	reject H_0 if $Z < -Z_\alpha$

The *Chi-Square Test*

16.1 Introduction

The *chi-square test* is used to compare two independent binomial proportions, p_1 and p_2. In the analysis of clinical data, the binomial proportion typically represents a response rate, cure rate, survival rate, abnormality rate, or some other '*event*' rate as introduced in the previous chapter. Often, you want to compare such 'response' rates between a treated group and a parallel control group.

The *chi-square test* is an approximate test, which may be used when the normal approximation to the binomial distribution is valid (see Chapter 15). A popular alternative, *Fisher's exact test* (Chapter 17), is based on exact probabilities and it is often applied when conditions for using the *chi-square test* are not met.

16.2 Synopsis

Observation is made of X_1 responders out of n_1 patients who are studied in one group, and X_2 non-responders out of n_2 patients in a second, independent group, as shown in Table 16.1.

TABLE 16.1. Layout for the Chi-Square Test

	Number of Responders	Number of Non-Responders	Total
Group 1	X_1	$n_1 - X_1$	n_1
Group 2	X_2	$n_2 - X_2$	n_2
Combined	$X_1 + X_2$	$N - (X_1 + X_2)$	$N = n_1 + n_2$

Assume that each of the n_i patients in Group i (i =1, 2) have the same chance, p_i, of responding, so that X_1 and X_2 are independent binomial random variables (see Chapter 15). The goal is to compare population 'response' rates (p_1 vs. p_2) based on these sample data. Compute

$$NUM = \frac{(X_1 \cdot n_2 - X_2 \cdot n_1)}{N}$$

and

$$DEN = \frac{n_1 \cdot n_2 \cdot (X_1 + X_2) \cdot (N - X_1 - X_2)}{N^3}$$

Assuming that the normal approximation to the binomial distribution is applicable (see Section 16.4.2), the *chi-square test* summary is

null hypothesis:	H_0: $p_1 = p_2$
alt. hypothesis:	H_A: $p_1 \neq p_2$
test statistic:	$\chi^2 = \dfrac{NUM^2}{DEN}$
decision rule:	reject H_0 if $\chi^2 > \chi_1^2(\alpha)$

The rejection region is found by obtaining the critical chi-square value based on 1 degree of freedom, denoted as $\chi_1^2(\alpha)$, from chi-square tables (Appendix A.3) or by using the SAS function CINV($1-\alpha$, *df*). For $\alpha = 0.05$, the critical chi-square value is 3.841 (=CINV(0.95,1) from SAS).

This computing formula for the chi-square statistic can be shown to be equivalent to the more popular form

$$\chi^2 = \sum_{i=1}^{4} \frac{(O_i - E_i)^2}{E_i}$$

where the O_i's and E_i's are the observed and expected cell frequencies, respectively, as shown in Table 16.2.

TABLE 16.2. Observed (O) and Expected (E) Cell Frequencies

i	O_i	E_i
1	X_1	$n_1(X_1+X_2)/N$
2	X_2	$n_2(X_1+X_2)/N$
3	n_1-X_1	$n_1(N-X_1-X_2)/N$
4	n_2-X_2	$n_2(N-X_1-X_2)/N$

16.3 Examples

Example 16.1 -- ADR Frequency with Antibiotic Treatment

A study was conducted to monitor the incidence of gastro-intestinal (GI) adverse drug reactions of a new antibiotic used in lower respiratory tract infections (LRTI). Two parallel groups were included in the study. One group consisted of 66 LRTI patients randomized to receive the new treatment and a reference group of 52 LRTI patients randomized to receive erythromycin. There were 22 patients in the test group and 28 patients in the control (erythromycin) group who reported one or more GI complaints during 7 days of treatment. Is there evidence of a difference in GI side effect rates between the two groups?

Solution

Define 'response' as the event that a patient develops one or more GI reactions during the study, and let p_1 and p_2 represent the probabilities that a randomly selected LRTI patient has such a 'response' when treated with the test drug and the control drug, respectively. The data are normally summarized in a 2×2 contingency table as shown in Table 16.3.

TABLE 16.3. Response Frequencies for Example 16.1

	Number of Responders	Number of Non-Responders	Total
Test Drug	22 (33.3%)	44	66
Control	28 (53.8%)	24	52
Combined	50 (42.4%)	68	118

Compute

$$NUM = \frac{(22 \cdot 52) - (28 \cdot 66)}{118} = -5.966$$

and

$$DEN = \frac{66 \cdot 52 \cdot 50 \cdot 68}{118^3} = 7.102$$

At a signific

ance level of 0.05, the test summary is

> **null hypothesis:** H_0: $p_1 = p_2$
>
> **alt. hypothesis:** H_A: $p_1 \neq p_2$
>
> **test statistic:** $\chi^2 = \frac{(-5.966)^2}{7.102} = 5.012$
>
> **decision rule:**   reject H_0 if $\chi^2 > \chi^2_1 (0.05) = 3.841$
>
> **conclusion:**   Because $5.012 > 3.841$, you reject H_0 and conclude there is a significant difference in the incidence of GI adverse effects between treatment groups at a 0.05 level of significance.

The p-value can be obtained from SAS by using the PROBCHI function as, $p = 1 - PROBCHI(5.012,1)$, which returns the value of 0.0252.

SAS Analysis of Example 16.1

The SAS code for conducting the *chi-square test* using PROC FREQ is shown next. The TABLES statement ❶ identifies the row and column variables that are used to form the 2×2 table. The row variable (specified first in the TABLES statement) is the treatment group (GRP), and the column variable is the response (RESP). The CHISQ option in the TABLES statement specifies that you want the *chi-square test*.

The WEIGHT statement ❷ specifies that the response variable, CNT, represents the cell frequencies. If the response data (i.e., YES or NO) are input individually for each patient, the CNT variable is not used and the WEIGHT statement is omitted from PROC FREQ.

Output 16.1 confirms the chi-square statistic of 5.012, with a p-value of 0.0252 ❸.

SAS Code for Example 16.1

```
DATA ADR;
    INPUT GRP RESP $ CNT @@;
    DATALINES;
1 YES 22   1 _NO 44
2 YES 28   2 _NO 24
;

/* GRP 1 = Test Drug,  GRP 2 = Control */
PROC FREQ DATA = ADR;
    TABLES GRP*RESP / CHISQ NOPERCENT NOROW;      ❶
    WEIGHT CNT;                                    ❷
    TITLE1 'The Chi-Square Test';
    TITLE2 'Example 16.1: ADR Frequency with Antibiotic Treatment';
RUN;
```

OUTPUT 16.1. SAS Output for Example 16.1

```
                    The Chi-Square Test
      Example 16.1: ADR Frequency with Antibiotic Treatment

                    The FREQ Procedure
                   Table of GRP by RESP

           GRP        RESP

           Frequency,
           Row Pct  |   YES  |    NO  |  Total
           ---------+--------+--------+
                  1 |    22  |    44  |    66
                    |  33.33 |  66.67 |
           ---------+--------+--------+
                  2 |    28  |    24  |    52
                    |  53.85 |  46.15 |
           ---------+--------+--------+
           Total          50       68      118

              Statistics for Table of GRP by RESP
      Statistic                  DF      Value      Prob
      ------------------------------------------------------
      Chi-Square                  1      5.0119  ❸ 0.0252
      Likelihood Ratio Chi-Square 1      5.0270    0.0250
      Continuity Adj. Chi-Square  1      4.2070  ❹ 0.0403
      Mantel-Haenszel Chi-Square  1      4.9694    0.0258
      Phi Coefficient                   -0.2061
      Contingency Coefficient            0.2018
      Cramer's V                        -0.2061

                   Fisher's Exact Test
           ----------------------------------
           Cell (1,1) Frequency (F)       22
           Left-sided Pr <= F         0.0201
           Right-sided Pr >= F        0.9925

           Table Probability (P)      0.0125
           Two-sided Pr <= P          0.0385
                 Sample Size = 118
```

Chi-Square Tests for the g×r Contingency Table

This discussion about the *chi-square test*, so far, has focused on its simplest form, namely that of a 2×2 table. In **statistics**, *chi-square test* is a generic reference for any inferential statistic that has a chi-square or approximate chi-square probability distribution. There are many situations that involve a hypothesis that can be tested with a *chi-square test*, and several different forms can be used with frequency tables.

A frequency table with g rows and r columns is called a '$g \times r$ contingency table'. The row and column variables can be nominal or ordinal. Nominal levels are descriptive; ordinal levels are quantitative and have a hierarchical ordering. Examples of nominal and ordinal variables are shown in Table 16.4.

TABLE 16.4. Examples of Nominal and Ordinal Variables

Type	Variable	Levels (Categories)
Nominal	RACE	Caucasian, Black, Hispanic, Oriental
	LESION SITE	Leg, Back, Arm, Face, Chest
	TREATMENT	Active, Placebo, Reference
Ordinal	IMPROVEMENT	Worse, None, Some, Marked, Cured
	SEVERITY	None, Mild, Moderate, Severe
	DOSAGE	10 mg, 20 mg, 40 mg, 80 mg

In comparative clinical trials, it is often the case that the row variable refers to a group, such as treatment group or dose group, and the column variable refers to a response category. A typical $g \times r$ contingency table has the following layout, with X_{ij} representing the frequency of events in Group i and Response Category j.

TABLE 16.5. Layout for a g×r Contingency Table

Group	----------- Response Category ---------			
	1	2	...	r
1	X_{11}	X_{12}	...	X_{1r}
2	X_{21}	X_{22}	...	X_{2r}
...	...			
g	X_{g1}	X_{g2}	...	X_{gr}

The most common form of the *chi-square test* for contingency table analysis is for testing 'general association' between the Group and Response variables. The null hypothesis is that there is no association. The alternative hypothesis is that the distribution over response categories differs among Group levels, or more generally, that Response is 'associated' with Group. This is tested by using a version of the *chi-square test* in the form already introduced.

If the Response variable is ordinal, you can compare mean responses among the Group levels by assigning numerically coded values called 'scores' to the response categories. Here, 'table' or 'integer' scores are used, which are simply the ranks of the categories when ordered from smallest to largest. In this case, the alternative hypothesis is that mean scores differ among groups. A different form of the *chi-square test* can be used to test this hypothesis. A mean score can be computed as the sum of all scores for a specific row (i.e., score × frequency summed over all scores) divided by the row total.

If the Group and Response variables are both ordinal, you can use another type of *chi-square* statistic to test whether there is a trend or correlation between increasing response scores and the Group scores.

The following three cases are tested using the *chi-square test* for 'general association' (χ^2_{GA}) based on $(g-1)\cdot(r-1)$ degrees of freedom, the *chi-square test* for 'row mean scores differ' (χ^2_{MSD}) based on $g-1$ degrees of freedom and the *chi-square test* for 'non-zero correlation' (χ^2_{COR}) based on 1 degree of freedom, respectively, as shown in Table 16.6. Notice that the 'correlation' test is only meaningful when both the Response and Group categories are ordinal, and 'mean scores' within a row make sense only when the Response category is ordinal.

TABLE 16.6. Types of Chi-Square Tests for Contingency Tables

Response (columns)	Group (rows)	Alternative Hypothesis		
		General Association	Row Mean Scores Differ	Non-Zero Correlation
Nominal	Nominal	χ^2_{GA}	--	--
Nominal	Ordinal	χ^2_{GA}	--	--
Ordinal	Nominal	χ^2_{GA}	χ^2_{MSD}	--
Ordinal	Ordinal	χ^2_{GA}	χ^2_{MSD}	χ^2_{COR}

The 3×3 tables which follow illustrate patterns of cell frequencies that can be associated with the three alternative hypotheses above. Table (i) shows a significant general association, which indicates a difference among groups in the distribution of responses. Table (ii) indicates a significant difference in mean scores among groups. The mean scores are 1.67, 2.33, and 2.00 for Groups A, B, and C, respectively (based on 'table' scores). A pattern resulting in significant correlation is shown in Table (iii), under the assumption that the Group factor is ordinal with A, B, and C representing increasing values (e.g., increasing dosage). Notice that the only difference between Tables (ii) and (iii) is that the row frequencies for the B and C groups have been exchanged, so that the row mean scores increase with increasing Group levels.

Table (i): General Association

Group	Response 1	2	3		Test	p-Value
A	10	15	5		χ^2_{GA}	0.0423
B	10	10	10		χ^2_{MSD}	0.2905
C	10	5	15		χ^2_{COR}	0.1159

Table (ii): Row Mean Scores Differ

Group	Response 1	2	3		Test	p-Value
A	15	10	5		χ^2_{GA}	0.0423
B	5	10	15		χ^2_{MSD}	0.0071
C	10	10	10		χ^2_{COR}	0.1159

Table (iii): Non-Zero Correlation

Group	Response 1	2	3		Test	p-Value
A	15	10	5		χ^2_{GA}	0.0423
B	10	10	10		χ^2_{MSD}	0.0071
C	5	10	15		χ^2_{COR}	0.0017

The *chi-square statistic* for general association can be computed in a way similar to that demonstrated for the 2×2 table. The mean scores chi-square value is a function of the sample group means and variances, and the correlation statistic is, computationally, a multiple of the correlation coefficient. These can easily be obtained in SAS using the CMH option in the TABLES statement in PROC FREQ, as demonstrated in the code for the sample data in Tables (i), (ii) and (iii) that follows.

Example SAS Code for Chi-Square Tests for Tables (i), (ii) and (iii) Using SAS

```
DATA G_BY_R;
    INPUT TBL GROUP $ RESP $ CNT @@;
    DATALINES;
1 A 1 10    1 A 2 15    1 A 3  5
1 B 1 10    1 B 2 10    1 B 3 10
1 C 1 10    1 C 2  5    1 C 3 15
2 A 1 15    2 A 2 10    2 A 3  5
2 B 1  5    2 B 2 10    2 B 3 15
2 C 1 10    2 C 2 10    2 C 3 10
3 A 1 15    3 A 2 10    3 A 3  5
3 B 1 10    3 B 2 10    3 B 3 10
3 C 1  5    3 C 2 10    3 C 3 15
;

ODS SELECT
    CMH;
PROC FREQ ORDER = DATA DATA = G_BY_R;
    BY TBL;
    TABLES GROUP*RESP / CMH NOPERCENT NOCOL;
    WEIGHT CNT;
    TITLE1 'Chi-Square Test for 3-by-3 Table';
RUN;
```

OUTPUT 16.2. CMH Tests for 3-by-3 Tables

```
                Chi-Square Test for 3-by-3 Table

                      The FREQ Procedure

               Summary Statistics for GROUP by RESP
        Cochran-Mantel-Haenszel Statistics (Based on Table Scores)

----------------------------- TBL=1 -----------------------------

Statistic    Alternative Hypothesis    DF    Value    Prob
-----------------------------------------------------------------
    1        Nonzero Correlation        1    2.4722   0.1159
    2        Row Mean Scores Differ      2    2.4722   0.2905
    3        General Association         4    9.8889   0.0423

----------------------------- TBL=2 -----------------------------

Statistic    Alternative Hypothesis    DF    Value    Prob
-----------------------------------------------------------------
    1        Nonzero Correlation        1    2.4722   0.1159
    2        Row Mean Scores Differ      2    9.8889   0.0071
    3        General Association         4    9.8889   0.0423

----------------------------- TBL=3 -----------------------------

Statistic    Alternative Hypothesis    DF    Value    Prob
-----------------------------------------------------------------
    1        Nonzero Correlation        1    9.8889   0.0017
    2        Row Mean Scores Differ      2    9.8889   0.0071
    3        General Association         4    9.8889   0.0423
```

Binomial Response with More Than Two Groups

The binomial response (r=2) for more than two groups (g>2) is a special, but frequently encountered, case of the $g \times r$ table just discussed. In this case, the null hypothesis is that response rates are the same among all groups ($p_1 = p_2 = \ldots = p_g$).

One alternative hypothesis is that response rates differ among groups. With binomial responses, the hypothesis of 'general association' is equivalent to the hypothesis of 'row mean scores differ' because the row mean is a linear function of the probability of response, as binomial response categories can always be coded 0 ('no response') and 1 ('response'). When the Group factor is ordinal, the test for 'non-zero correlation' is actually a linear 'trend' test. This can be used to test for dose response, for example, when the Group factor represents dose level.

Example 16.2 -- Comparison of Dropout Rates for 4 Dose Groups

The following table summarizes dropout rates for patients randomized to 4 dose groups in a clinical study. (i) Is there a difference in dropout rates among groups, and (ii) do dropout rates have a linear correlation with dosage?

TABLE 16.7. Frequency Table for Example 16.2

Group	------ Dropout? ------	
	YES	NO
10 mg	5	35
20 mg	6	29
40 mg	10	28
80 mg	12	27

SAS Analysis of Example 16.2

The CMH option in the TABLES statement produces the output entitled 'Cochran-Mantel-Haenszel Statistics', which shows the tests for 'general association', 'row mean scores differ' and 'non-zero correlation' (Output 16.3). You see $\chi^2_{GA} = \chi^2_{MSD} = 4.7516$ based on 3 degrees of freedom with a p-value of 0.1909 ❺. From this, you can conclude that response rates are not significantly different among the dose groups. However, the *chi-square test* for non-zero correlation, χ^2_{COR} is 4.217 based on 1 degree of freedom with a p-value of 0.0400 ❻, which indicates a significant trend in response rates with increasing dosage. It's not unusual to be unable to detect a difference in response rates among groups, yet find that a dose-response trend exists, as this example illustrates.

The *chi-square test* produced by the CHISQ option in the TABLES statement is also a test of 'general association' ❼. This is simply a multiple $(N/(N-1))$ of χ^2_{GA}, and the two forms are essentially equivalent for large N. The Mantel-Haenszel *chi-square test* ❽ is equivalent to χ^2_{COR} ❻ in a non-stratified layout as presented here.

SAS Code for Example 16.2

```
DATA DORATE;
    INPUT DOSE_MG RESP $ CNT @@;
    DATALINES;
10 YES 5    10 _NO 35
20 YES 6    20 _NO 29
40 YES 10   40 _NO 28
80 YES 12   80 _NO 27
;

PROC FREQ DATA = DORATE;
    TABLES DOSE_MG*RESP / CHISQ CMH TREND NOPERCENT NOCOL;
    WEIGHT CNT;
    TITLE1 'The Chi-Square Test';
    TITLE2 'Example 16.2: Comparison of Dropout Rates for 4
           Dose Groups';
RUN;
```

OUTPUT 16.3. SAS Output for Example 16.2

```
                     The Chi-Square Test
        Example 16.2: Comparison of Dropout Rates for 4 Dose Groups

                      The FREQ Procedure

                   Table of DOSE_MG by RESP

        DOSE_MG     RESP
        Frequency,
        Row Pct  |YES     |_NO     | Total
        ---------+--------+--------+
              10 |      5 |     35 |    40
                 |  12.50 |  87.50 |
        ---------+--------+--------+
              20 |      6 |     29 |    35
                 |  17.14 |  82.86 |
        ---------+--------+--------+
              40 |     10 |     28 |    38
                 |  26.32 |  73.68 |
        ---------+--------+--------+
              80 |     12 |     27 |    39
                 |  30.77 |  69.23 |
        ---------+--------+--------+
        Total          33      119     152
```

OUTPUT 16.3. SAS Output for Example 16.2 (*continued*)

```
                    Statistics for Table of DOSE_MG by RESP

        Statistic                     DF       Value      Prob
        -----------------------------------------------------------
        Chi-Square                     3       4.7831     0.1884      ❼
        Likelihood Ratio Chi-Square    3       4.9008     0.1792
        Mantel-Haenszel Chi-Square     1       4.2171     0.0400      ❽
        Phi Coefficient                        0.1774
        Contingency Coefficient                0.1747
        Cramer's V                             0.1774


                        Cochran-Armitage Trend Test
                        ---------------------------
                        Statistic (Z)        2.0603      ❾
                        One-sided Pr >  Z    0.0197
                        Two-sided Pr > |Z|   0.0394


                          Sample Size = 152

                  Summary Statistics for DOSE_MG by RESP

        Cochran-Mantel-Haenszel Statistics (Based on Table Scores)

        Statistic   Alternative Hypothesis    DF      Value      Prob
        -----------------------------------------------------------------
            1       Nonzero Correlation        1      4.2171     0.0400   ❻
            2       Row Mean Scores Differ     3      4.7516     0.1909
            3       General Association        3      4.7516     0.1909   ❺

                          Total Sample Size = 152
```

Multinomial Responses

Comparison of two groups ($g=2$) when there are more than two response categories ($r > 2$) is also a special case of the $g \times r$ table that was discussed previously. In this case, you use a $2 \times r$ table, where r (>2) is the number of response levels. For example, if patients randomized to active and placebo groups had responses categorized as 'none', 'partial' or 'complete', the 2×3 table would be

TABLE 16.8. Layout for a 2×r Contingency Table

Group	---------------- Response ----------------		
	None	Partial	Complete
Active	X_{11}	X_{12}	X_{13}
Placebo	X_{21}	X_{22}	X_{23}

The hypothesis of 'general association' is equivalent to the hypothesis that the distribution of responses differs between groups. This test can be used regardless of whether the response levels are ordinal or nominal. When the response is ordinal, the 'row mean scores differ' hypothesis is equivalent to the 'non-zero correlation' hypothesis in the $2 \times r$ table.

✎ **Example 16.3** -- Active vs. Placebo Comparisons of Degree of Response

The following table contains the number of patients who show complete, partial, or no response after treatment with either active medication or a placebo. Is there a difference between treatment groups in response distributions?

TABLE 16.9. Frequency Table for Example 16.3

Group	---------------- Response ----------------		
	None	Partial	Complete
Active	16	26	29
Placebo	24	26	18

SAS Analysis of Example 16.3

The CMH option in the TABLES statement in PROC FREQ requests the *chi-square tests* for general association and linear correlation, as shown in the SAS code that follows. In Output 16.4, you see a chi-square value of 4.0727 based on 1 degree of freedom, and a p-value of 0.0436 ❿, which indicates a significant correlation or 'trend' between treatment group and response. The test for general association ⓫ is non-significant (p=0.1299), which indicates a lack of evidence of differing response distributions between the active and the placebo groups.

SAS Code for Example 16.3

```
DATA MULTI;
    INPUT TRT $ RESP $ CNT @@;
    DATALINES;
ACT NONE 16  ACT PART 26  ACT FULL 29
PBO NONE 24  PBO PART 26  PBO FULL 18
;

PROC FREQ ORDER = DATA DATA = MULTI;
    TABLES TRT*RESP / CMH CHISQ TREND NOPERCENT NOCOL;
    WEIGHT CNT;
    TITLE1 'The Chi-Square Test;
    TITLE2 'Example 16.3: Active vs. Placebo Comparison of
            Degree of Response';
RUN;
```

Notice that the default scoring system in PROC FREQ is the 'tables' scores. If you want to explicitly include the score, specify SCORES=TABLES.

OUTPUT 16.4. SAS Output for Example 16.3

```
                         The Chi-Square Test
       Example 16.3: Active vs. Placebo Comparison of Degree of Response

                         The FREQ Procedure

                      Table of TRT by RESP

            TRT        RESP

            Frequency|
            Row Pct  |NONE    |PART    |FULL    |  Total
            ---------+--------+--------+--------+
            ACT      |     16 |     26 |     29 |     71
                     |  22.54 |  36.62 |  40.85 |
            ---------+--------+--------+--------+
            PBO      |     24 |     26 |     18 |     68
                     |  35.29 |  38.24 |  26.47 |
            ---------+--------+--------+--------+
            Total          40       52       47      139


                 Statistics for Table of TRT by RESP

        Statistic                      DF       Value      Prob
        ------------------------------------------------------------
        Chi-Square                      2      4.1116     0.1280
        Likelihood Ratio Chi-Square     2      4.1446     0.1259
        Mantel-Haenszel Chi-Square      1      4.0727     0.0436
        Phi Coefficient                        0.1720
        Contingency Coefficient                0.1695
        Cramer's V                             0.1720


                   Cochran-Armitage Trend Test
                   --------------------------
                   Statistic (Z)        2.0254
                   One-sided Pr >  Z    0.0214
                   Two-sided Pr > |Z|   0.0428              ⓬

                   Sample Size = 139


                 Summary Statistics for TRT by RESP

          Cochran-Mantel-Haenszel Statistics (Based on Table Scores)

        Statistic    Alternative Hypothesis    DF      Value      Prob
        -----------------------------------------------------------------
            1        Nonzero Correlation        1      4.0727     0.0436  ❿
            2        Row Mean Scores Differ      1      4.0727     0.0436
            3        General Association         2      4.0821     0.1299  ⓫


                   Total Sample Size = 139
```

16.4 Details & Notes

▶ **16.4.1.** An equivalent test to the *chi-square test* for comparing two binomial proportions is based on the Z-test statistic as follows:

$$Z = \frac{\hat{p}_1 - \hat{p}_2}{\sqrt{\overline{p}(1-\overline{p}) \cdot (\frac{1}{n_1} + \frac{1}{n_2})}}$$

where $\hat{p}_i = \frac{X_i}{n_i}$ and $\overline{p} = \frac{(X_1 + X_2)}{(n_1 + n_2)}$

When H_0 is true and values for n_1 and n_2 are large, Z has an approximate standard normal distribution, and you reject H_0 if $|Z| > Z_{\alpha/2}$.

Because the square of a standard normal variable is a chi-square with 1 degree of freedom, Z^2 has a chi-square distribution and can be shown, algebraically, to be equivalent to the chi-square test statistic already introduced. In Example 16.1, the response rate estimates are found as follows:

TABLE 16.10. Estimating Response Rates for Example 16.1

	Test Group (i=1)	Control Group (i=2)	Combined
X_i	22	28	50
n_i	66	52	118
Est. of p	0.3333	0.5385	0.4237

and the Z-test statistic is

$$Z = \frac{0.3333 - 0.5385}{\sqrt{(0.4237) \cdot (0.5763) \cdot (\frac{1}{66} + \frac{1}{52})}}$$

$$= -2.2387$$

Because $2.2387 > 1.96$, you reject H_0 based on the Z-statistic at a 0.05 level of significance.

Notice that $Z^2 = (-2.2387)^2 = 5.012$ is the chi-square value that was obtained previously. The critical chi-square value with 1 degree of freedom (from the chi-square tables) corresponds to the square of the critical Z value from the normal tables. For $\alpha = 0.05$, the critical value is $\chi^2(0.05) = 3.841 = 1.96^2 = (Z_{0.025})^2$.

▶ **16.4.2.**   In conducting a two-sample binomial comparison using either the *chi-square test* or the Z-statistic, the normal approximation to the binomial distribution must be valid. The tests described here might not be valid if X_i or $n_i – X_i$ is small for $i = 1$ or 2. Generally, the analyst should be wary of results that use this approximate test if any cell frequency is less than 5. *Fisher's exact test* (Chapter 17) might be applicable for cases that involve small cell frequencies.

The normal approximation to the binomial is usually a good approximation if

$$n_i \cdot p_i - 2\sqrt{n_i \cdot p_i \cdot (1-p_i)} \geq 0$$

and

$$n_i \cdot p_i + 2\sqrt{n_i \cdot p_i \cdot (1-p_i)} \leq n_i$$

for $i = 1$ and $i = 2$ (see Section 15.4.2).

For small values of n_1 and n_2, the normal approximation can be improved by adjusting the test statistic with a 'continuity correction', $C = 0.5(1/n_1 + 1/n_2)$. The adjustment is made by subtracting C from the numerator of the Z-test statistic if the numerator is greater than 0, or by adding C to the numerator of Z if it is less than 0.

In Example 16.1, the Z-statistic using the continuity correction is

$$Z = \frac{(0.3333 - 0.5385) + 0.5(\dfrac{1}{66} + \dfrac{1}{52})}{\sqrt{0.4237 \cdot (0.5763) \cdot (\dfrac{1}{66} + \dfrac{1}{52})}} = -2.051$$

The continuity-corrected chi-square value is the square of this Z-value, $(-2.051)^2 = 4.207$. This adjusted value is shown in Output 16.1, with a p-value of 0.0403 ❹.

▶ **16.4.3.**   An approximate 95% confidence interval for the proportion, p_i, is given by

$$\hat{p}_i \pm 1.96 \cdot \sqrt{\frac{\hat{p}_i \cdot (1-\hat{p}_i)}{n_i}} \quad \text{where} \quad \hat{p}_i = \frac{X_i}{n}$$

An approximate 95% confidence interval for the difference in proportions, $p_1 – p_2$, is given by

$$(\hat{p}_1 - \hat{p}_2) \pm 1.96 \cdot \sqrt{\frac{\hat{p}_1 \cdot (1-\hat{p}_1)}{n_1} + \frac{\hat{p}_2 \cdot (1-\hat{p}_2)}{n_2}}$$

With $X_1/n_1 = 22/66 = 0.333$ and $X_2/n_2 = 28/52 = 0.538$ in Example 16.1, a 95% confidence interval for $p_1 - p_2$ is

$$0.333 - 0.538 \pm 1.96 \cdot \left(\frac{(0.333 \cdot 0.667)}{66} + \frac{(0.538 \cdot 0.462)}{52} \right)^{\frac{1}{2}} =$$

$$-0.21 \pm 0.18 = (-0.39 \text{ to } -0.03)$$

▶ **16.4.4.**   Because Example 16.1 tests for a difference from the hypothesized value in either direction, a two-tailed test is used. A one-tailed test would be used if you want to test whether one population proportion is strictly *greater than* or *strictly less* than the other. Use the rejection region according to the alternative hypothesis as follows:

Type of Test	Alternative Hypothesis	Corresponding Rejection Region
two-tailed	H_A: $p \neq p_2$	reject H_0 if $Z > Z_{\alpha/2}$ or $Z < -Z_{\alpha/2}$
one-tailed (right)	H_A: $p > p_2$	reject H_0 if $Z > Z_\alpha$
one-tailed (left)	H_A: $p < p_2$	reject H_0 if $Z < -Z_\alpha$

Notice that the *chi-square test* is a two-tailed test because large chi-square values within the rejection region occur when Z is a very large positive *or* large negative value. To conduct a one-tailed *chi-square test*, the nominal significance level, α, should be doubled when looking up the critical chi-square values. The critical values for a rejection region that correspond to a significance level of $\alpha = 0.05$ are

Test	One-Tailed	Two-Tailed
Z-Test	1.645	1.960
Chi-Square	2.706	3.841

The p-value for a *chi-square test* in the SAS output corresponds to a two-tailed test. The one-tailed p-value is found by halving this value.

▶ **16.4.5.**   For the case of $n_1 = n_2$, a method for estimating sample sizes to detect a difference in response rates, $\Delta = p_1 - p_2$, is shown in Chapter 2.

▶ **16.4.6.**   In addition to the *chi-square test* for 'non-zero correlation', the *Cochran-Armitage test* for trend can also be used to test for linear correlation between a binomial response and an ordinal Group variable. This test is based on a *Z-test* statistic that has the standard normal distribution for large N. The *Mantel-Haenszel* chi-square and the *Cochran-Armitage test* for trend can be used interchangeably when Response and Group are ordinal factors and one of these factors has only two levels. When the total sample size, N, is large, they are equivalent. The *Mantel-Haenszel* chi-square is simply Z^2 adjusted by a factor of $(N-1)/N$.

For Example 16.2, the *Cochran-Armitage test* results are printed by using the TREND option in the TABLES statement in PROC FREQ. Output 16.3 shows a Z statistic of 2.0603 ❾. With N=152, the *Mantel-Haenszel* chi-square can be confirmed as $(151/152) \cdot 2.0603^2 = 4.217$. The *Cochran-Armitage test* is also printed in Output 16.4 ❿.

▶ **16.4.7.** When comparing binomial proportions among more than two groups, a significant test for general association would imply that response rates differ for at least one pair of group levels. Multiple comparisons using a series of 2×2 tables can be used to determine which pairs actually differ. This might require multiplicity adjustments for multiple comparisons, which are discussed in Appendix E.

▶ **16.4.8.** When there are only two categories (i.e., $g=2$ or $r=2$), the scores of 0 and 1 can be assigned to the levels regardless of whether the factor is nominal or ordinal. Therefore, when there are only two groups ($g=2$), the alternative hypothesis of 'row mean scores differ' is equivalent to the 'non-zero correlation' hypothesis. When there are only two response categories ($r=2$), the hypothesis of 'general association' is equivalent to the 'row mean scores differ' hypothesis.

▶ **16.4.9.** 'Table' scores are the simplest and most commonly used scores for ordinal response categories when conducting *chi-square tests*. One criticism in using table scores is that, because they are equally spaced, they might not give an accurate representation of the ordinal nature of categories, which are thought not to be equally spaced. For example, if response is 'degree of improvement' with categories 'none', 'some', 'marked', and 'cured', the relative difference between 'marked' and 'cured' might be clinically more important than the difference between 'none' and 'some'.

Rank, log-rank, ridit, and modified ridit scores are alternatives to the table scores available with PROC FREQ in SAS. Of these, modified ridit scores are probably the most frequently encountered in clinical trials. These scores are based on the mid-ranks of the column totals, standardized by dividing by $(N+1)$.

For example, suppose 50 patients were classified in four response categories as 'none' (n=20), 'some' (n=13), 'marked' (n=10), and 'cured' (n=7). Computation of the modified ridit scores is shown in Table 16.11.

TABLE 16.11. Sample Calculation of Modified Ridit Scores

	None	Some	Marked	Cured
Column Total	20	13	10	7
Midrank	10.5	27	38.5	47
Mod. Ridit Score	0.206	0.529	0.755	0.922

The SCORES=MODRIDIT option in the TABLES statement in PROC FREQ is used to perform the *chi-square test* based on modified ridit scores in SAS.

Mid-ranks are computed as

None:	$(20 + 1)/2 = 10.5$
Some:	$(20 + (13 + 1)/2) = 27$
Marked	$(20 + 13 + (10 + 1)/2) = 38.5$
Cured:	$(20 + 13 + 10 + (7 + 1)/2) = 47$

Custom scoring systems can also be used when the relative importance of the response categories is well defined. In the preceding example, you can assign scores of 0, 2, 5, and 10, for example, to reflect the clinical importance of the response relative to other responses. However, in the rare cases when such relative importance can be meaningfully assigned, it is usually easier to treat the response as a numeric rather than categorical variable when determining the best analysis to use. If the relative clinical importance of the response categories is not clear, the analyst should examine the robustness of the results under various scoring assignments before making a conclusion.

▶ **16.4.10.** The *chi-square tests* that were discussed for ordinal responses are invariant over linear transformations of the scores. For example, if there are four ordered-response categories as shown in Table 16.11, you can code the categories by using table scores of 1-2-3-4, or scores based on any linear transformation of these scores, such as 0-1-2-3 or 5-10-15-20, and obtain the same results. The same invariance principle holds when using modified ridit scores. The modified ridit scores found in Table 16.11 can be compared with the table scores using the linear transformation shown in Table 16.12.

TABLE 16.12. Comparison of Ridit Scores with Table Scores

	None	Some	Marked	Cured
Mod. Ridit Score	0.206	0.529	0.755	0.922
Subtract 0.206	0	0.323	0.549	0.716
Multiply by 4.19	0	1.35	2.30	3.00
Table Scores	0	1	2	3

This representation more easily depicts the spacing of the modified ridit scores relative to the table scores. Using a similar approach, examples of modified ridit scores transformed to a 0-3 interval for comparison with the table scores are shown in Table 16.13 for various overall distributions of the response category (i.e., column totals). Notice that the modified ridit scores are equivalent to table scores when the distribution is uniform.

TABLE 16.13. Comparison of Ridit Scores for Various Marginal Distributions

Distribution		None	Some	Marked	Cured
Uniform	Column Total	25	25	25	25
	Scaled Mod. Ridit	0	1	2	3
Normal	Column Total	10	40	40	10
	Scaled Mod. Ridit	0	0.83	2.17	3
Bimodal	Column Total	40	10	10	40
	Scaled Mod. Ridit	0	1.25	1.75	3
Exponential	Column Total	60	20	14	6
	Scaled Mod. Ridit	0	1.80	2.55	3
Skewed	Column Total	5	15	55	25
	Scaled Mod. Ridit	0	0.35	1.59	3

▶ **16.4.11.** In a g×r contingency table with ordinal responses, the *chi-square test* for the 'row mean scores differ' hypothesis is identical to the *Kruskal-Wallis test* (Chapter 14) when modified ridit scores are used. This is clear when you recognize that a contingency table is simply a summary of responses in which frequencies represent the numbers of tied values. The *Kruskal-Wallis test* is based on ranks of the data with average ranks assigned to tied values. These are the same as the mid-ranks used in the modified ridit scores.

Fisher's Exact Test

17.1 Introduction

Fisher's exact test is an alternative to the *chi-square test* (Chapter 16) for comparing two independent binomial proportions, p_1 and p_2. This method is based on computing exact probabilities of observing a given result or a more extreme result, when the hypothesis of equal proportions is true. *Fisher's exact test* is useful when the normal approximation to the binomial might not be applicable, such as in the case of small cell sizes or extreme proportions.

17.2 Synopsis

Using the same notation as in Chapter 16, you observe X_1 'responders' out of n_1 patients studied in one group and X_2 'responders' of n_2 patients in a second independent group, as shown in Table 17.1.

TABLE 17.1. Layout for Fisher's Exact Test

	Number of Responders	Number of Non-Responders	Total
Group 1	X_1	$n_1 - X_1$	n_1
Group 2	X_2	$n_2 - X_2$	n_2
Combined	$X_1 + X_2$	$N - (X_1 + X_2)$	$N = n_1 + n_2$

Given equal proportions, $p_1 = p_2$, the probability of observing the configuration shown in Table 17.1, when the marginal totals are fixed, is found by the 'hypergeometric probability distribution' as

$$\text{prob} = \frac{\binom{n_1}{X_1} \cdot \binom{n_2}{X_2}}{\binom{N}{X_1+X_2}} \quad \text{where} \quad \binom{a}{b} = \frac{a!}{b! \cdot (a-b)!}$$

is the combinatorial symbol that represents "the number of ways 'b' items can be selected from a set of 'a' items". The probability of the table configuration simplifies to

$$\text{prob} = \frac{(X_1+X_2)! \cdot (N-X_1-X_2)! \cdot (n_1)! \cdot (n_2)!}{N! \cdot X_1! \cdot X_2! \cdot (n_1-X_1)! \cdot (n_2-X_2)!}$$

The p-value for the test, Fisher's exact probability, is the probability of the observed configuration plus the sum of the probabilities of all other configurations with a more extreme result for fixed row and column totals.

17.3 Examples

Example 17.1 -- CHF Incidence in CABG after ARA

A new adenosine-releasing agent (ARA), thought to reduce side effects in patients undergoing coronary artery bypass surgery (CABG), was studied in a pilot trial that enrolled 35 patients who received active medication and 20 patients who received a placebo. Follow-up observation revealed that 2 patients who received active medication and 5 patients who received the placebo had shown symptoms of congestive heart failure (CHF) within 90 days post surgery. Is this evidence of a reduced rate of CHF for patients treated with the ARA compound?

Solution

Let p_1 and p_2 represent the CHF rates for the active-medication and placebo groups, respectively. You want to test for equal proportions vs. the one-tailed alternative because you are looking for improvement.

H_0: $p_1 = p_2$

H_A: $p_1 < p_2$

The summary results are shown in Table 17.2.

TABLE 17.2. CHF Frequency Summary for Example 17.1

	Active Group (i=1)	Placebo Group (i=2)	Combined
X_i	2	5	7
n_i	35	20	55
Estimate of p	0.057	0.250	0.127

The conditions for using the *chi-square test* (Chapter 16) are not met in this case because of the small cell sizes. However, *Fisher's exact test* can be used as demonstrated next. The observed table and tables with a more extreme result that have the same row and column totals are shown in Table 17.3.

TABLE 17.3. Configuration of 'Extreme' Tables for Calculation of Fisher's Exact Probability

	Table (i)		Table (ii)		Table (iii)		Row Total
	X	n–X	X	n–X	X	n–X	n
ACT	2	33	1	34	0	35	35
PBO	5	15	6	14	7	13	20
Column Total	7	48	7	48	7	48	55

Under the null hypothesis, H_0, the probability for Table (i) is found by

$$\text{prob}_1 = \frac{(7)! \cdot (48)! \cdot (35)! \cdot (20)!}{(55)! \cdot (2)! \cdot (5)! \cdot (33)! \cdot (15)!} = 0.04546$$

Similarly, the probabilities for Tables (ii) and (iii) can be computed as $\text{prob}_2 = 0.00669$ and $\text{prob}_3 = 0.00038$, respectively. The exact one-tailed p-value is $p = 0.04546 + 0.00669 + 0.00038 = 0.05253$. Because this value is greater than 0.05, you would not reject the hypothesis of equal proportions at a significance level of 0.05. (This is close to 0.05, however, and it might encourage a researcher to conduct a larger study).

SAS Analysis of Example 17.1

Fisher's exact test can be performed by using the FISHER option in the TABLES statement in PROC FREQ, as shown in the SAS code for Example 17.1 ❶. This example uses the WEIGHT statement ❷ because the summary results are input. If you use the data set that contains the observations for individual patients, the WEIGHT statement would be omitted. Notice that, with a 2×2 table, either the FISHER or the CHISQ option in the TABLES statement will print both the *chi-square test* and the *Fisher's exact test* results.

Fisher's exact probability is printed in Output 17.1, with a one-tailed value of 0.0525 ❸. Notice that SAS prints a warning about using the *chi-square test* when cell sizes are too small.

SAS Code for Example 17.1

```
DATA CABG;
    INPUT GRP RESP $ CNT  @@;
    DATALINES;
1 YES   2   1 _NO 33
2 YES   5   2 _NO 15
;

/* GRP 1 = Active Group,  GRP 2 = Placebo */
PROC FREQ DATA = CABG;
    TABLES GRP*RESP / FISHER NOPERCENT NOCOL;      ❶
    WEIGHT CNT;                                    ❷
    TITLE1 "Fisher's Exact Test";
    TITLE2 'Example 17.1:  CHF Incidence in CABG after ARA';
RUN;
```

OUTPUT 17.1. SAS Output for Example 17.1

```
                        Fisher's Exact Test
          Example 17.1:  CHF Incidence in CABG after ARA

                        The FREQ Procedure

                      Table of GRP by RESP

          GRP         RESP

          Frequency,
          Row Pct  |YES     |_NO     |  Total
          ---------+--------+--------+
              1 |      2 |     33 |     35
                |   5.71 |  94.29 |
          ---------+--------+--------+
              2 |      5 |     15 |     20
                |  25.00 |  75.00 |
          ---------+--------+--------+
          Total          7       48       55

          Statistics for Table of GRP by RESP

     Statistic                    DF      Value      Prob
     --------------------------------------------------------
     Chi-Square                    1      4.2618     0.0390
     Likelihood Ratio Chi-Square   1      4.1029     0.0428
     Continuity Adj. Chi-Square    1      2.7024     0.1002
     Mantel-Haenszel Chi-Square    1      4.1843     0.0408
     Phi Coefficient                     -0.2784
     Contingency Coefficient              0.2682
     Cramer's V                          -0.2784

       WARNING: 50% of the cells have expected counts less
                than 5. Chi-Square may not be a valid test.


                      Fisher's Exact Test
          ------------------------------------
          Cell (1,1) Frequency (F)          2
          Left-sided Pr <= F           0.0525   ❸
          Right-sided Pr >= F          0.9929

           Table Probability (P)       0.0455
          Two-sided Pr <= P            0.0857   ❹

                    Sample Size = 55
```

17.4 Details & Notes

▶ **17.4.1.** *Fisher's exact test* is considered a non-parametric test because it does not rely on any distributional assumptions.

▶ **17.4.2.** Manual computations for Fisher's exact probabilities can be very tedious if you use a calculator, especially, with larger cell sizes. A statistical program, such as SAS, is recommended to facilitate the computations.

▶ **17.4.3.** *Fisher's* probabilities are not necessarily symmetric. Although some analysts will double the one-tailed p-value to obtain the two-tailed result, this method is usually overly conservative.

To obtain the two-tailed p-value, first compute the probabilities associated with all possible tables that have the same row and column totals. The 2-tailed p-value is then found by adding the probability of the observed table with the sum of the probabilities of each table whose probability is less than that of the observed table. To obtain the *two-tailed test* for Example 17.1 in this way, first compute the probabilities for each table as follows:

TABLE 17.4. Individual Table Probabilities for Example 17.1

Table	Group	Responders	Non-Responders	Probabilities		
1	Active	0	35			
	Placebo	7	13	0.0004	+	
2	Active	1	34			
	Placebo	6	14	0.0067	+	
3	Active	2	33			
	Placebo	5	15	0.0455	+	(Observed)
4	Active	3	32			
	Placebo	4	16	0.1563		
5	Active	4	31			
	Placebo	3	17	0.2941		
6	Active	5	30			
	Placebo	2	18	0.3040		
7	Active	6	29			
	Placebo	1	19	0.1600		
8	Active	7	28			
	Placebo	0	20	0.0331	+	
			TOTAL:	1.0000		

+ = Probability included in two-tailed p-value

The observed Table 3 has probability 0.0455. Tables 1, 2, and 8 have probabilities less than 0.0455 and are included in the p-value for the two-tailed alternative. Thus, the two-tailed p-value is

$$P = 0.0004 + 0.0067 + 0.0455 + 0.0331 = 0.0857$$

As noted in Output 17.1, both the one-tailed ❸ and two-tailed results ❹ for *Fisher's exact test* are provided.

▶ **17.4.4.** *Fisher's exact test* can be extended to situations that involve more than two treatment groups or more than two response levels. This is sometimes referred to as the *generalized Fisher's exact test* or the *Freeman-Halton test*. With g treatment groups, you would establish a $g \times 2$ table of responses by extending the 2×2 table. We may also extend this method to multinomial responses, i.e., responses that can result in one of r possible outcomes ($r > 2$). With two treatment groups, the 2×2 table would be extended to a $2 \times r$ table, or more generally, to a $g \times r$ table.

An example that illustrates the *generalized Fisher's exact test* applied to a 3×6 table is shown in the "SAS/STAT User's Guide". The alternative hypothesis that is tested by the generalized *Fisher's exact test* is the hypothesis that corresponds to 'general association', as discussed in Chapter 16.

In SAS, the FISHER or EXACT option must be specified in the TABLES statement in PROC FREQ to perform the *Fisher's exact test* when the table has more than two rows or two columns.

McNemar's Test

18.1 Introduction

McNemar's test is a special case of the *binomial test* (Chapter 15) for comparing two proportions using paired samples. *McNemar's test* is often used in a clinical trials application when dichotomous outcomes are recorded twice for each patient under different conditions. The conditions might represent different treatments or different measurement times, for example. The goal is to compare response rates under the two sets of conditions. Because measurements come from the same patients, the assumption of independent groups, which is needed for the *chi-square test* and *Fisher's exact test,* is not met.

Typical examples where *McNemar's test* might be applicable include testing for a shift in the proportion of abnormal responses from before treatment to after treatment in the same group of patients, or comparing response rates of two ophthalmic treatments when both are given to each patient, one treatment in each eye.

18.2 Synopsis

In general, there are n patients, each observed under two conditions (time points, treatments, etc.) with each condition resulting in a dichotomous outcome. The results can be partitioned into 4 subgroups: the number of patients who respond under both conditions (A), the number of patients who respond under the first but not the second condition (B), the number of patients who respond under the second but not the first condition (C), and the number of patients who fail to respond under either condition (D), as shown in the 2×2 table which follows.

TABLE 18.1. Layout for McNemar's Test

Condition 2

		Number of Responders	Number of Non-Responders	Total
Condition 1	Number of Responders	A	B	A+B
	Number of Non-Responders	C	D	C+D
	Total	A+C	B+D	n = A+B+C+D

The hypothesis of interest is the equality of the response proportions, p_1 and p_2, under conditions 1 and 2, respectively. The test statistic is based on the difference in the discordant cell frequencies (B,C) as shown in the test summary below. This statistic has an approximate chi-square distribution when H_0 is true.

---

null hypothesis: H_0: $p_1 = p_2$

alt. hypothesis: H_A: $p_1 \neq p_2$

test statistic: $\chi^2 = \dfrac{(B - C)^2}{B + C}$

decision rule: reject H_0 if $\chi^2 > \chi^2_1(\alpha)$

The rejection region is found by obtaining the critical chi-square value based on 1 degree of freedom, $\chi^2_1(\alpha)$, from chi-square tables or by using the SAS function CINV($1-\alpha$, df). For $\alpha = 0.05$, the critical chi-square value is 3.841 (see Table A.3 in Appendix A.3, or the SAS function CINV(0.95,1)).

18.3 Examples

Example 18.1 -- Bilirubin Abnormalities Following Drug Treatment

Eighty-six patients were treated with an experimental drug for 3 months. Pre- and post-study clinical laboratory results showed abnormally high total bilirubin values (above the upper limit of the normal range) as indicated in Table 18.2. Is there evidence of a change in the pre- to post-treatment rates of abnormalities?

TABLE 18.2. Raw Data for Example 18.1

Patient Number	Pre-	Post-	Patient Number	Pre-	Post-	Patient Number	Pre-	Post-
1	N	N	31	N	N	61	N	N
2	N	N	32	N	N	62	N	N
3	N	N	33	Y	N	63	N	N
4	N	N	34	N	N	64	N	N
5	N	N	35	N	N	65	N	N
6	N	Y	36	N	N	66	N	N
7	Y	Y	37	N	N	67	N	N
8	N	N	38	N	Y	68	N	N
9	N	N	39	N	Y	69	N	Y
10	N	N	40	N	N	70	N	Y
11	N	N	41	N	N	71	Y	Y
12	Y	N	42	N	Y	72	N	N
13	N	N	43	N	N	73	N	N
14	N	Y	44	Y	N	74	N	Y
15	N	N	45	N	N	75	N	N
16	N	N	46	N	N	76	N	Y
17	N	N	47	Y	Y	77	N	N
18	N	N	48	N	N	78	N	N
19	N	N	49	N	N	79	N	N
20	N	Y	50	N	Y	80	N	N
21	N	N	51	Y	N	81	Y	Y
22	Y	N	52	N	N	82	N	N
23	N	N	53	N	Y	83	N	N
24	N	N	54	N	N	84	N	N
25	Y	N	55	Y	Y	85	N	N
26	N	N	56	N	N	86	N	N
27	N	N	57	N	N			
28	Y	Y	58	N	N			
29	N	Y	59	N	N			
30	N	Y	60	N	N			

N = normal, Y = abnormally high

Solution

Let p_1 and p_2 represent the proportions of patients who have abnormally high bilirubin values (Y) before and after treatment, respectively. The data are summarized in Table 18.3.

TABLE 18.3. Abnormality Frequency Summary for Example 18.1

		Post-Treatment		
		N	Y	Total
Pre-Treatment	N	60	14	74
	Y	6	6	12
	Total	66	20	86

Y = Total bilirubin above upper limit of normal range

The test summary is

null hypothesis: H_0: $p_1 = p_2$

alt. hypothesis: H_A: $p_1 \neq p_2$

test statistic:

$$\chi^2 = (14 - 6)^2 / (14 + 6)$$

$$= 64 / 20 = 3.20$$

decision rule: reject H_0 if $\chi^2 > 3.841$

conclusion: Because 3.20 is not > 3.841, you do not reject H_0, concluding that, at a significance level of 0.05, there is insufficient evidence that a shift in abnormality rates occurs with treatment.

The actual p-value of 0.074 for the chi-square value of 3.20 can be found by using the SAS expression 1–PROBCHI(3.20,1).

SAS Analysis of Example 18.1

Use the AGREE option in the TABLES statement in the FREQ procedure ❶ to conduct *McNemar's test* in SAS. The SAS code and output for Example 18.1 follow. The chi-square value of 3.20 ❷ with a p-value of 0.074 ❸ are shown in the output.

SAS Code for Example 18.1

```
PROC FORMAT;
    VALUE RSLTFMT 0 = 'N'  1 = 'Y';
RUN;

DATA BILI;
    INPUT PAT PRE PST @@;
    DATALINES;
 1 0 0   2 0 0   3 0 0   4 0 0   5 0 0   6 0 1
 7 1 1   8 0 0   9 0 0  10 0 0  11 0 0  12 1 0
13 0 0  14 0 1  15 0 0  16 0 0  17 0 0  18 0 0
19 0 0  20 0 1  21 0 0  22 1 0  23 0 0  24 0 0
25 1 0  26 0 0  27 0 0  28 1 1  29 0 1  30 0 1
31 0 0  32 0 0  33 1 0  34 0 0  35 0 0  36 0 0
37 0 0  38 0 1  39 0 1  40 0 0  41 0 0  42 0 1
43 0 0  44 1 0  45 0 0  46 0 0  47 1 1  48 0 0
49 0 0  50 0 1  51 1 0  52 0 0  53 0 1  54 0 0
55 1 1  56 0 0  57 0 0  58 0 0  59 0 0  60 0 0
61 0 0  62 0 0  63 0 0  64 0 0  65 0 0  66 0 0
67 0 0  68 0 0  69 0 1  70 0 1  71 1 1  72 0 0
73 0 0  74 0 1  75 0 0  76 0 1  77 0 0  78 0 0
79 0 0  80 0 0  81 1 1  82 0 0  83 0 0  84 0 0
85 0 0  86 0 0
;

ODS EXCLUDE
    SimpleKappa;
PROC FREQ DATA = BILI;
    TABLES PRE*PST / AGREE NOROW NOCOL;          ❶
    FORMAT PRE PST RSLTFMT.;
    TITLE1 "McNemar's Test";
    TITLE2 'Example 18.1: Bilirubin Abnormalities Following
            Drug Treatment';
RUN;
```

OUTPUT 18.1. SAS Output for Example 18.1

```
                        McNemar's Test
      Example 18.1: Bilirubin Abnormalities Following Drug Treatment

                       The FREQ Procedure

                     Table of PRE by PST

          PRE          PST

          Frequency|
          Percent  |      N  |      Y  |  Total
          ---------+--------+--------+
          N        |     60  |     14  |     74
                   |  69.77  |  16.28  |  86.05
          ---------+--------+--------+
          Y        |      6  |      6  |     12
                   |   6.98  |   6.98  |  13.95
          ---------+--------+--------+
          Total          66       20       86
                       76.74    23.26   100.00


           Statistics for Table of PRE by PST

                    McNemar's Test
                 ----------------------
                 Statistic (S)    3.2000      ❷
                 DF                    1
                 Pr > S           0.0736      ❸

                   Sample Size = 86
```

Three Response Categories

Many situations arise in clinical data analysis in which the data are paired and the response has three categorical levels. The bilirubin response in Example 18.1, for example, can be classified as 'normal', 'above normal', or 'below normal'. Clinical laboratory data are often analyzed using pre- to post-study 'shift' tables, which show the frequencies of patients shifting among these three categories from baseline to some point in the study following treatment. Such data can be analyzed using the *Stuart-Maxwell test,* which is an extension of *McNemar's test.*

The *Stuart-Maxwell test* is also a *chi-square test* based on the cell frequencies from a layout similar to that shown in Table 18.4. The null hypothesis is that the distribution of responses among the three categories is the same under both conditions, in this case, pre- and post-study.

TABLE 18.4. Layout for a Paired Experiment with a Trinomial Response

		--------------Post-Study -----------		
		Low	Normal	High
Pre-Study	Low	n_{11}	n_{12}	n_{13}
	Normal	n_{21}	n_{22}	n_{23}
	High	n_{31}	n_{32}	n_{33}

Compute

$$d_1 = (n_{12} + n_{13}) - (n_{21} + n_{31})$$
$$d_2 = (n_{21} + n_{23}) - (n_{12} + n_{32})$$
$$d_3 = (n_{31} + n_{32}) - (n_{13} + n_{23})$$

and, for $i \neq j$,

$$\bar{n}_{ij} = (n_{ij} + n_{ji}) / 2$$

For $i = 1, 2, 3$, let $p_i(1)$ represent the probability of being classified in Category i under Condition 1 and $p_i(2)$ represent the probability of being classified in Category i under Condition 2, the test summary is

null hypothesis: H_0: $p_i(1) = p_i(2)$ for $i = 1, 2,$ and 3

alt. hypothesis: H_A: $p_i(1) \neq p_i(2)$ for $i = 1, 2,$ or 3

test statistic:
$$S = \frac{(\bar{n}_{23} \cdot d_1^2) + (\bar{n}_{13} \cdot d_2^2) + (\bar{n}_{12} \cdot d_3^2)}{2 \cdot ((\bar{n}_{12} \cdot \bar{n}_{23}) + (\bar{n}_{12} \cdot \bar{n}_{13}) + (\bar{n}_{13} \cdot \bar{n}_{23}))}$$

decision rule: reject H_0 if $S > \chi_2^2(\alpha)$

When H_0 is true, S has an approximate chi-square distribution with 2 degrees of freedom. For $\alpha = 0.05$, the critical chi-square value, $\chi_2^2(\alpha)$, is 5.991 from Table A.3 (Appendix A) or by using the SAS function =CINV(0.95,2) .

Example 18.2 -- Symptom Frequency Before and After Treatment

Patients characterized their craving of certain high-fat food products before and two weeks after an experimental diet therapy as 'never', 'occasional' or 'frequent', as summarized in Table 18.5. Does the diet appear to have an effect on the frequency of these cravings?

TABLE 18.5. Cell Frequencies for Example 18.2

		--------------- Two Weeks --------------		
		Never	Occasional	Frequent
Pre-Study	Never	14	6	4
	Occasional	9	17	2
	Frequent	6	12	8

Solution

Compute

$$d_1 = (6+4) - (9+6) = -5$$
$$d_2 = (9+2) - (6+12) = -7$$
$$d_3 = (6+12) - (4+2) = 12$$

and

$$\bar{n}_{12} = (n_{12} + n_{21})/2 = (6+9)/2 = 7.5$$
$$\bar{n}_{13} = (n_{13} + n_{31})/2 = (4+6)/2 = 5$$
$$\bar{n}_{23} = (n_{23} + n_{32})/2 = (2+12)/2 = 7$$

The test statistic is

$$S = \frac{(7 \cdot (-5)^2) + (5 \cdot (-7)^2) + (7.5 \cdot (12)^2)}{2 \cdot ((7.5 \cdot 7) + (7.5 \cdot 5) + (5 \cdot 7))} = 6.00$$

which is larger than the critical chi-square value of 5.991. Therefore, there has been a significant shift in the distribution of responses at the $\alpha = 0.05$ level. The marginal response probabilities are estimated as

TABLE 18.6. Marginal Response Probabilities for Example 18.2

	Pre-Study	2 Weeks
Never	24 / 78 = 30.8%	29 / 78 = 37.2%
Occasional	28 / 78 = 35.9%	35 / 78 = 44.9%
Frequent	26 / 78 = 33.3%	14 / 78 = 17.9%

18.4 Details & Notes

▶ **18.4.1.** For *McNemar's test*, the estimate of p_1 is $(A+B)/n$, and the estimate of p_2 is $(A+C)/n$. The difference in proportions, $p_1 - p_2$, is estimated by $((A+B)/n) - ((A+C)/n) = (B-C)/n$. An approximate 95% confidence interval for p_1-p_2 is given by

$$\frac{(B-C)}{n} \pm 1.96 \cdot \left(\frac{1}{n}\right) \cdot \sqrt{B + C - \frac{(B-C)^2}{n}}$$

For Example 18.1, the approximate 95% confidence interval for $p_1 - p_2$ is

$$\frac{(14-6)}{86} \pm 1.96 \cdot \left(\frac{1}{86}\right) \cdot \sqrt{14 + 6 - \frac{(14-6)^2}{86}}$$

$$= 0.093 \pm 0.100 \text{ or } (-0.007 \text{ to } 0.193)$$

▶ **18.4.2.** Note that the chi-square test statistic is based only on the discordant cell sizes (B, C) and ignores the concordant cells (A, D). However, the estimates of p_1, p_2 and the size of the confidence interval are based on all cells because they are inversely proportional to the total sample size, n.

▶ **18.4.3.** A continuity correction can be used with *McNemar's test* as follows:

$$\chi^2 = \frac{(|B-C|-1)^2}{B+C}$$

This adjustment results in a more conservative test, and the correction factor may be omitted as B+C gets larger. Re-analyzing the data in Example 18.1 with the continuity correction, the test statistic becomes $\chi^2 = 2.45$, which is seen to be smaller and less significant (p=0.118) than the uncorrected value.

▶ **18.4.4.** A well-known relationship in probability theory is that if a random variable, Z, has a standard normal distribution (i.e., mean 0 and variance 1), then Z^2 has a chi-square distribution with 1 degree of freedom. This principle can be used to show the relationship of the *McNemar chi-square* to the *binomial test* using the normal approximation as follows.

When the null hypothesis is true, the discordant values, B and C, should be about the same, that is B/(B+C) should be about 1/2. *McNemar's test* is equivalent to using the *binomial test* (Chapter 15) to test H_0: $p = 0.5$, where p equals the fraction of the events that fall in 1 of the 2 discordant cells. Using the setup of Chapter 15 with $n = B+C$ and $X = B$, the normal approximation to the *binomial test* (expressed as a standard normal Z when H_0 is true), is

$$ Z = \frac{(\, |\hat{p} - 0.5| - \dfrac{1}{2(B+C)} \,)}{\sqrt{\dfrac{0.5 \cdot 0.5}{(B+C)}}} = \frac{|B - C| - 1}{\sqrt{B+C}} $$

because $\quad \hat{p} = \dfrac{B}{(B+C)}$

Therefore,

$$ Z^2 = \frac{(\, |B - C| - 1 \,)^2}{(B+C)} = \chi^2 $$

▶ **18.4.5.** Because *McNemar's test* is identical to the *binomial test* using a normal approximation, it should be used only when the conditions for the normal approximation apply (see Chapter 15). Using the notation here, these conditions can be simplified as $B^2 \geq C(4-B)$ and $C^2 \geq B(4-C)$. Notice that these conditions need to be checked only if either B or C is less than 4. If the conditions are not satisfied, the exact binomial probabilities should be used rather than the normal approximation or the chi-square statistic.

▶ **18.4.6.** The above application of the *binomial test* is an example of the *sign test* mentioned in Chapter 15. In applying the *sign test*, the number of increases (+) are compared with the number of decreases (–), ignoring tied values. In Example 18.1, B represents the number of increases, C represents the number of decreases, and the concordant values (A and D) represent the tied values, which are ignored.

▶ **18.4.7.** The p-value in the SAS output corresponds to a *two-tailed hypothesis test*. The *one-tailed* p-value can be found by halving this value.

▶ **18.4.8.** *McNemar's test* is often used to detect shifts in response rates between pre- and post-treatment measurement times within a single treatment group. A comparison in shifts can be made between two treatment or dose groups (e.g., Group 1 and Group 2) using a normal approximation as follows. As in Table 18.1, let A_i, B_i, C_i, D_i, and n_i represent the cell and overall frequencies for Group i (i = 1, 2). The proportional shift for Group i is

$$ D_i = \frac{A_i + C_i}{n_i} - \frac{A_i + B_i}{n_i} = \frac{C_i - B_i}{n_i} $$

To test for a difference between groups in these proportional shifts, you can use

$$Z = \frac{|D_1 - D_2|}{\sqrt{\sigma_{D_1}^2 + \sigma_{D_2}^2}}$$

as a test statistic that has an approximate standard normal distribution under the hypothesis of no difference in shifts between groups. Above, the variance of D_i is computed as

$$\sigma_{D_i}^2 = \frac{n_i(B_i + C_i) - (B_i - C_i)^2}{n_i^3}$$

▶ **18.4.9.** The *Stuart-Maxwell test* is sometimes referred to as a test for 'marginal homogeneity' because it tests for equality between the two conditions in the marginal response probabilities. Another alternative hypothesis that might be of interest is that of symmetry. Symmetry occurs when the off-diagonal cell probabilities are the same for each 2×2 sub-table. This implies that changes in response levels between the conditions (e.g., pre- and post-) occur in both directions with the same probability.

With dichotomous outcomes, the conditions of marginal homogeneity and symmetry are equivalent. With more than two response categories, symmetry is a stronger condition and implies marginal homogeneity. The 3×3 tables in Table 18.6 show a pattern of marginal homogeneity with symmetry (Table i) and without symmetry (Table ii).

TABLE 18.6. Examples of Symmetry (i) and non-Symmetry (ii) in a 3 x 3 Table

Table i		Condition 2			
		1	2	3	
Condition 1	1	30	15	5	50
	2	15	5	10	30
	3	5	10	5	20
		50	30	20	100

Table ii		Condition 2			
		1	2	3	
Condition 1	1	30	0	20	50
	2	20	10	0	30
	3	0	20	0	20
		50	30	20	100

Bowker's test can be used to test for symmetry in 3×3 or larger tables. The test statistic is found by adding the *McNemar* chi-square statistics for each 2×2 sub-table. For a table with k categories, there are $k \cdot (k-1)/2$ 2×2 sub-tables. For example, the 3×3 table contains three 2×2 sub-tables with categories 1 and 2, 1 and 3, and 2 and 3. *Bowker's test* for k categories is a *chi-square test* with $k \cdot (k-1)/2$ degrees of freedom.

Bowker's test for symmetry can be performed in SAS in the same way that *McNemar's test* is run (by using the AGREE option in the TABLES statement in PROC FREQ). If SAS detects k > 2, the test for symmetry is automatically performed. *Bowker's test* results for Example 18.2 are found by using the SAS program that follows. The output shows a chi-square test statistic of 8.1429 ❹, which indicates a significant departure from the hypothesis of symmetry (p=0.0431).

```
DATA DIET;
    INPUT PRE WK2 CNT @@;
    DATALINES;
0 0 14  0 1 6   0 2 4
1 0 9   1 1 17  1 2 2
2 0 6   2 1 12  2 2 8
;

ODS SELECT
    SymmetryTest;
PROC FREQ DATA = DIET;
    TABLES PRE*WK2 / AGREE NOCOL NOROW;
    WEIGHT CNT;
RUN;
```

OUTPUT 18.2. Output for Symmetry Test in Example 18.2

```
            Statistics for Table of PRE by WK2

                  Test of Symmetry
            -----------------------
            Statistic (S)     8.1429        ❹
            DF                     3
            Pr > S            0.0431

                Sample Size = 78
```

▶ **18.4.10.**   Notice that Section 18.4.8 shows one method for comparing the magnitude of shifts in conditions based on correlated responses among independent groups. If there are more than two groups or more than two response levels, or the design involves other stratification factors, a more complex analysis is required. Stokes, Davis, and Koch (2000) illustrate the analysis of examples that involve *repeated measures* using PROC CATMOD in SAS.

CHAPTER 19

The *Cochran-Mantel-Haenszel Test*

19.1 Introduction

The *Cochran-Mantel-Haenszel test* is used in clinical trials to compare two binomial proportions from independent populations based on stratified samples. This test provides a means of combining a number of 2×2 tables of the type discussed in Chapters 16 and 17 when each is from a separate, independent stratum.

The stratification factor can represent patient subgroups, such as study centers, gender, age group, or disease severity, and acts similar to the blocking factor in a *two-way ANOVA* (Chapter 7). The *Cochran-Mantel-Haenszel test* obtains an overall comparison of response rates adjusted for the stratification variable. The adjustment is simply a weighting of the 2×2 tables in proportion to the within-strata sample sizes.

The *Cochran-Mantel-Haenszel test* is often used in the comparison of response rates between two treatment groups in a multi-center study using the study centers as strata.

19.2 Synopsis

Assume there are k strata ($k \geq 2$). Within Stratum j, there are N_j patients ($j = 1, 2, ..., k$), randomly allocated to one of two groups. In Group 1, there are n_{j1} patients, X_{j1} of whom are considered 'responders'. Similarly, Group 2 has n_{j2} patients with X_{j2} 'responders', as shown in Table 19.1.

TABLE 19.1. Layout for the Cochran-Mantel-Haenszel Test

Stratum	Group	Responders	Non-Responders	Total
1	1	X_{11}	$n_{11} - X_{11}$	n_{11}
	2	X_{12}	$n_{12} - X_{12}$	n_{12}
	Total	$X_{11} + X_{12}$	$N_1 - (X_{11} + X_{12})$	N_1

Stratum	Group	Responders	Non-Responders	Total
2	1	X_{21}	$n_{21} - X_{21}$	n_{21}
	2	X_{22}	$n_{22} - X_{22}$	n_{22}
	Total	$X_{21} + X_{22}$	$N_2 - (X_{21} + X_{22})$	N_2

$\vdots$

Stratum	Group	Responders	Non-Responders	Total
k	1	X_{k1}	$n_{k1} - X_{k1}$	n_{k1}
	2	X_{k2}	$n_{k2} - X_{k2}$	n_{k2}
	Total	$X_{k1} + X_{k2}$	$N_k - (X_{k1} + X_{k2})$	N_k

Let p_1 and p_2 denote the overall response rates for Group 1 and Group 2, respectively. For Stratum j, compute the quantities

$$NUM_j = \frac{X_{j1} \cdot n_{j2} - X_{j2} \cdot n_{j1}}{N_j}$$

and

$$DEN_j = \frac{n_{j1} \cdot n_{j2} \cdot (X_{j1} + X_{j2}) \cdot (N_j - X_{j1} - X_{j2})}{N_j^2 \cdot (N_j - 1)}$$

The Cochran-Mantel-Haenszel test summary is

null hypothesis: H_0: $p_1 = p_2$

alt. hypothesis: H_A: $p_1 \neq p_2$

test statistic:
$$\chi^2_{CMH} = \frac{\left(\sum_{j=1}^{k} NUM_j \right)^2}{\sum_{j=1}^{k} DEN_j}$$

decision rule: reject H_0 if $\chi^2_{CMH} > \chi^2_1(\alpha)$

As in previous chapters, $\chi_1^2(\alpha)$ represents the critical chi-square value with significance level α and 1 degree of freedom.

19.3 Examples

Example 19.1 -- *Dermotel* Response in Diabetic Ulcers

A multi-center study with 4 centers is testing an experimental treatment, Dermotel, used to accelerate the healing of dermal foot ulcers in diabetic patients. Sodium hyaluronate was used in a control group. Patients who showed a decrease in ulcer size after 20 weeks treatment of at least 90% by surface area measurements were considered 'responders'. The numbers of responders in each group are shown in Table 19.2 for each study center. Is there an overall difference in response rates between the Dermotel and control groups?

TABLE 19.2. Response Frequencies by Study Center for Example 19.1

Study Center	Treatment Group	Response	Non-Response	TOTAL
1	*Dermotel*	26	4	30
	Control	18	11	29
	Total	44	15	59

2	*Dermotel*	8	3	11
	Control	7	5	12
	Total	15	8	23

3	*Dermotel*	7	5	12
	Control	4	6	10
	Total	11	11	22

4	*Dermotel*	11	6	17
	Control	9	5	14
	Total	20	11	31

Solution

Consider the study centers as separate strata. For Study Center 1, compute

$$NUM_1 = \frac{X_{11} \cdot n_{12} - X_{12} \cdot n_{11}}{N_1}$$

$$= \frac{26 \cdot 29 - 18 \cdot 30}{59} = 3.6271$$

and

$$DEN_1 = \frac{n_{11} \cdot n_{12} \cdot (X_{11} + X_{12}) \cdot (N_1 - X_{11} - X_{12})}{N_1^2 \cdot (N_1 - 1)}$$

$$= \frac{30 \cdot 29 \cdot 44 \cdot 15}{59^2 \cdot 58} = 2.8440$$

These quantities can be computed in a similar way for the other centers, and the results are shown in Table 19.3.

TABLE 19.3. Computational Summary for CMH Test Statistic of Example 19.1

STUDY CENTER (j)	NUM$_j$	DEN$_j$
1	3.6271	2.8440
2	0.8261	1.3611
3	1.000	1.4286
4	0.0322	1.8162
TOTAL	5.4855	7.4500

The test summary using the *Cochran-Mantel-Haenszel test* at a significance level of 0.05 is

null hypothesis: H_0: $p_1 = p_2$

alt. hypothesis: H_A: $p_1 \neq p_2$

test statistic:
$$\chi^2_{CMH} = \frac{\left(\sum\limits_{j=1}^{4} NUM_j \right)^2}{\sum\limits_{j=1}^{4} DEN_j}$$

$$= 5.4855^2 / 7.4500 = 4.039$$

decision rule: reject H_0 if $\chi^2_{CMH} > 3.841$

conclusion: Because $4.039 > 3.841$, you reject H_0 at a significance level of $\alpha = 0.05$ and conclude that there is a significant difference in response rates between the *Dermotel* treatment and the control.

SAS Analysis of Example 19.1

The CMH option in the FREQ procedure in SAS can be used to conduct the *Cochran-Mantel-Haenszel test*, as shown on the following pages. The stratification factor (CNTR) must be specified first in the TABLES statement as shown in the SAS code ❶. Use the NOPERCENT and NOCOL options to suppress printing of unneeded results (the row percentages will be printed because the NOROW option is not specified).

The output shows the 2×2 tables for each study center ❷. These can be omitted using the NOFREQ option in the TABLES statement. The row percentages are printed under the cell frequencies, and the percent for RESP = YES represents the estimated response rate. The *Cochran-Mantel-Haenszel test* results are shown on the subsequent output page ❸, confirming the chi-square statistic of 4.039. Note that the tests for 'general association', 'row mean scores differ' and 'non-zero correlation' are all equivalent for 2×2 tables. The p-value of 0.0445 indicates significance when tested at $\alpha = 0.05$.

The SAS code includes an overall *chi-square test* (Chapter 16), ignoring the stratification factor (Study Center), which is not significant (p=0.0513) ❹. This is discussed more in Section 19.4.2.

SAS Code for Example 19.1

```
DATA ULCR;
    INPUT CNTR $ TRT $ RESP $ FRQ @@;
    DATALINES;
1 ACT YES 26  1 CTL YES 18
1 ACT _NO  4  1 CTL _NO 11
2 ACT YES  8  2 CTL YES  7
2 ACT _NO  3  2 CTL _NO  5
3 ACT YES  7  3 CTL YES  4
3 ACT _NO  5  3 CTL _NO  6
4 ACT YES 11  4 CTL YES  9
4 ACT _NO  6  4 CTL _NO  5
;

/* Analysis using CNTR as stratification factor */
ODS EXCLUDE
    CommonRelRisks;
PROC FREQ DATA = ULCR;
    TABLES CNTR*TRT*RESP / CMH NOPERCENT NOCOL;          ❶
    WEIGHT FRQ;
    TITLE1 'The Cochran-Mantel-Haenszel Test';
    TITLE2 'Example 19.1:  Response to Dermotel in Diabetic
            Ulcers';
RUN;

/* Analysis without stratification (ignoring CNTR) */
PROC FREQ DATA = ULCR;                                   ❹
    TABLES TRT*RESP / CHISQ NOPERCENT NOCOL;
    WEIGHT FRQ;
RUN;
```

OUTPUT 19.1. SAS Output for Example 19.1

```
                 The Cochran-Mantel-Haenszel Test
        Example 19.1:  Response to Dermotel in Diabetic Ulcers

                        The FREQ Procedure

                      Table 1 of TRT by RESP
                      Controlling for CNTR=1
                                                            ❷
              TRT        RESP

              Frequency|
              Row Pct  |    YES  |     NO  |  Total
              ---------+---------+---------+
              ACT      |    26   |     4   |    30
                       |  86.67  |  13.33  |
              ---------+---------+---------+
              CTL      |    18   |    11   |    29
                       |  62.07  |  37.93  |
              ---------+---------+---------+
              Total         44         15       59
```

OUTPUT 19.1. SAS Output for Example 19.1 (*continued*)

```
                         The Cochran-Mantel-Haenszel Test
              Example 19.1:  Response to Dermotel in Diabetic Ulcers


                              Table 2 of TRT by RESP
                              Controlling for CNTR=2            ❷

                         TRT       RESP

                         Frequency|
                         Row Pct  |   YES  |    NO  |  Total
                         ---------+--------+--------+
                         ACT      |     8  |     3  |    11
                                  |  72.73 |  27.27 |
                         ---------+--------+--------+
                         CTL      |     7  |     5  |    12
                                  |  58.33 |  41.67 |
                         ---------+--------+--------+
                         Total         15        8       23




                              Table 3 of TRT by RESP
                              Controlling for CNTR=3            ❷

                         TRT       RESP

                         Frequency|
                         Row Pct  |   YES  |    NO  |  Total
                         ---------+--------+--------+
                         ACT      |     7  |     5  |    12
                                  |  58.33 |  41.67 |
                         ---------+--------+--------+
                         CTL      |     4  |     6  |    10
                                  |  40.00 |  60.00 |
                         ---------+--------+--------+
                         Total         11       11       22




                              Table 4 of TRT by RESP
                              Controlling for CNTR=4            ❷

                         TRT       RESP

                         Frequency|
                         Row Pct  |   YES  |    NO  |  Total
                         ---------+--------+--------+
                         ACT      |    11  |     6  |    17
                                  |  64.71 |  35.29 |
                         ---------+--------+--------+
                         CTL      |     9  |     5  |    14
                                  |  64.29 |  35.71 |
                         ---------+--------+--------+
                         Total         20       11       31
```

OUTPUT 19.1. SAS Output for Example 19.1 (*continued*)

```
                  The Cochran-Mantel-Haenszel Test
        Example 19.1:   Response to Dermotel in Diabetic Ulcers

                    Summary Statistics for TRT by RESP
                          Controlling for CNTR

      Cochran-Mantel-Haenszel Statistics (Based on Table Scores)

      Statistic    Alternative Hypothesis    DF      Value     Prob
      -----------------------------------------------------------------
          1        Nonzero Correlation        1      4.0391    0.0445
          2        Row Mean Scores Differ     1      4.0391    0.0445
          3        General Association        1      4.0391    0.0445


                         Breslow-Day Test for
                      Homogeneity of the Odds Ratios
                      -------------------------------
                      Chi-Square              1.8947
                      DF                           3
                      Pr > ChiSq              0.5946

                       Total Sample Size = 135

                       Table of TRT by RESP

                  TRT         RESP
                  Frequency|
                  Row Pct  |   YES  |   NO  |  Total
                  ---------+--------+--------+
                  ACT      |    52  |   18  |    70
                           | 74.29  | 25.71 |
                  ---------+--------+--------+
                  CTL      |    38  |   27  |    65
                           | 58.46  | 41.54 |
                  ---------+--------+--------+
                  Total         90       45     135

                  Statistics for Table of RESP by TRT
      Statistic                       DF     Value      Prob
      --------------------------------------------------------------
      Chi-Square                       1     3.7978    0.0513
      Likelihood Ratio Chi-Square      1     3.8136    0.0508
      Continuity Adj. Chi-Square       1     3.1191    0.0774
      Mantel-Haenszel Chi-Square       1     3.7697    0.0522
      Phi Coefficient                        0.1677
      Contingency Coefficient                0.1654
      Cramer's V                             0.1677

                         Fisher's Exact Test
                      ------------------------------------
                      Cell (1,1) Frequency (F)       52
                      Left-sided Pr <= F         0.9837
                      Right-sided Pr >= F        0.0385

                      Table Probability (P)      0.0222
                      Two-sided Pr <= P          0.0676

                         Sample Size = 135
```

19.4 Details & Notes

▶ **19.4.1.** A convenient way to summarize the test results by stratum is shown for Example 19.1 in Table 19.4. The response rate for Group i, Stratum j is estimated by $100(X_{ji}/n_{ji})\%$. The overall response rate for Group i is estimated by $100((X_{1i}+X_{2i}+X_{3i}+X_{4i})/(n_{1i}+n_{2i}+n_{3i}+n_{4i}))\%$.

TABLE 19.4. Summary of Results for Example 19.1

Study Center	Response Rates Active	(n)	Response Rates Control	(n)	Chi-Square	p-Value
1	86.7%	(30)	62.1%	(29)	4.706	0.030*
2	72.7%	(11)	58.3%	(12)	0.524	0.469
3	58.3%	(12)	40.0%	(10)	0.733	0.392
4	64.7%	(17)	64.3%	(14)	0.001	0.981
Overall	74.3%	(70)	58.5%	(65)	4.039	0.044*

Although not included in the SAS output for this example, the chi-square values and p-values can be output for each stratum using the CHISQ option in the TABLES statement of PROC FREQ.

▶ **19.4.2.** By ignoring the strata and combining all the data of Example 19.1 into one simple *chi-square test* (Chapter 16), you obtain the following results, as shown in Output 19.1❹:

TABLE 19.5. Chi-Square Test for Example 19.1, Ignoring Strata

Group	Response	Non-Response	Total
Active	52 (74.3%)	18	70
Control	38 (58.5%)	27	65
Total	90 (100.0%)	45	135

chi-square value = 3.798, p = 0.051

The test statistic does not quite attain significance at the 0.05 level as with the *Cochran-Mantel-Haenszel test*. In this example, the within-strata information used by the *Cochran-Mantel-Haenszel test* is advantageous in revealing greater statistical significance. This will often be the case when there is a big difference in sample sizes among strata and the largest strata show the biggest response rate differences.

▶ **19.4.3.** With some algebraic manipulation,

$$NUM_j = \frac{X_{j1} \cdot n_{j2} - X_{j2} \cdot n_{j1}}{N_j}$$

can be expressed as

$$w_j \cdot (\hat{p}_{j1} - \hat{p}_{j2})$$

where $\hat{p}_{ji} = \dfrac{X_{ji}}{n_{ji}}$ is the estimate of p_{ji}, and w_j is a function of the group sample sizes

$$w_j = \left(\frac{1}{n_{j1}} + \frac{1}{n_{j2}} \right)^{-1}$$

Written in this way, the *Cochran-Mantel-Haenszel* statistic is seen to be based on the within-strata response rate differences combined over all strata, weighted by w_j. Because w_j increases with the n_{ij}'s, it is seen that greater weights are assigned to those strata that have larger sample sizes.

▶ **19.4.4.** The *Cochran-Mantel-Haenszel test* was originally developed for use with retrospective data in epidemiological applications. The same methodology has been widely applied to prospective clinical trials, such as those illustrated here. A number of alternative statistics, similar but with minor variations to the version presented, have also been used.

For example, *Cochran's (chi-square) test* is computed in the same way as the *Cochran-Mantel-Haenszel* statistic with the exception that the denominator of DEN_j is N_j^3 instead of $N_j^2(N_j-1)$. The *Cochran-Mantel-Haenszel test* is an attempt to improve on *Cochran's test* by giving the strata with fewer patients less weight in the overall analysis, while leaving strata with large N_j's relatively unaltered. Notice that if *Cochran's test* is used with only one stratum ($k = 1$), the chi-square value is $(NUM_1)^2 / DEN_1$, which is identical to the *chi-square test* discussed in Chapter 16.

Another variation of the *Cochran-Mantel-Haenszel* statistic is the continuity-corrected value as follows:

$$\chi^2_{CMH} = \frac{\left(\left| \sum_{j=1}^{k} NUM_j \right| - 0.5 \right)^2}{\sum_{j=1}^{k} DEN_j}$$

The continuity correction should be used if there are many small cell sizes. However, use of the continuity correction might produce overly conservative results, and it can generally be omitted for reasonable cell sizes.

▶ **19.4.5.** An interaction exists if the differences in response rates between groups are not consistent among strata. An example of an interaction is an Active vs. Control response rate comparison of 60% vs. 30% in one stratum and 30% vs. 60% in another stratum. Combining strata might mask this interaction, which leads to offsetting responses and no overall differences.

In the presence of an interaction or lack of 'homogeneity' among response differences, each stratum should be analyzed separately, and further analyses might be pursued in an attempt to explain the interaction.

The *Breslow-Day test* for homogeneity among strata is included in the SAS output when conducting the *Cochran-Mantel-Haenszel test*. This test provides an indication of the presence of an interaction even though it is based on the odds ratios (see Chapter 20) rather than the differences in response rates. A significant *Breslow-Day test* does not invalidate the results of the *CMH test*, but indicates caution should be used in its interpretation, and that perhaps individual strata should be further investigated. The SAS output for Example 19.1 shows a non-significant *Breslow-Day test* with a p-value of 0.5946 ❺.

▶ **19.4.6.** Combining data across strata into a single 2×2 table should only be considered when the individual tables have like proportions. To show the problems that can arise by automatically combining tables without carefully examining each, consider the results for two strata (shown in Table 19.6).

TABLE 19.6. Example of 2×2 Tables with Counter-Intuitive Combined Results

Stratum	Group	Responders	Non-Responders	Total	Response Rate
1	A	10	38	48	21%
	B	4	21	25	16%
2	A	20	10	30	67%
	B	27	17	44	61%
Combined	A	30	48	78	38%
	B	31	38	69	45%

The response rates for Group A are greater than those of Group B within each stratum. But the overall response rate for Group B is greater for the combined strata. This situation can occur if there is a big difference in response rates among strata, and sample sizes are imbalanced between groups in opposite ways among strata.

▶ **19.4.7.**   The *Cochran-Mantel-Haenszel test* can be extended to contingency tables larger than the 2×2 tables considered here. The general layout is based on k strata of g×r contingency tables, where g (number of rows) and r (columns) typically represent the number of treatment groups and the number of response categories, respectively. The FREQ procedure in SAS can also be used to analyze results for this more general setup. The CMH option in the TABLES statement prints the results for the 'general association', 'row mean scores differ' and 'non-zero correlation' hypotheses when samples are stratified in the same way as the unstratified case discussed in Chapter 16. Caution must be used with larger values of g and r due to interpretation difficulties, smaller cell sizes, and the increased potential for interactions.

▶ **19.4.8.**   In Chapter 16, you see that the *chi-square test* for 2×2 tables is equivalent to using a normal approximation to the binomial distribution, and for general use, the cell frequencies should be large enough to validate that approximation. A conservative "rule-of-thumb" is to require expected cell frequencies of at least 5. This rule can be loosened somewhat for stratified data, as long as the combined cell frequencies over all strata are sufficiently large. The requirement for larger cell frequencies becomes even less important when the response variable is ordinal and has more than two categories.

> Details about sample size guidelines for applying the *CMH test* are discussed in the highly recommended "*Categorical Data Analysis Using the SAS System*, Second Edition" by Stokes, Davis, and Koch. This book was written under the SAS Books by Users program.

▶ **19.4.9.**   The *Cochran-Mantel-Haenszel test* as presented here is a *two-tailed test*. The p-value from the SAS output can be halved to obtain a *one-tailed test*.

Logistic Regression

20.1 Introduction

Logistic regression analysis is a statistical modeling method for analyzing dichotomous response data while accommodating adjustments for one or more explanatory variables or 'covariates'. This method is analogous to *analysis of covariance* (Chapter 11), which is useful for comparing two or more groups while adjusting for various background factors (covariates). Although both methods include covariate adjustments, *ANCOVA* analyzes *means* of numeric response measures; *logistic regression* analyzes *proportions* based on categorical responses, most commonly binary responses (e.g., success rates, survival rates, or cure rates).

Historically, *logistic regression* techniques have been widely used for identifying risk factors associated with disease in epidemiological studies. *Logistic regression* also is popular for analyzing prospective clinical trials and in identifying potentially important covariates in exploratory analyses of clinical research data.

Examples from clinical research where *logistic regression* might be useful include:

- comparing survival rates in cancer patients among various treatment groups adjusted for age and duration of disease.

- comparing proportions of patients whose dermal ulcers show complete healing between an active and placebo group adjusted for baseline ulcer size.

- comparing the proportion of normalized hypertensive patients between two anti-hypertensive treatment groups adjusted for age, cholesterol level, tobacco use, and exercise habits.

20.2 Synopsis

The Logit Model: One Covariate

Consider response variables, Y, that take one of two possible values (yes-no, normal-abnormal, present-absent, cured-not cured, died-survived, etc.), with coded values 0 and 1. A response of Y=1 indicates that the *event* of interest occurs (event), and a response of Y=0 indicates that the *event* does not occur (non-event). If you suspect that one or more background factors will affect the response, you want the analysis to reflect this relationship, and you must incorporate the values of the covariates (X) into the analysis.

The methods used to develop *ANCOVA* procedures (Chapter 11) are not applicable because the responses are not normally distributed. Instead, you apply a transformation of the data called the 'logit function',

$$Y^* = \ln\left(\frac{P}{1-P}\right)$$

where P is the expected value of Y for a specified set of X-values and 'ln' represents the natural-logarithm function.

For now, assume there is just one covariate, X. Because Y only takes the values 0 or 1 for a given value of X, the mean of Y equals the probability that Y=1. You denote this probability by P_X, where $0 \le P_X \le 1$. *Logistic regression* assumes that P_X is related to X in a sigmoidal fashion (Figure 20.1), represented by the equation

$$P_X = \frac{1}{1 + e^{-(\alpha + \beta X)}}$$

With some algebraic manipulation, this can be re-expressed as

$$\ln\left(\frac{P_X}{1 - P_X}\right) = \alpha + \beta\, X$$

the left side of which is the logistic transformation or 'logit' function (Y*). $P_X/(1-P_X)$ is known as the 'odds' that Y=1, i.e., the odds that the *event* of interest occurs. The logit is sometimes referred to as the 'log-odds'. The log-odds becomes a linear function of the covariate, X, when a sigmoidal relationship is assumed between X and P_X, as illustrated in Figure 20.1.

FIGURE 20.1. Logistic Probability Function

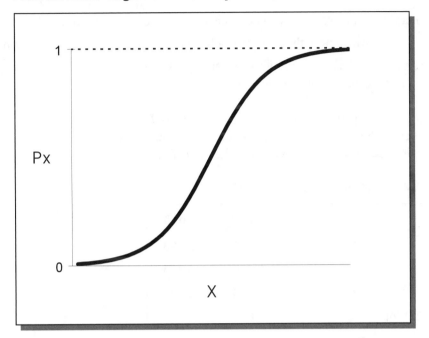

The Odds Ratio

Note that the odds for a specific covariate value of $X=x$ is

$$Odds_x = e^{\alpha+\beta x}$$

and the odds for a covariate value of $X=x+1$ is

$$Odds_{x+1} = e^{\alpha+\beta(x+1)}$$

so that the ratio of the odds based on a 1-unit increment in X is simply

$$\frac{Odds_{x+1}}{Odds_x} = e^{\beta}$$

This is called the 'odds ratio' (OR) for the covariate X. By subtracting 1 from the OR and multiplying by 100, you obtain the percent change in the odds of *event* occurrence when the covariate (X) increases by 1 unit. If X is a dichotomous variable, such as Gender with values 'Male' and 'Female', you assign numeric values to its levels, e.g., 0=Male and 1=Female, in which case the OR represents the factor by which the odds of *event* increases for females relative to males.

Model Estimation

For a fixed value of the covariate, such as $X = x$, one way to estimate P_x is by using $\hat{p}_x = y_x / n_x$, where n_x is the number of observations at $X = x$ and y_x is the number of *events* out of the n_x observations. Because y_x is a binomial random variable, $\hat{p}_x$ will be a better estimate when n_x is large.

Suppose 12 patients with ulcers secondary to *H. pylori* were cured out of 20 patients who were treated with an antibiotic. The study results were broken down by the ulcer history (X, in years) as shown in Table 20.1:

TABLE 20.1. Naïve Estimates of P_x

x	y_x	n_x	P_x (est)	Logit
1	4	6	0.667	0.693
2	6	10	0.600	0.405
3	2	4	0.500	0.000
TOTAL	12	20	0.600	

You might estimate the chance of cure with the antibiotic for patients with a 1-year history ($x = 1$) by $\hat{p}_1 = 4/6 = 0.667$. The logit of $\hat{p}_1$ is $\ln(0.667/0.333) = 0.693$.

Another way to estimate P_x is to obtain an estimate of the *logistic regression* model, then plug in the value of x and solve for P_x. This approach is based on a method known as maximum likelihood, which uses all the data to determine the estimate of each model parameter. These estimates are determined in a way that maximizes the likelihood of observing the data collected, and they are called 'maximum likelihood estimates' (MLE). In addition to having some powerful statistical properties, MLEs have the advantage that data need not be grouped, as in the above example, and the resulting model can be used to estimate P_x even for unobserved values of X.

Although the mathematical derivations based on the maximum likelihood method are complex and beyond the scope of this book, this method yields a set of simultaneous equations that can be solved for **a** and **b**, the estimates of α and β. These equations, which do not have a closed solution, have the form

$$\sum_{i=1}^{N} Y_i = \sum_{i=1}^{N} \left(1 + e^{-(a+b_{xi})}\right)^{-1}$$

and

$$\sum_{i=1}^{N} X_i \cdot Y_i = \sum_{i=1}^{N} X_i \cdot \left(1 + e^{-(a+b_{xi})}\right)^{-1}$$

Numerical techniques, such as iteratively weighted least-squares and Newton-Raphson algorithms, are used by SAS and other computer programs to solve these equations.

The Logit Model: Multiple Covariates

In general, the *logistic regression* layout has N patients and k covariates, $X_1, X_2, ..., X_k$, and a typical data set can have the following layout:

TABLE 20.2. Layout for Logistic Regression

Patient Number	Response Y	Covariates X_1	X_2	...	X_k
1	y_1	x_{11}	x_{21}	...	x_{k1}
2	y_2	x_{12}	x_{22}	...	x_{k2}
...	...	...	...	...	...
N	y_N	x_{1N}	x_{2N}	...	x_{kN}

The X_i's can be known, numeric-valued, concomitant factors, such as age, WBC, or fasting glucose level, or they can represent levels of ordinal categorical variables, such as small-medium-large or none-mild-moderate-severe. You can also use nominal level categorical explanatory variables, as discussed later (see Section 20.4.6). In controlled clinical studies, at least one of the X_i's is included to represent the treatment or dose group.

The model for the probability of '*event*', P, is

$$P = \frac{1}{1 + e^{-(\alpha + \beta_1 x_1 + \beta_2 x_2 + ... + \beta_k x_k)}}$$

so the logit becomes the linear function

$$\ln\left(\frac{P}{1-P}\right) = \alpha + \beta_1 x_1 + \beta_2 x_2 + ... + \beta_k x_k$$

The odds can be expressed as

$$\left(\frac{P}{1-P}\right) = e^{(\alpha + \beta_1 x_1 + \beta_2 x_2 + ... + \beta_k x_k)}$$

and the odds ratio for X_i is

$$OR_{x_i} = e^{\beta_i}$$

with the interpretation that

$$100 \cdot (e^{\beta_i} - 1)$$

represents the percent increase in the odds of '*event*' occurrence when X_i increases by 1 unit and all other X's are held constant.

The importance of each covariate (X_i) for predicting the *event* probability is measured by the magnitude of the parameter coefficient, β_i. Estimates of these parameters can be found by the method of maximum likelihood using PROC LOGISTIC in SAS. For large samples, these estimates (b_i) have an approximate normal distribution. If s_b represents the standard error of the estimate, b_i, then b_i / s_b has an approximate standard normal distribution under the null hypothesis that $\beta_i = 0$, and its square has the chi-square distribution with 1 degree of freedom. The test summary for each model parameter, β_i, is based on this *Wald chi-square*, summarized as follows:

---

null hypothesis: H_0: $\beta_i = 0$
alternative hypothesis: H_A: $\beta_i \neq 0$

test statistic: $\chi^2_w = \left(\dfrac{b_i}{s_b} \right)^2$

decision rule: reject H_0 if $\chi^2_w > \chi^2_1(\alpha)$

Example 20.1 illustrates a *logistic regression* analysis for k=2 using PROC LOGISTIC in SAS.

20.3 Examples

Example 20.1 -- Relapse Rate Adjusted for Remission Time in AML

One hundred and two patients with acute myelogenous leukemia (AML) in remission were enrolled in a study of a new antisense oligonucleotide (asODN). The patients were randomly assigned to receive a 10-day infusion of asODN or no treatment (Control), and the effects were followed for 90 days. The time of remission from diagnosis or prior relapse (X, in months) at study enrollment was considered an important covariate in predicting response. The response data are shown in Table 20.3 with Y=1 indicating relapse, death, or major intervention, such as bone marrow transplant before Day 90. Is there any evidence that administration of asODN is associated with a decreased relapse rate?

TABLE 20.3. Raw Data for Example 20.1

-- asODN Group --

Patient Number	X	Y	Patient Number	X	Y	Patient Number	X	Y
1	3	0	32	9	0	67	12	0
2	3	1	33	6	1	69	12	0
4	3	1	36	6	0	71	12	0
6	6	1	39	6	0	73	9	1
7	15	0	42	6	0	74	6	1
10	6	1	44	3	1	77	12	0
11	6	1	46	18	0	79	6	0
14	6	1	49	9	0	81	15	1
15	15	0	50	12	1	83	9	0
17	15	0	52	6	0	85	3	1
20	12	0	54	9	1	88	9	0
21	18	0	56	9	1	90	9	0
22	6	1	58	3	0	92	9	0
25	15	0	60	9	1	94	9	0
26	6	1	62	12	0	95	9	1
28	15	0	63	12	0	98	12	1
29	12	1	66	3	0	99	3	1
						102	6	1

-- Control Group --

Patient Number	X	Y	Patient Number	X	Y	Patient Number	X	Y
3	9	1	38	15	0	72	9	1
5	3	0	40	15	1	75	15	0
8	12	1	41	9	0	76	15	0
9	3	1	43	9	0	78	12	0
12	3	1	45	12	1	80	9	0
13	15	1	47	3	1	82	12	0
16	9	1	48	6	1	84	15	0
18	12	1	51	6	1	86	18	1
19	3	1	53	12	0	87	12	0
23	9	1	55	12	0	89	15	1
24	15	1	57	12	1	91	15	0
27	9	1	59	3	1	93	15	0
30	6	1	61	12	1	96	18	0
31	9	1	64	3	1	97	18	1
34	6	1	65	12	1	100	18	0
35	12	0	68	6	1	101	18	0
37	9	0	70	6	1			

Solution

You want to compare relapse rates between treatment groups adjusted for prior remission time. By constructing a series of 2×2 contingency tables from the data (one table for each X value), you obtain the following summary table:

TABLE 20.4. Naïve Estimates of Response Rates for Example 20.1

X (months)	asODN Group			Control Group		
	Number of Events	N	Estimated P_x	Number of Events	N	Estimated P_x
3	5	8	0.625	6	7	0.857
6	9	14	0.643	6	6	1.000
9	5	12	0.417	6	10	0.600
12	3	10	0.300	6	12	0.500
15	1	6	0.167	4	10	0.400
18	0	2	0.000	2	5	0.400
TOTAL	23	52	0.442	30	50	0.600

If prior remission time (X) is ignored, overall relapse rates are estimated as 0.442 for the asODN group and 0.600 for the Control group. This is not a significant difference if you use the *chi-square test* discussed in Chapter 16 ($\chi^2 = 2.54$, p = 0.111).

You can also proceed by treating prior remission time as a grouped stratification factor and applying the *Cochran-Mantel-Haenszel test* (Chapter 19). This approach would satisfy the goal of comparing relapse rates between groups by controlling for prior remission time. However, the ordinality of the stratification variable is ignored with the *CMH test*, and logistic modeling might be preferable in such situations. The modeling technique allows for interpolation based on unobserved values of the numeric covariate, provides estimates of the odds ratios, and permits the inclusion of interactions and additional covariates.

A plot of the summary data (Figure 20.2) shows that the probability of relapse (P_x) seems to depend on the length of prior remission, with higher probabilities of relapse associated with shorter remission times. Using this information in a *logistic regression* analysis provides an adjusted treatment group comparison that is found to be significant (p=0.0165), as shown in Output 20.1.

FIGURE 20.2. Probability of Relapse (P_x) vs. Remission Time (X) for Example 20.1

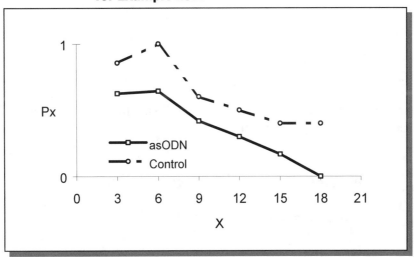

To perform *logistic regression*, include a treatment factor, say X_1, and a remission time covariate, say X_2. Define X_1 as

$X_1 = 0$ if no treatment (Control Group)

$\quad = 1$ if treated (asODN Group)

Prior remission time (X_2) is considered a continuous numeric covariate (X in Table 20.3). The *logistic regression* model incorporates both X_1 and X_2 as covariates,

$$P = \frac{1}{1 + e^{-(\alpha + \beta_1 X_1 + \beta_2 X_2)}}$$

Use PROC LOGISTIC in SAS to fit this model, as shown in the analysis that follows.

SAS Analysis of Example 20.1

In the input data set, define the treatment effect (TRT) as a dichotomous explanatory variable with values 0 (placebo group) and 1 (active group) ❶. Code the response variable Y as 1 if the patient relapsed, and 0 if relapse did not occur ❷.

The SAS code for performing the *logistic regression* analysis is shown following the data input (see SAS code for Example 20.1) and the results are given in Output 20.1. The DESCENDING option is used in the PROC LOGISTIC statement ❸ to let SAS know that the *event* of interest is 'relapse' or Y = 1. Otherwise, SAS will model the smaller value of Y (Y = 0) as the *event*.

The MLEs of the model parameters, α, β_1, and β_2, are seen to be $a = 2.6135$, $b_1 = -1.1191$, and $b_2 = -0.1998$ ❹, which result in an estimated *logistic regression* equation of

$$\hat{P} = \frac{1}{1 + e^{-(2.6135 - 1.1191 \cdot X_1 - 0.1998 \cdot X_2)}}$$

One question of interest is whether X_2 = remission time (X in SAS analysis) is an important covariate, tested as follows:

null hypothesis: H_0: $\beta_2 = 0$

alt. hypothesis: H_A: $\beta_2 \neq 0$

test statistic: $\chi^2_w = 12.72$

decision rule: reject H_0 if $\chi^2_w > \chi^2_1 (0.05)$ $(= 3.841)$

conclusion: Because $12.72 > 3.841$, you reject H_0 indicating a significant covariate, X.

The output indicates that the time since prior remission (X) is a highly significant background factor for predicting the probability of a relapse within 90 days (p=0.0004) ❺. This is not taken into account in the unadjusted *chi-square test*, which yields relapse rates of 44.2% and 60.0% for the Active and Control groups, respectively (p=0.111) ❻.

Similarly, comparison of relapse rates between treatment groups (TRT) adjusted for the covariate is tested by the hypothesis

H_0: $\beta_1 = 0$

The SAS output indicates a significant Wald chi-square value of 5.7446 with a p-value of 0.0165 ❼. The estimate of β_1 is -1.1191, and the estimate of the treatment OR is $e^{-1.1191} = 0.327$. This means that, adjusted for prior remission time, there is a $100 \cdot (0.327 - 1) = -67.3\%$ increase, or 67.3% reduction, in the odds of relapse associated with the active treatment group ($X_1 = 1$) compared with the placebo group ($X_1 = 0$). Beginning with SAS Version 8, the odds ratios and 95% confidence intervals are printed in the output ❽.

SAS Code for Example 20.1

```
DATA AML;
    INPUT PAT GROUP $  X  RELAPSE $ @@;
    TRT = (GROUP = 'ACT')  ;                    ❶
    Y = (RELAPSE = 'YES');                       ❷
    DATALINES;
  1 ACT  3 NO     2 ACT  3 YES    4 ACT  3 YES
  6 ACT  6 YES    7 ACT 15 NO    10 ACT  6 YES
 11 ACT  6 YES   14 ACT  6 YES   15 ACT 15 NO
 17 ACT 15 NO    20 ACT 12 NO    21 ACT 18 NO
 22 ACT  6 YES   25 ACT 15 NO    26 ACT  6 YES
 28 ACT 15 NO    29 ACT 12 YES   32 ACT  9 NO
 33 ACT  6 YES   36 ACT  6 NO    39 ACT  6 NO
 42 ACT  6 NO    44 ACT  3 YES   46 ACT 18 NO
 49 ACT  9 NO    50 ACT 12 YES   52 ACT  6 NO
 54 ACT  9 YES   56 ACT  9 YES   58 ACT  3 NO
 60 ACT  9 YES   62 ACT 12 NO    63 ACT 12 NO
 66 ACT  3 NO    67 ACT 12 NO    69 ACT 12 NO
 71 ACT 12 NO    73 ACT  9 YES   74 ACT  6 YES
 77 ACT 12 NO    79 ACT  6 NO    81 ACT 15 YES
 83 ACT  9 NO    85 ACT  3 YES   88 ACT  9 NO
 90 ACT  9 NO    92 ACT  9 NO    94 ACT  9 NO
 95 ACT  9 YES   98 ACT 12 YES   99 ACT  3 YES
102 ACT  6 YES    3 PBO  9 YES    5 PBO  3 NO
  8 PBO 12 YES    9 PBO  3 YES   12 PBO  3 YES
 13 PBO 15 YES   16 PBO  9 YES   18 PBO 12 YES
 19 PBO  3 YES   23 PBO  9 YES   24 PBO 15 YES
 27 PBO  9 YES   30 PBO  6 YES   31 PBO  9 YES
 34 PBO  6 YES   35 PBO 12 NO    37 PBO  9 NO
 38 PBO 15 NO    40 PBO 15 YES   41 PBO  9 NO
 43 PBO  9 NO    45 PBO 12 YES   47 PBO  3 YES
 48 PBO  6 YES   51 PBO  6 YES   53 PBO 12 NO
 55 PBO 12 NO    57 PBO 12 YES   59 PBO  3 YES
 61 PBO 12 YES   64 PBO  3 YES   65 PBO 12 YES
 68 PBO  6 YES   70 PBO  6 YES   72 PBO  9 YES
 75 PBO 15 NO    76 PBO 15 NO    78 PBO 12 NO
 80 PBO  9 NO    82 PBO 12 NO    84 PBO 15 NO
 86 PBO 18 YES   87 PBO 12 NO    89 PBO 15 YES
 91 PBO 15 NO    93 PBO 15 NO    96 PBO 18 NO
 97 PBO 18 YES  100 PBO 18 NO   101 PBO 18 NO
;

PROC LOGISTIC DATA = AML DESCENDING;            ❸
    MODEL Y = TRT X;
    TITLE1 'Logistic Regression';
    TITLE2 'Example 20.1:  Relapse Rate Adjusted for Remission
          Time in AML';
RUN;

PROC FREQ DATA = AML;
    TABLES TRT*Y / CHISQ NOCOL NOPERCENT NOCUM;
    TITLE3 'Chi-Square Test Ignoring the Covariate';
RUN;
```

OUTPUT 20.1. SAS Output for Example 20.1

```
                          Logistic Regression
         Example 20.1:  Relapse Rate Adjusted for Remission Time in AML

                          The LOGISTIC Procedure

                            Model Information
              Data Set                    WORK.AML
              Response Variable           Y
              Number of Response Levels   2
              Number of Observations      102
              Link Function               Binary Logit
              Optimization Technique      Fisher's scoring

                            Response Profile
                   Ordered                      Total
                    Value          Y          Frequency

                      1            1             53
                      2            0             49

                       Model Convergence Status
              Convergence criterion (GCONV=1E-8) satisfied.

                          Model Fit Statistics
                                                  Intercept
                                    Intercept        and
                  Criterion           Only        Covariates

                   AIC              143.245         129.376
                   SC               145.870         137.251
                   -2 Log L         141.245         123.376


                  Testing Global Null Hypothesis: BETA=0

          Test                   Chi-Square      DF      Pr > ChiSq

          Likelihood Ratio         17.8687        2        0.0001
          Score                    16.4848        2        0.0003
          Wald                     14.0612        2        0.0009

                  Analysis of Maximum Likelihood Estimates

                                   Standard
          Parameter   DF   Estimate    Error    Chi-Square   Pr > ChiSq
                               ❹
          Intercept    1    2.6135     0.7149     13.3662      0.0003
          TRT          1   -1.1191     0.4669 ❾   5.7446       0.0165 ❼
          X            1   -0.1998     0.0560     12.7187      0.0004 ❺

                          Odds Ratio Estimates

                           Point          95% Wald
               Effect     Estimate    Confidence Limits

               TRT         0.327 ❿    0.131      0.815 ❽
               X           0.819      0.734      0.914
```

OUTPUT 20.1. SAS Output for Example 20.1 (*continued*)

```
                        Logistic Regression
Example 20.1:  Relapse Rate Adjusted for Remission Time in AML

Association of Predicted Probabilities and Observed Responses

          Percent Concordant     68.5    Somers' D    0.454
          Percent Discordant     23.1    Gamma        0.496
          Percent Tied            8.4    Tau-a        0.229
          Pairs                  2597    c            0.727
```

```
                  Chi-Square Test Ignoring the Covariate

                         The FREQ Procedure

                         Table of TRT by Y

           TRT          Y

           Frequency|
           Row Pct  |       0|       1|  Total
           ---------+--------+--------+
                  0 |     20 |     30 |     50
                    |  40.00 |  60.00 |
           ---------+--------+--------+
                  1 |     29 |     23 |     52
                    |  55.77 |  44.23 |
           ---------+--------+--------+
           Total          49       53      102


                  Statistics for Table of TRT by Y

           Statistic                  DF     Value      Prob
           ------------------------------------------------------
           Chi-Square                  1     2.5394    0.1110
           Likelihood Ratio Chi-Square 1     2.5505    0.1103
           Continuity Adj. Chi-Square  1     1.9469    0.1629
           Mantel-Haenszel Chi-Square  1     2.5145    0.1128
           Phi Coefficient                   -0.1578
           Contingency Coefficient            0.1559
           Cramer's V                        -0.1578


                         Fisher's Exact Test
           ----------------------------------
           Cell (1,1) Frequency (F)        20
           Left-sided Pr <= F          0.0813
           Right-sided Pr >= F         0.9637

           Table Probability (P)       0.0450
           Two-sided Pr <= P           0.1189

                        Sample Size = 102
```

❻ (marker beside TRT by Y table)

❻ (marker beside Chi-Square statistic row)

Multinomial Responses

In addition to dichotomous outcomes, *logistic regression* methods can be used in cases that involve ordinal categorical responses with more than two levels. The strategy uses a 'proportional odds' model, which simultaneously fits $m-1$ binary *logistic regression* models of the form just discussed, when there are m (>2) ordinal response levels.

Consider an example in which the response, Y, is measured on an ordinal improvement scale of 'worse', 'no change', 'improved', or 'cured'. In this case, m is equal to 4, so you can define three 'cumulative' binary responses as follows:

1. $Y_1 = 0$ if Y = 'worse'
           $= 1$ if Y = 'no change', 'improved', or 'cured'

2. $Y_2 = 0$ if Y = 'worse' or 'no change'
           $= 1$ if Y = 'improved' or 'cured'

3. $Y_3 = 0$ if Y = 'worse', 'no change', or 'improved'
           $= 1$ if Y = 'cured'

The first dichotomous response variable, Y_1, is measuring whether the patient's condition does not deteriorate. Similarly, Y_2 measures whether the patient improves, and Y_3 measures whether the patient is cured. Taken together, you can use Y_1, Y_2, and Y_3 as an overall measure of improvement.

You fit dichotomous *logistic regression* models for Y_j ($j = 1, 2$ and 3) of the form

$$\ln\left(\frac{P_j}{1-P_j}\right) = \alpha_j + \beta_{1j}x_1 + \beta_{2j}x_2 + ... + \beta_{kj}x_k$$

with the constraint that the slopes must be equal (i.e., $\beta_{11}=\beta_{12}=\beta_{13}$, $\beta_{21}=\beta_{22}=\beta_{23}$, etc.), so you actually fit the model

$$\ln\left(\frac{P_j}{1-P_j}\right) = \alpha_j + \beta_1 x_1 + \beta_2 x_2 + ... + \beta_k x_k$$

Requiring equal slopes among the $m-1$ levels for each covariate is called the 'proportional odds assumption'. Using *logistic regression* analysis, you fit the model by obtaining estimates of the coefficients of each covariate under this constraint. As before, e^{β_i} is the odds ratio that represents the proportional increase in odds of improvement for each 1-unit increase in x_i ($i = 1, 2, ..., k$).

In SAS, PROC LOGISTIC automatically fits the proportional odds model when it detects more than two quantitative response levels, as shown in Example 20.2.

// **Example 20.2** -- Symptom Relief in Gastroparesis

Patients with severe symptoms of gastroparesis were randomized to receive an experimental therapy (A) or dietary changes with 'watchful waiting' (B). Response was measured after 7 days, using the following scale: 1=no response, 2=some response, 3=marked response, or 4=complete response, based on the degree of symptom relief. A patient's history of severe gastroparesis, thought to be an important covariate, was also recorded as 'no prior episodes' (0), 'one prior episode' (1), or 'more than one prior episode' (2). The data are shown in Table 20.5. Is there any difference in response between the patients who received the experimental therapy and the untreated patients?

TABLE 20.5. Raw Data for Example 20.2

New Treatment (A)			Untreated Group (B)		
Patient Number	History	Response	Patient Number	History	Response
101	1	3	103	1	3
102	2	3	105	1	3
104	1	2	107	1	2
106	0	4	110	2	3
108	2	1	111	2	1
109	0	4	112	0	4
113	1	3	118	0	3
114	1	4	119	2	2
115	0	4	120	1	1
116	2	2	122	2	1
117	1	3	123	1	4
121	2	1	126	0	2
124	1	4	129	2	2
125	1	2	131	1	3
127	2	4	134	1	2
128	0	3	136	2	3
130	1	4	138	2	1
132	1	3	139	0	4
133	1	1	141	1	3
135	1	4	142	2	4
137	0	3	146	1	2
140	2	4	148	1	1
143	1	3	150	1	2
144	2	3	152	1	3
145	2	2			
147	1	4			
149	2	1			
151	2	4			
153	1	2			
154	1	2			
155	1	4			

Solution

The response, Y, is ordinal with 4 levels, so the proportional odds approach is used by fitting three dichotomous *logistic regression* models as shown in Table 20.6. There are two categorical covariates, Study Group (X_1) with levels A and B, and History of severe gastroparesis (X_2) with levels 0, 1, and 2. You will look at a main effects model, so there will be a total of 5 parameters to estimate (one 'α' for each of the three models and one 'β' for each of the two covariates).

TABLE 20.6. Dichotomous Sub-Models for the Proportional Odds Model

	Dichotomous Categories	Interpretation	Model (logit)
(i)	4 vs. 1,2,3	'complete' vs. 'incomplete response'	$\alpha_1 + \beta_1 X_1 + \beta_2 X_2$
(ii)	3,4 vs. 1,2	'marked or complete response' vs. 'some or no response'	$\alpha_2 + \beta_1 X_1 + \beta_2 X_2$
(iii)	2,3,4 vs. 1	'response' vs. 'no response'	$\alpha_3 + \beta_1 X_1 + \beta_2 X_2$

Maximum-likelihood estimates are easily found by using SAS, as shown in the analysis that follows.

SAS Analysis of Example 20.2

In this case, the syntax used in PROC LOGISTIC is similar to that used in Example 20.1 for a dichotomous response. The main difference here is that the Study Group effect has character values (A and B). Rather than use the DATA step to convert them to numeric values (1 and 0, respectively) you use a CLASS statement in PROC LOGISTIC, which tells SAS that the values have not yet been converted[11]. You use the PARAM=REF option to specify that SAS assign values of 0 and 1 to the levels (the default assignment with dichotomous class variables is –1 and +1).

The REF paramaterization specifies that SAS treat one of the levels of the class variable as a reference level, assign it a value of 0, and compare the other levels to it. The default selection for the reference level is the last value (alphabetically or numerically). In this case, Group B is the reference level, so SAS assigns the numeric values of 0 to B and 1 to A [12].

Notice also the use of the DESCENDING option in the PROC LOGISTIC statement. As in the Example 20.1, this ensures that SAS models increasing response.

Estimates of the model parameters are given under the heading 'Analysis of Maximum Likelihood Estimates' [13] in Output 20.2. The fitted models, (i), (ii), and (iii) are

(i) $\quad \ln\left(\dfrac{P_1}{1-P_1}\right) = -0.3890 + 0.8682X_1 - 0.9741X_2$

(ii) $\quad \ln\left(\dfrac{P_2}{1-P_2}\right) = 1.0756 + 0.8682X_1 - 0.9741X_2$

(iii) $\quad \ln\left(\dfrac{P_3}{1-P_3}\right) = 2.4430 + 0.8682X_1 - 0.9741X_2$

The odds ratio for the Study Group effect is $e^{0.8682} = 2.383$ **⑭**, with the interpretation that the odds of some degree of response with Group A (experimental treatment) is 138% greater than that of the untreated group (B), adjusted for history of prior experience with severe gastroporesis. The p-value is not quite significant (p=0.0863) **⑮**. You also see that the HIST covariate (X_2) is significant (p=0.0112) **⑯** with an odds ratio of $e^{-0.9741} = 0.378$ **⑰**.

SAS Code for Example 20.2

```
DATA GI;
    INPUT PAT RX $ HIST  RESP  @@;
    /* A = new treatment, B = untreated               */
    /* HIST = 0 if no prior episodes, HIST = 1 if one  */
    /* prior episode, HIST = 2 if >1 prior episodes    */
    /* RESP = 1 (none), 2 (some), 3 (marked), 4 (complete) */
    DATALINES;
101 A 1 3    102 A 2 3    103 B 1 3    104 A 1 2
105 B 1 3    106 A 0 4    107 B 1 2    108 A 2 1
109 A 0 4    110 B 2 3    111 B 2 1    112 B 0 4
113 A 1 3    114 A 1 4    115 A 0 4    116 A 2 2
117 A 1 3    118 B 0 3    119 B 2 2    120 B 1 1
121 A 2 1    122 B 2 1    123 B 1 4    124 A 1 4
125 A 1 2    126 B 0 2    127 A 2 4    128 A 0 3
129 B 2 2    130 A 1 4    131 B 1 3    132 A 1 3
133 A 1 1    134 B 1 2    135 A 1 4    136 B 2 3
137 A 0 3    138 B 2 1    139 B 0 4    140 A 2 4
141 B 1 3    142 B 2 4    143 A 1 3    144 A 2 3
145 A 2 2    146 B 1 2    147 A 1 4    148 B 1 1
149 A 2 1    150 B 1 2    151 A 2 4    152 B 1 3
153 A 1 2    154 A 1 2    155 A 1 4
;

PROC LOGISTIC DESCENDING DATA = GI;
    CLASS RX / PARAM = REF ;                    ⑪
    MODEL RESP = RX HIST;
    TITLE1 'Logistic Regression';
    TITLE2 'Example 20.2: Symptom Relief in Severe
            Gastroparesis';
RUN;
```

OUTPUT 20.2. SAS Output for Example 20.2

```
                        Logistic Regression
        Example 20.2: Symptom Relief in Severe Gastroparesis

                        The LOGISTIC Procedure

                          Model Information

          Data Set                      WORK.GI
          Response Variable             RESP
          Number of Response Levels     4
          Number of Observations        55
          Link Function                 Cumulative Logit
          Optimization Technique        Fisher's scoring


                          Response Profile

            Ordered                            Total
             Value         RESP             Frequency

               1            4                  16
               2            3                  17
               3            2                  13
               4            1                   9

Probabilities modeled are cumulated over the lower Ordered Values.

                      Class Level Information

                                        Design
                                       Variables
                 Class      Value          1

                 RX         A              1          ⓬
                            B              0


                     Model Convergence Status

          Convergence criterion (GCONV=1E-8) satisfied.

          Score Test for the Proportional Odds Assumption

              Chi-Square        DF        Pr > ChiSq

                2.5521           4          0.6353       ⓲


                       Model Fit Statistics

                                          Intercept
                            Intercept        and
               Criterion       Only       Covariates

               AIC            155.516       149.907
               SC             161.538       159.944
               -2 Log L       149.516       139.907
```

OUTPUT 20.2. SAS Output for Example 20.2 (*continued*)

```
                        Logistic Regression

        Example 20.2: Symptom Relief in Severe Gastroparesis

                       The LOGISTIC Procedure

                Testing Global Null Hypothesis: BETA=0

        Test                Chi-Square        DF      Pr > ChiSq

        Likelihood Ratio      9.6084           2        0.0082
        Score                 9.0147           2        0.0110
        Wald                  8.7449           2        0.0126


                    Type III Analysis of Effects

                                   Wald
              Effect      DF    Chi-Square     Pr > ChiSq

              RX           1      2.9426         0.0863
              HIST         1      6.4304         0.0112


              Analysis of Maximum Likelihood Estimates

                               Standard
        Parameter     DF   Estimate    Error    Chi-Square    Pr > ChiSq
                                    ⓭

        Intercept4     1   -0.3890    0.5831      0.4449        0.5048
        Intercept3     1    1.0756    0.6001      3.2123        0.0731
        Intercept2     1    2.4430    0.6698     13.3018        0.0003
        RX       A     1    0.8682    0.5061      2.9426        0.0863 ⓯
        HIST           1   -0.9741    0.3841      6.4304        0.0112 ⓰


                        Odds Ratio Estimates

                          Point           95% Wald
            Effect      Estimate      Confidence Limits

            RX    A vs B   2.383  ⓮   0.884        6.425
            HIST           0.378  ⓱   0.178        0.802


    Association of Predicted Probabilities and Observed Responses

            Percent Concordant    57.6    Somers' D    0.339
            Percent Discordant    23.7    Gamma        0.417
            Percent Tied          18.7    Tau-a        0.255
            Pairs                 1115    c            0.670
```

Clustered Binomial Data

In Chapter 19, you saw how the *Cochran-Mantel-Haenszel test* can be used to analyze binomial responses from stratified groups. In that case, observations within strata are considered independent, generally arising from different patients.

Sometimes binary responses within strata are correlated, in which case the *CMH test* would not be appropriate. Such situations arise frequently in clinical trials when a number of binary outcomes are observed in each of several patients.

For example, suppose migraine patients are prescribed a new 'as needed' medication and are asked to keep a diary of the number of migraine headaches they experience and the number of those which are resolved within two hours of taking the medication. In this case, each migraine occurrence results in the binary outcome 'resolved' or 'not resolved' within two hours of medication. While independence can be assumed among patients, there is a natural clustering of observations for each patient for whom you could reasonably assume responses are correlated.

Such data can be analyzed by using PROC LOGISTIC with a correction for overdispersion as shown in Example 20.3. This procedure essentially re-scales the correlation matrix that is used to estimate the standard errors of the parameter estimates. Without this adjustment, the within-cluster correlation might lead to underestimating the standard errors, which, in turn, leads to results that are overly significant.

Example 20.3 -- Intercourse Success Rate in Erectile Dysfunction

Male patients who experienced erectile dysfunction following prostate surgery were enrolled in a parallel study to compare a new anti-impotence treatment with a marketed drug. Patients were asked to keep a diary for one month to record the number of attempts at sexual intercourse after taking the study medication, and the number of those attempts that were 'successful'. Data, including patient's age, which is thought to be an important covariate, are shown in Table 20.7. Is there any difference in 'success' rates between the new medication and the product already on the market?

TABLE 20.7. Raw Data for Example 20.3

Reference Control				New Drug			
Patient Number	Age (yrs.)	Number of Successes	Number of Attempts	Patient Number	Age (yrs.)	Number of Successes	Number of Attempts
1	41	3	6	2	57	3	8
3	44	5	15	4	54	10	12
5	62	0	4	7	65	0	0
6	44	1	2	9	51	5	8
8	70	3	8	10	53	8	10
11	35	4	8	12	44	17	22
13	72	1	6	14	66	2	3
15	34	5	15	16	55	9	11
18	61	1	7	17	37	6	8
22	35	5	5	19	40	2	4
24	52	6	8	20	44	9	16
25	66	1	7	21	64	5	9
27	35	4	10	23	78	1	3
30	61	4	8	26	51	6	12
31	55	2	5	28	67	5	11
34	41	7	9	29	44	3	3
37	53	2	4	32	65	7	18
39	72	4	6	33	69	0	2
40	68	0	0	35	53	4	14
41	56	12	17	36	49	5	8
44	53	8	15	38	74	10	15
45	45	3	4	42	39	4	9
48	40	14	20	43	35	8	10
				46	47	4	5
				47	46	6	7

Solution

In this case, each patient represents a cluster of like binomial responses. It is natural to assume that within-patient responses might be correlated, certainly more so than among different patients. If you perform a *logistic regression* analysis of response rates for treatment Group and Age that ignores this clustering, you might get inaccurate results, so you proceed with a *logistic regression* analysis that uses a correction for overdispersion.

SAS Analysis of Example 20.3

Two patients with no attempts ⓲ are excluded from the analysis, which leaves 46 patients or 'clusters' of response data. The *logistic regression* model is specified in SAS in the usual way using PROC LOGISTIC, except that in this case, you use the 'events/trials' form, which is an alternative specification for the dependent variable in the MODEL statement. The 'events' are the number of successes (SUCC), and the 'trials' are the number of attempts (ATTPT). Include treatment group (TRT) as a dichotomous explanatory variable and age (AGE) as a continuous numeric covariate in the model.

Several different methods for re-scaling the covariance matrix are available in SAS. Williams' method often works well with data of this type, especially when sample sizes differ among the clusters. This approach is implemented by specifying the SCALE=WILLIAMS option in the MODEL statement ⓴.

The results indicate a significant treatment effect ㉑ (p=0.0291) with an estimated odds ratio of 1.738 ㉒. This means that the age-adjusted odds of success increase by 73.8% for the new drug relative to the control. Age is shown to be a significant covariate ㉓ (p=0.0124). It's odds ratio is 0.973 ㉔, which means that the odds of success decrease by about 2.7% for each year the patient ages.

SAS Code for Example 20.3

```
DATA DIARY;
    INPUT PAT TRT AGE SUCC ATTPT @@;
    /* TRT = 1 for new drug, TRT = 0 for reference control */
    IF ATTPT = 0 THEN DELETE;              ⓲
    DATALINES;
  1 0 41  3  6     3 0 44  5 15     5 0 62  0  4     6 0 44  1  2
  8 0 70  3  8    11 0 35  4  8    13 0 72  1  6    15 0 34  5 15
 18 0 61  1  7    22 0 35  5  5    24 0 52  6  8    25 0 66  1  7
 27 0 35  4 10    30 0 61  4  8    31 0 55  2  5    34 0 41  7  9
 37 0 53  2  4    39 0 72  4  6    40 0 68  0  0    41 0 56 12 17
 44 0 53  8 15    45 0 45  3  4    48 0 40 14 20     2 1 57  3  8
  4 1 54 10 12     7 1 65  0  0     9 1 51  5  8    10 1 53  8 10
 12 1 44 17 22    14 1 66  2  3    16 1 55  9 11    17 1 37  6  8
 19 1 40  2  4    20 1 44  9 16    21 1 64  5  9    23 1 78  1  3
 26 1 51  6 12    28 1 67  5 11    29 1 44  3  3    32 1 65  7 18
 33 1 69  0  2    35 1 53  4 14    36 1 49  5  8    38 1 74 10 15
 42 1 39  4  9    43 1 35  8 10    46 1 47  4  5    47 1 46  6  7
 ;

PROC LOGISTIC DATA = DIARY;
    MODEL SUCC/ATTPT = TRT AGE / SCALE = WILLIAMS;       ⓴
    TITLE1 'Logistic Regression';
    TITLE2 'Example 20.3: Intercourse Success Rate in Erectile
        Dysfunction';
RUN;
```

OUTPUT 20.3. SAS Output for Example 20.3

```
                        Logistic Regression
       Example 20.3: Intercourse Success Rate in Erectile Dysfunction

                        The LOGISTIC Procedure

                          Model Information

     Data Set                         WORK.DIARY
     Response Variable (Events)       SUCC
     Response Variable (Trials)       ATTPT
     Number of Observations           46
     Weight Variable                  1 / ( 1 + 0.056638 * (ATTPT - 1) )  ㉖
     Sum of Weights                   268.53902437
     Link Function                    binary logit
     Optimization Technique           Fisher's scoring

                          Response Profile

            Ordered       Binary         Total             Total
            Value         Outcome        Frequency         Weight

                1         Event            234           149.48211
                2         Nonevent         183           119.05692


                     Model Convergence Status

        Convergence criterion (GCONV=1E-8) satisfied.

        Deviance and Pearson Goodness-of-Fit Statistics

     Criterion        DF        Value      Value/DF     Pr > ChiSq

     Deviance         43       48.2014      1.1210        0.2706
     Pearson          43       42.9997      1.0000        0.4713


        Number of events/trials observations: 46
```

NOTE: Because the Williams method was used to accommodate ㉕ overdispersion, the Pearson chi-squared statistic and the deviance can no longer be used to assess the goodness of fit of the model.

```
                    Model Fit Statistics

                                        Intercept
                        Intercept          and
     Criterion            Only          Covariates

     AIC                 370.820          364.792
     SC                  374.853          376.891
     -2 Log L            368.820          358.792

        Testing Global Null Hypothesis: BETA=0

     Test                Chi-Square       DF      Pr > ChiSq

     Likelihood Ratio     10.0277          2        0.0066
     Score                 9.9254          2        0.0070
     Wald                  9.6295          2        0.0081
```

OUTPUT 20.3. SAS Output for Example 20.3 (*continued*)

```
                          Logistic Regression
        Example 20.3: Intercourse Success Rate in Erectile Dysfunction

                          The LOGISTIC Procedure

                   Analysis of Maximum Likelihood Estimates

                                    Standard
        Parameter    DF    Estimate      Error    Chi-Square    Pr > ChiSq

        Intercept     1      1.3384     0.5732        5.4515        0.0196
        TRT           1      0.5529     0.2534        4.7614        0.0291 ㉑
        AGE           1     -0.0271     0.0108        6.2497        0.0124 ㉓


                            Odds Ratio Estimates

                          Point            95% Wald
             Effect     Estimate       Confidence Limits

               TRT       1.738 ㉒     1.058       2.856
               AGE       0.973 ㉔     0.953       0.994


        Association of Predicted Probabilities and Observed Responses

               Percent Concordant     57.9     Somers' D    0.194
               Percent Discordant     38.5     Gamma        0.201
               Percent Tied            3.6     Tau-a        0.096
               Pairs                 42822     c            0.597
```

20.4 Details & Notes

▶   **20.4.1.**   *Logistic regression* is a useful tool for conducting exploratory analyses to identify background factors that might help explain trends observed in treatment comparisons. SAS prints out two measures, Akaike's Information Criterion (AIC) and the Schwarz Criterion (SC), whose relative values can be used to assess the goodness of fit of the model. Covariates can be added or removed in a stepwise fashion to obtain the most appropriate model by attempting to minimize the values of the AIC and SC.

When you use the SCALE option in the MODEL statement in PROC LOGISTIC, two other goodness-of-fit tests, the *Pearson* and *Deviance tests*, are printed. Non-significance of these tests, which have an approximate chi-square distribution with sufficiently large sample sizes, provides an indication of adequate fit. As noted in Output 20.3 ㉕, these goodness-of-fit tests are not valid when the Williams' correction for overdispersion is made.

The AGGREGATE option in the MODEL statement can be used to identify subgroups defined by combinations of factor levels for assessing goodness-of-fit. These same subgroups are then used to compare relative goodness-of-fit measures among competing models.

When one or more of the explanatory variables is measured on a continuous numeric scale, you might prefer to use the LACKFIT option to assess goodness of fit. This option performs a goodness-of-fit test based on a division of the range of the continuous numeric covariates into intervals.

Assessing the fit of a *logistic regression* model can be a complex process, and the details are beyond the scope of this introduction to *logistic regression*. Examples that demonstrate goodness-of-fit methods and provide additional details can be found in many excellent references, including two highly recommended SAS BBU books: Allison (1999), and Stokes, Davis, and Koch (2000).

▶ **20.4.2.** In clinical trials, equality of response rates between groups is usually tested by the hypothesis of a 0 difference, as you have seen in previous chapters. You can also compare response rates by measuring how close their ratio is to 1. This ratio is called 'relative risk' and is often discussed in epidemiological studies along with the odds ratio.

In a modeling procedure such as *logistic regression*, any comparison of response rates between treatment groups will depend on the values of other covariates in the model. With the logit function, the odds ratio is the 'cleanest' way of comparing levels of a model factor such as a treatment effect. The treatment effect odds ratio is adjusted for other covariates, but does not depend on their specific values.

▶ **20.4.3.** In Example 20.1, notice that the unadjusted odds (ignoring remission time) are

0.442 / 0.558 = 0.792 (Active group)

0.600 / 0.400 = 1.500 (Control group)

A comparison of these odds results in an odds ratio of 0.792 / 1.500 = 0.528, which is considerably larger than the odds ratio (0.327) found by using the covariance adjustment.

▶ **20.4.4.** An approximate 95% confidence interval can be constructed for the odds ratios by exponentiating the upper and lower confidence limits for the model parameter, β_i. Because the MLEs of the model parameters have asymptotic normal distributions, confidence limits can be constructed in the usual manner. In Example 20.1, the confidence limits for the TRT parameter, β_1, is represented by

$$b_1 \pm 1.96 \cdot s(b_1)$$

where b_1 and $s(b_1)$ can be obtained from the SAS output ❾. Output 20.1 shows $b_1 = -1.1191$ and $s(b_1) = 0.4669$, resulting in a 95% confidence interval for β_1 as

$$-1.1191 \pm 1.96 \cdot (0.4669)$$
or
$$(\text{-2.034 to } -0.204)$$

An approximate 95% confidence interval for the odds of response on active treatment relative to control is

$$(e^{-2.034} \text{ to } e^{-0.204})$$
or
$$(0.131 \text{ to } 0.815)$$

Beginning with SAS, Version 8, estimates of the odds ratios and 95% confidence limits are automatically printed in SAS output ❽. In versions of SAS prior to V8, confidence intervals can be obtained by using the RISKLIMITS option in the MODEL statement in PROC LOGISTIC (see the SAS Help and Online Documentation for PROC LOGISTIC).

▶ **20.4.5.**   Other transformations, such as the probit (based on the inverse normal distribution) can be used in a manner similar to the logit. The logistic transformation enjoys popular usage because of its application ease and appropriateness as a model for a wide range of natural phenomena. As illustrated in a plot of P vs. its logit function (Figure 20.3), $\ln(P/(1-P))$ is fairly linear in P over a large portion of the range of P (approximately 0.2 to 0.8). For very large or very small values of P, the logit of P is greatly magnified. This is consistent with a model based on intuition, in which a change in response rates, say from 45% to 50%, might not be as clinically relevant as a change from 5% to 10%.

The logistic transformation also has the advantage of mapping a limited range of observable values (0 to 1) onto an unlimited range ($-\infty$ to $+\infty$). Thus, the potential problem of obtaining estimates outside the observable range is eliminated.

FIGURE 20.3. Plot of Transformation from P to the Logit(P)

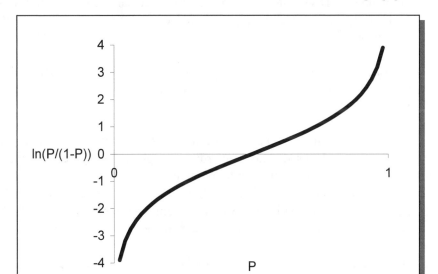

▶ **20.4.6.** This chapter presents an introduction to *logistic regression* using covariates that have either numeric or ordinal values. These methods include both ordinal and nominal dichotomous explanatory variables, because the dichotomous levels can always be coded as 0 to 1. *Logistic regression* can also be used with nominal-level, categorical explanatory variables that have more than two levels by defining dummy variables that correspond to the levels. For example, suppose geographic region is a covariate of interest, with levels A (North), B (South), C (Midwest), and D (West). One of the levels, e.g., A, is designated as a reference, and three dummy variables are created as follows:

$X_1 = 1$ if from Region B
$X_1 = 0$ otherwise

$X_2 = 1$ if from Region C
$X_2 = 0$ otherwise

$X_3 = 1$ if from Region D
$X_3 = 0$ otherwise

Using a *logistic regression* model with these variables as covariates, the odds-ratios represent the odds of response relative to Region A.

While these dummy variables can easily be created by using a DATA step in SAS, this can become cumbersome for categorical variables that have large numbers of levels. Beginning with SAS, Version 8, PROC LOGISTIC automatically creates the dummy variables when the variable is included in a CLASS statement. This also makes it easy to specify interaction terms in the MODEL statement by using GLM-type specifications (e.g., A*B). In versions of SAS prior to V8, PROC LOGISTIC requires interactions to be explicitly defined in the DATA step. In Example 20.2, you can include the Study Group-by-History interaction simply by including RX*HIST in the MODEL statement.

Logistic regression can also be carried out by using the SAS procedure CATMOD. This procedure is recommended for categorical modeling with nominal categorical covariates.

▶ **20.4.7.**   By making the proportional odds assumption, *logistic regression* techniques can be used to analyze ordinal categorical responses with more than two levels. A test for this assumption is included in the SAS output from PROC LOGISTIC. In Example 20.2, a 'Score' test is used based on the chi-square distribution, which shows a non-significant result (p=0.6353) **⑱**. This supports the assumption of equal slope parameters.

If this test is significant, caution should be used in the interpretation. If it is not possible to justify the proportional odds assumption, an alternative method can be used with PROC GENMOD by considering the response levels to be nominal.

▶ **20.4.8.**   Model building by adding or removing explanatory variables in the logistic model should be performed under constant assumptions regarding the covariance structure of the response variable. When observations arise from different patients, the assumption of independent observations is usually valid, so this is not a problem. In the clustered binomial case, the variance-covariance matrix is weighted using a scale parameter that is estimated by SAS and included in the output. For the SCALE=WILLIAMS adjustment used in Example 20.3, this estimate is 0.056638, as shown in the output for Weight Variable **㉖**. To maintain the same covariance structure for alternative models, you can include the scale parameter in parenthesis in the SCALE option to request that the same weightings be used when adding or removing model effects, e.g., SCALE = WILLIAMS(0.056638).

▶ **20.4.9.**   In addition to PROC LOGISTIC, two other SAS procedures, PROC CATMOD and PROC GENMOD, can be used for *logistic regression* analysis. PROC CATMOD uses a 'weighted least squares' approach (WLS) in addition to maximum likelihood. This is often preferable when all covariates are categorical and for cases of a multinomial response on a nominal scale.

PROC GENMOD, which is a more generalized modeling procedure, can be used for *logistic regression* by specifying the logit as the link function. PROC GENMOD is very useful when observations are correlated, such as in a *repeated measures* experiment. Details about using these alternative procedures in SAS for *logistic regression* can be found in other books, including Stokes, Davis, and Koch (2000), and Allison (1999), which were written under the SAS Books by Users Program.

▶ **20.4.10.** In Output 20.1, you see that the odds ratio for the treatment effect is 0.327 ⓾, which means that the odds of relapse for active treatment is 67.3% less than that for the placebo. This estimate does not depend on the other covariate, prior remission time. However, in comparative clinical trials, it is often decided to report covariate-adjusted response rates for each treatment group. Estimates of these response rates do, however, depend on other covariates in the model. Table 20.4 shows the 'naïve' estimates of the covariate-adjusted response rates.

Substituting 1 and 0, respectively, for X_1 in the estimated *logistic regression* model for Example 20.1, you obtain

$$\hat{P}_{(A)} = \frac{1}{1 + e^{-(1.4944 - 0.1998 \cdot X_2)}} \quad \text{(Active group)}$$

$$\hat{P}_{(C)} = \frac{1}{1 + e^{-(2.6135 - 0.1998 \cdot X_2)}} \quad \text{(Control group)}$$

Given a prior remission time of $X_2=4$ months, for example, the predicted relapse rates for the active and placebo groups are estimated from the preceding equations, namely, 67% for the active group and 86% for the control group. This method can be repeated for any other values of prior remission time in the range of observed X_2 values (3 to 18 months), which includes unobserved values such as the overall mean remission time. Caution must be used when extrapolating beyond the experimental region.

These predicted values can be written to an output data set in SAS by specifying the OUTPUT statement following the MODEL statement in PROC LOGISTIC. When the P= option is used, SAS includes estimated probabilities in the output data set for each combination of observed covariate values. If you want predicted probabilities for non-observed values, additional observations with missing values for the response variable and the covariate values that you choose can be included in the data set. Notice that if the response variable is missing for an observation, that observation is not used by PROC LOGISTIC in estimating the model.

In Example 20.1, you can obtain the relapse rates for each group by creating a dummy data set of observations that contains the values of the covariate and concatenate this with the analysis data set. For example, to include estimated probabilities for $X_2 = 3$, 4, ..., 18, concatenate the data set ADDON (see below) with the AML data set.

> Note: Concatenation refers to the process of appending one data set with observations from another data set. This is done with the SET statement in the SAS DATA step. For more information, see "The Little SAS Book, a Primer" by Delwiche and Slaughter (page 126), which is written under the SAS Books by Users program.

```
DATA ADDON;
    DO I = 1 TO 16;
        X = I + 2;
        TRT =  0; OUTPUT;
        TRT =  1; OUTPUT;
    END;
RUN;
```

By adding the statement

```
OUTPUT OUT = ESTIM  P = P_EST;
```

following the MODEL statement in PROC LOGISTIC, the estimated
probabilities are included in the output data set ESTIM, which can be rearranged to display the results, as shown in Table 20.8 and plotted as shown in
Figure 20.4. Confidence intervals for these predicted values can also be easily
obtained in the output data set (see the SAS Help and Online Documentation
for PROC LOGISTIC).

TABLE 20.8. Estimated Relapse Rates for Various Remission Times (X) in Example 20.1

X	Control	Active	X	Control	Active
3	0.88	0.71	11	0.60	0.33
4	0.86	0.67	12	0.55	0.29
5	0.83	0.62	13	0.50	0.25
6	0.80	0.57	14	0.45	0.21
7	0.77	0.52	15	0.41	0.18
8	0.73	0.47	16	0.36	0.15
9	0.69	0.42	17	0.31	0.13
10	0.65	0.38	18	0.27	0.11

FIGURE 20.4. Plot of Estimated Relapse Probabilities vs. Time since Prior Remission (X)

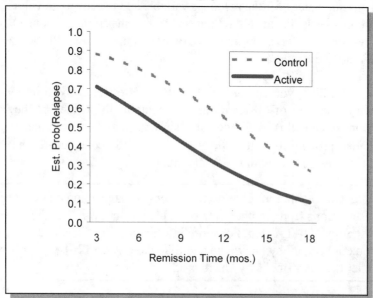

20.4.11. Example 20.2 uses an ordinal response with 4 levels, so the estimated probabilities are provided for each of the three dichotomous models used (i, ii, and iii in Table 20.6). For $X_1=1$ (Group A) and $X_2= 0$ (no previous episodes), these models result in the following estimated probabilities:

(i) $\ln(P_1 / (1-P_1)) = -0.3890 + 0.8682 = 0.479$ or $P_1 = 0.6175$

(ii) $\ln(P_2 / (1-P_2)) = 1.0756 + 0.8682 = 1.944$ or $P_2 = 0.8747$

(iii) $\ln(P_3 / (1-P_3)) = 2.4430 + 0.8682 = 3.311$ or $P_3 = 0.9648$

P_1 represents the probability of 'complete' response, P_2 is the probability of 'marked' or 'complete' response, and P_3 is the probability of any response ('some', 'marked', or 'complete'). You can obtain these estimated probabilities for each combination of covariate levels by using the OUTPUT statement as shown in Section 20.4.10. The results are shown in Table 20.9.

TABLE 20.9. Estimated Probabilities for Example 20.2

| History (X₂) | Model | --------- Group (X₁) --------- | |
		A	B
0	(i)	0.618	0.404
	(ii)	0.875	0.746
	(iii)	0.965	0.920
1	(i)	0.379	0.204
	(ii)	0.725	0.525
	(iii)	0.912	0.813
2	(i)	0.187	0.088
	(ii)	0.499	0.295
	(iii)	0.796	0.621

20.4.12. The X_2 covariate in Example 20.2 (history of severe gastroparesis) is used as an ordinal covariate with 3 levels: 'no prior episodes', 'one prior episode', and 'more than one prior episode'. The odds ratio seen in Output 20.2 is 0.378 **[17]**, which means that the odds of improving response decreases by 62.2% for each incremental increase in the history category.

This analysis assumes that the log-odds is related to incremental changes in X_2 in a linear way. If there is reason to believe that the log-odds of 'one prior episode' vs. 'no prior episodes' should be different from the log-odds of 'more than one prior episode' vs. 'one prior episode', the slope cannot be assumed to be linear. In this case, a quadratic term for prior history (HIST*HIST) can be included in the model, or, alternatively, the HIST variable can be included in the class statement. When used as a class variable, PROC LOGISTIC estimates β's and odds ratios separately for each level of HIST relative to the reference value.

▶ **20.4.13.** Just as *analysis of covariance* assumes equal slopes among groups, *logistic regression* also assumes that the slope of the logit function is similar among groups. This assumption can be checked by a preliminary plot of the data along with the inclusion of the interaction terms between the appropriate X-variables in the *logistic regression* model. Caution must be used in the interpretation of treatment group differences in the presence of interactions.

▶ **20.4.14.** The maximum-likelihood equations might not always give a solution. In cases with small sample sizes, convergence to a unique solution based on the iterative calculations might not be attainable. Although conservative, a general guideline is that the sample size N should be at least 10 times the number of covariates when fitting a *logistic regression* model. Beginning with SAS Version 8, when sample sizes are small, exact methods for fitting *logistic regression* models are available. However, other categorical methods might be more appropriate in clinical trials applications when sample sizes are very small.

The *Log-Rank Test*

21.1   Introduction

The *log-rank test* is a statistical method for comparing distributions of time until the occurrence of an *event* of interest among independent groups. The *event* is often death due to disease, but *event* might be any binomial outcome, such as cure, response, relapse, or failure. The elapsed time from initial treatment or observation until the *event* is the *event* time, often referred to as 'survival time', even when the *event* is not 'death'.

The *log-rank test* provides a method for comparing 'risk-adjusted' *event* rates. This is useful when patients in a clinical study are subject to varying degrees of opportunity to experience the *event*. Such situations arise frequently in clinical trials due to the finite duration of the study, early termination of the patient from the study, or interruption of treatment before the *event* occurs.

Examples where use of the *log-rank test* might be appropriate include comparing survival times in cancer patients who are given a new treatment with patients who receive standard chemotherapy, or comparing times-to-cure among several doses of a topical antifungal preparation where the patient is treated for 10 weeks or until cured, whichever comes first.

Usually, *event* times are not well-modeled using the normal distribution. Modeling techniques using specific distributional assumptions are discussed in Chapter 22. The *log-rank test* is a non-parametric test and, as such, does not require any distributional assumptions about the *event* times. If every patient were followed until the *event* occurrence, the *event* times could be compared between two groups using the *Wilcoxon rank-sum test* (Chapter 13). However, some patients might drop out or complete the study before the *event* occurs. In such cases, the actual time to *event* is unknown because the *event* does not occur while under study observation.

The *event* times for these patients are based on the last known time of study observation, and are called 'censored' observations because they represent the lower-bound of the true, unknown *event* times. The *Wilcoxon rank-sum test* can be highly biased in the presence of censored data. The *log-rank test* adjusts for censoring, thereby, accounting for the patient's opportunity to experience the *event*.

21.2 Synopsis

The null hypothesis tested by the *log-rank test* is that of equal *event* time distributions among groups. Equality of the distributions of *event* times implies similar risk-adjusted *event* rates among groups not only for the clinical trial as a whole, but also for any arbitrary time point during the trial. Rejection of the null hypothesis indicates that the *event* rates differ among groups at one or more time points during the study.

Here, you will examine the case of two independent groups, although the same method is easily extended to more than two groups. A typical data-set layout has the following form, where Y represents the time from initial treatment to the *event* occurrence, and a † indicates a censored value.

TABLE 21.1. Layout for the Log-Rank Test

GROUP 1		GROUP 2	
Patient Number	*Event* Time	Patient Number	*Event* Time
101	Y_{11}	102	Y_{21} †
103	Y_{12} †	105	Y_{22}
104	Y_{13}	106	Y_{23}
.	.	.	.
.	.	.	.
.	.	.	.
N_1	Y_{1N_1} †	N_2	Y_{2N_2} †

† indicates censored time

Divide the study into k distinct time periods, t_1, t_2, ..., t_k, where t_j (j = 1, 2, ..., k) represents the jth time point when one or more patients in the combined samples becomes *event*-positive. Let d_{ij} represent the number of patients in Group i (i = 1, 2) who first experience the *event* at time period t_j, and let n_{ij} represent the number of patients in Group i who are at risk at the beginning of time period t_j. At risk describes the patients who are '*event*-negative' and still in the study. Let $d_j = d_{1j} + d_{2j}$ and let $n_j = n_{1j} + n_{2j}$. For j = 1, 2, ..., k, compute

$$e_{1j} = \frac{n_{1j} \cdot d_j}{n_j} \quad \text{and} \quad v_j = \frac{n_{1j} \cdot n_{2j} \cdot d_j \cdot (n_j - d_j)}{n_j^2 \cdot (n_j - 1)}$$

Finally, you obtain

$$O_1 = \sum_{j=1}^{k} d_{1j}$$

$$E_1 = \sum_{j=1}^{k} v_j$$

and

$$V = \sum_{j=1}^{k} v_j$$

Denote by Y_i a random variable that represents the *event* time for Group i (i=1, 2), and let $S_i(t) = \text{Prob}(Y_i \geq t)$. The test summary for the *log-rank test* is as follows:

---

null hypothesis: H_0: $S_1(t) = S_2(t)$ (for all times, t)

alt. hypothesis: H_A: $S_1(t) \neq S_2(t)$ (for at least one time, t)

test statistic: $\chi^2 = \dfrac{(O_1 - E_1)^2}{V}$

decision rule: reject H_0 if $\chi^2 > \chi_1^2(\alpha)$

where, $\chi_1^2(\alpha)$ is the critical chi-square value with significance level, α, and 1 degree of freedom.

21.3 Examples

Example 21.1 -- HSV-2 Episodes following gD2 Vaccine

Forty-eight patients with genital herpes (HSV-2) were enrolled in a study of a new recombinant herpes vaccine based on the antigen glycoprotein, gD2. Patients were required to have a history of at least 6 HSV-2 episodal outbreaks in the 12 months prior to enrollment in the study and be in remission at the time of vaccination. Patients were randomly assigned to receive either a single gD2 vaccine injection (n=25) or a placebo (n=23), and their conditions were followed for 1 year. The data in Table 21.2 show the time (in weeks) to first recurrence of HSV-2 following immunization for each patient (Y), along with the number of episodes during the 12-month period prior to enrollment (X). Is there evidence that the distributions of the times to recurrence differ between the groups?

TABLE 21.2. Raw Data for Example 21.1

------------------------ gD2 Vaccine Group --------------------

Patient Number	X	Y		Patient Number	X	Y	
1	12	8		26	12	52	†
3	10	12	†	28	13	36	
6	7	52	†	31	8	52	†
7	10	28		33	10	9	
8	6	44		34	16	11	†
10	8	14		36	6	52	†
12	8	3		39	14	15	
14	9	52	†	40	13	13	
15	11	35		42	13	21	
18	13	6		44	16	24	†
20	7	12		46	13	52	†
23	13	7	†	48	9	28	
24	9	52	†				

-------------------------- Placebo Group ----------------------

Patient Number	X	Y		Patient Number	X	Y	
2	9	15		27	9	9	†
4	10	44	†	29	10	27	
5	12	2	†	30	17	1	
9	7	8		32	8	12	
11	7	12		35	8	20	
13	7	52	†	37	8	32	†
16	7	21		38	8	15	
17	11	19		41	14	5	
19	16	6		43	13	35	
21	16	10		45	9	28	
22	6	15	†	47	15	6	
25	15	4					

† indicates censored time

   (Note: Patients who had censored times of less than 52 weeks were study dropouts.)

Solution

This analysis will ignore the covariate, X. This example is also used in Chapter 22, which discusses the comparison of survival distributions using covariate-adjustments with the *Cox proportional hazards model.*

The first step in manual computation of the *log-rank test* is to construct a table for each *event* time as shown in Table 21.3. At each time period, t_j, the number of patients at risk, n_{ij}, is reduced by the number of *event*-positives (d_{ij}) and censored observations (w_{ij}) from the previous time period, t_{j-1}.

Let $S_1(t)$ and $S_2(t)$ represent the cumulative probability distributions of the times from vaccine administration until the first HSV-2 recurrence for the gD2 and placebo groups, respectively. The hypothesis test summary is

null hypothesis: H_0: $S_1(t) = S_2(t)$ (for all times, t)

alt. hypothesis: H_A: $S_1(t) \neq S_2(t)$ (for at least one time, t)

test statistic:

$$\chi^2 = \frac{(O_1 - E_1)^2}{V}$$

$$= \frac{(14 - 19.1556)^2}{6.8197} = 3.8976$$

decision rule: reject H_0 if $\chi^2 > \chi_1^2(0.05) = 3.841$.

conclusion: Because $3.897 > 3.841$, reject H_0 and conclude that the recurrence times are significantly different between the gD2 and placebo vaccine groups at a 0.05 level of significance.

TABLE 21.3. Preliminary Summary Table for Log-Rank Computations for Example 21.1

WEEK	gD2 VACCINE GROUP			PLACEBO GROUP			TOTAL		COMPUTATIONS	
t_j	d_{1j}	w_{1j}	n_{1j}	d_{2j}	w_{2j}	n_{2j}	d_j	n_j	e_1	v_1
1	0	0	25	1	0	23	1	48	0.5208	0.2496
2	0	0	25	0	1	22	0	47	0	0
3	1	0	25	0	0	21	1	46	0.5435	0.2481
4	0	0	24	1	0	21	1	45	0.5333	0.2489
5	0	0	24	1	0	20	1	44	0.5455	0.2479
6	1	0	24	2	0	19	3	43	1.6744	0.7046
7	0	1	23	0	0	17	0	40	0	0
8	1	0	22	1	0	17	2	39	1.1282	0.4788
9	1	0	21	0	1	16	1	37	0.5676	0.2454
10	0	0	20	1	0	15	1	35	0.5714	0.2449
11	0	1	20	0	0	14	0	34	0	0
12	1	1	19	2	0	14	3	33	1.7273	0.6870
13	1	0	17	0	0	12	1	29	0.5862	0.2426
14	1	0	16	0	0	12	1	28	0.5714	0.2449
15	1	0	15	2	1	12	3	27	1.6667	0.6838
19	0	0	14	1	0	9	1	23	0.6087	0.2382
20	0	0	14	1	0	8	1	22	0.6364	0.2314
21	1	0	14	1	0	7	2	21	1.3333	0.4222
24	0	1	13	0	0	6	0	19	0	0
27	0	0	12	1	0	6	1	18	0.6667	0.2222
28	2	0	12	1	0	5	3	17	2.1176	0.5450
32	0	0	10	0	1	4	0	14	0	0
35	1	0	10	1	0	3	2	13	1.5385	0.3254
36	1	0	9	0	0	2	1	11	0.8182	0.1488
44	1	0	8	0	1	2	1	10	0.8000	0.1600
52	0	7	7	0	1	1	0	8	0	0
	14 (O_1)			17			31		19.1556 (E_1)	6.8197 (V)

(Numbers in shaded rows do not affect the calculations of E_1 and V. These are shown only to account for all censored observations.)

SAS Analysis of Example 21.1

One way to identify censored values in SAS is to assign them a negative value as you read the *event* times (WKS) into the SAS data set (HSV), as shown in the SAS code for Example 21.1. The variable CENS is defined as an indicator variable that takes the value 1 if the observation is censored (WKS<1), and 0 if the observation is not censored ❶. A partial listing of the data is displayed in the output from PROC PRINT ❷.

The SAS procedure LIFETEST is used to perform the *log-rank test* ❸. The TIME statement, which follows the PROC LIFETEST statement, designates the variable WKS whose values are the *event* times, followed by the variable CENS that identifies which observations are censored (i.e., *CENS=1) ❹. The STRATA statement identifies the grouping or stratification variable, in this case, vaccine group (VAC) ❺.

Output 21.1 shows the *log-rank test* resulting in a chi-square value of 3.8976 ❻, which confirms the manual calculations. This is a significant result with a p-value of 0.0484 ❼. Also shown in the output are the values of $O_1 - E_1 = -5.1556$ ❽ and $V = 6.81973$ ❾.

SAS Code for Example 21.1

```
DATA HSV;
     INPUT VAC $ PAT WKS X @@;
     CENS = (WKS < 1);                                    ❶
     WKS  = ABS(WKS);
     TRT = (VAC = 'GD2');      /* used in Example 22.1 */
     DATALINES;
GD2   1    8 12  GD2   3 -12 10  GD2   6 -52   7
GD2   7   28 10  GD2   8  44  6  GD2  10  14   8
GD2  12    3  8  GD2  14 -52  9  GD2  15  35  11
GD2  18    6 13  GD2  20  12  7  GD2  23  -7  13
GD2  24  -52  9  GD2  26 -52 12  GD2  28  36  13
GD2  31  -52  8  GD2  33   9 10  GD2  34 -11  16
GD2  36  -52  6  GD2  39  15 14  GD2  40  13  13
GD2  42   21 13  GD2  44 -24 16  GD2  46 -52  13
GD2  48   28  9  PBO   2  15  9  PBO   4 -44  10
PBO   5   -2 12  PBO   9   8  7  PBO  11  12   7
PBO  13  -52  7  PBO  16  21  7  PBO  17  19  11
PBO  19    6 16  PBO  21  10 16  PBO  22 -15   6
PBO  25    4 15  PBO  27  -9  9  PBO  29  27  10
PBO  30    1 17  PBO  32  12  8  PBO  35  20   8
PBO  37  -32  8  PBO  38  15  8  PBO  41   5  14
PBO  43   35 13  PBO  45  28  9  PBO  47   6  15
;

PROC SORT DATA = HSV;
     BY VAC PAT;
PROC PRINT DATA = HSV;
     VAR VAC PAT WKS CENS X;
     TITLE1 'The Log-Rank Test';
     TITLE2 'Example 21.1: HSV-2 Episodes with gD2 Vaccine';
RUN;
```

```
ODS EXCLUDE
    ProductLimitEstimates;
PROC LIFETEST PLOTS=(S) LINEPRINTER DATA = HSV;      ❸
    TIME WKS*CENS(1);                                 ❹
    STRATA VAC;                                        ❺
RUN;
```

OUTPUT 21.1. SAS Output for Example 21.1

```
                    The Log-Rank Test
        Example 21.1: HSV-2 Episodes with gD2 Vaccine

        Obs     VAC     PAT     WKS     CENS      X

          1     GD2       1       8        0      12
          2     GD2       3      12        1      10
          3     GD2       6      52        1       7
          4     GD2       7      28        0      10
          5     GD2       8      44        0       6
          6     GD2      10      14        0       8
          7     GD2      12       3        0       8
          8     GD2      14      52        1       9
          9     GD2      15      35        0      11
         10     GD2      18       6        0      13
         11     GD2      20      12        0       7
         12     GD2      23       7        1      13
         13     GD2      24      52        1       9            ❷
         14     GD2      26      52        1      12
         15     GD2      28      36        0      13
         16     GD2      31      52        1       8
         17     GD2      33       9        0      10
          .
          .
          .
         43     PBO      37      32        1       8
         44     PBO      38      15        0       8
         45     PBO      41       5        0      14
         46     PBO      43      35        0      13
         47     PBO      45      28        0       9
         48     PBO      47       6        0      15
```

```
                  The LIFETEST Procedure

                  Stratum 1: VAC = GD2

         Summary Statistics for Time Variable WKS

                    Quartile Estimates

                   Point        95% Confidence Interval
        Percent    Estimate      (Lower        Upper)

           75        .           35.0000
           50       35.0000      15.0000          . ❶❸
           25       13.0000       8.0000       28.0000
```

OUTPUT 21.1. SAS Output for Example 21.1 (*continued*)

```
                       The Log-Rank Test
           Example 21.1: HSV-2 Episodes with gD2 Vaccine


               Mean      Standard Error

               28.7214          3.2823   ⑭

NOTE: The mean survival time and its standard error were underestimated
because the largest observation was censored and the estimation was
restricted to the largest event time.

                     Stratum 2: VAC = PBO

           Summary Statistics for Time Variable WKS

                     Quartile Estimates

                  Point     95% Confidence Interval
        Percent   Estimate    (Lower      Upper)

           75     28.0000     19.0000         .
           50     15.0000     10.0000     27.0000   ⑬
           25      8.0000      5.0000     15.0000


               Mean      Standard Error

               18.2397          2.5387   ⑭

NOTE: The mean survival time and its standard error were underestimated
because the largest observation was censored and the estimation was
restricted to the largest event time.


       Summary of the Number of Censored and Uncensored Values


                                                      Percent
        Stratum     VAC     Total  Failed   Censored  Censored

           1        GD2      25      14        11      44.00
           2        PBO      23      17         6      26.09
        ---------------------------------------------------------
          Total              48      31        17      35.42
```

OUTPUT 21.1. SAS Output for Example 21.1 (*continued*)

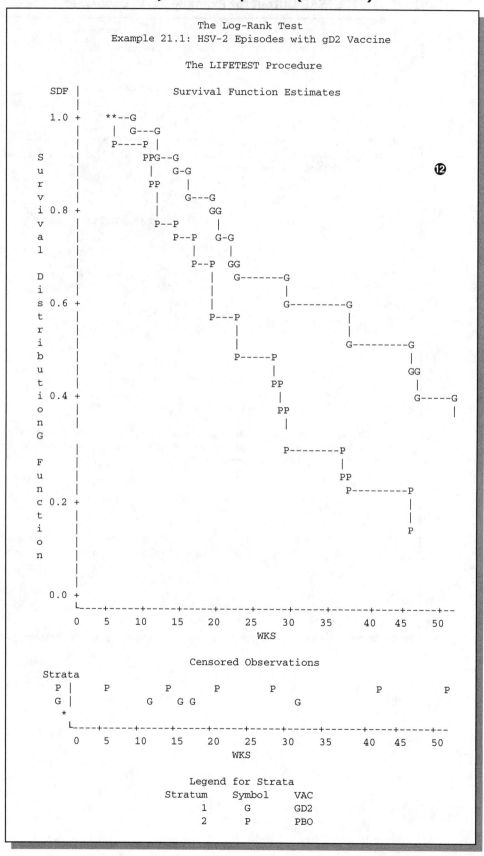

OUTPUT 21.1. SAS Output for Example 21.1 (*continued*)

```
                         The Log-Rank Test
            Example 21.1: HSV-2 Episodes with gD2 Vaccine

                      The LIFETEST Procedure


        Testing Homogeneity of Survival Curves for WKS over Strata

                           Rank Statistics

                VAC        Log-Rank      Wilcoxon

                GD2         -5.1556   ❽  -160.00
                PBO          5.1556       160.00


           Covariance Matrix for the Log-Rank Statistics

                VAC            GD2            PBO

                GD2         6.81973   ❾     -6.81973
                PBO        -6.81973          6.81973


           Covariance Matrix for the Wilcoxon Statistics

                VAC            GD2            PBO

                GD2         7136.46        -7136.46
                PBO        -7136.46         7136.46


               Test of Equality over Strata
                                            Pr >
            Test        Chi-Square    DF   Chi-Square

            Log-Rank      3.8976  ❻    1     0.0484   ❼
            Wilcoxon      3.5872       1     0.0582   ❿
            -2Log(LR)     4.2589       1     0.0390   ⓫
```

21.4 Details & Notes

▶ **21.4.1.**   Clinical study outcomes often have the goal of estimating response or *event* rates and comparing them among randomized groups. However, the selection of a time point during the clinical study at which to compare *event* rates is not always clear-cut. The last double-blind visit is often designated for such use, although drawbacks might exist for this choice. First, the duration of the study might be somewhat arbitrary or constrained by safety issues or other considerations unrelated to response. More importantly, the analysis ignores information prior to this evaluation time point that might have an important impact on the results.

If the data in Example 21.1 were analyzed with the *chi-square test* (Chapter 16) for comparing *event* rates at the final visit using a 'last-observation-carried-forward' method, you obtain

TABLE 21.4. Unadjusted Recurrence Rates for Example 21.1

Response	gD2 Group	Placebo Group	TOTAL
HSV-2 Recurrence	14 (56.0%)	17 (73.9%)	31 (64.6%)
No Recurrence	11	6	17
Total Enrolled	25	23	48

The HSV-2 recurrence rate comparison (56.0% vs. 73.9%) is not significant ($\chi^2 = 1.680$, p = 0.195) based on the *chi-square test* (Chapter 16), which ignores the time that patients were at risk. By analyzing time-to-*event* occurrence and accounting for censoring, the *log-rank test* uses *event* rates over the whole trial, rather than relying on a single time point.

▶ **21.4.2.** For the jth time period (t_j), you can construct a 2×2 contingency table as follows:

	GROUP 1	GROUP 2	TOTAL
Event Positive	d_{1j}	d_{2j}	d_j
Event Negative	$n_{1j} - d_{1j}$	$n_{2j} - d_{2j}$	$n_j - d_j$
Total	n_{1j}	n_{2j}	n_j

The *log-rank test* is equivalent to applying the *Cochran-Mantel-Haenszel test* (Chapter 19) using these 2×2 tables at each time point as the strata.

▶ **21.4.3.** Many variations of the *log-rank test* for comparing survival distributions exist. The most common variant has the form

$$\chi^2 = \frac{(O_1 - E_1)^2}{E_1} + \frac{(O_2 - E_2)^2}{E_2}$$

where O_i and E_i are computed for each group, as in the formulas given previously. This statistic also has an approximate chi-square distribution with 1 degree of freedom under H_0.

In Example 21.1, you have $O_1 = 14$, $O_2 = 17$, and $E_1 = 19.1556$. Using the relationship that $O_1 + O_2 = E_1 + E_2$, you obtain $E_2 = 14 + 17 - 19.1556 = 11.8444$, which results in

$$\chi^2 = \frac{(14 - 19.1556)^2}{19.1556} + \frac{(17 - 11.8444)^2}{11.8444} = 3.632$$

with a p-value of 0.0567. Although computationally easier, this *chi-square test* gives a more conservative result than the version presented.

A continuity correction can also be used by reducing the numerators by 0.5 before squaring. Using this type of correction leads to even further conservatism and may be omitted when sample sizes are moderate or large.

▶ **21.4.4.** Previously, it was noted that the *Wilcoxon rank-sum test* can be used to analyze the *event* times in the absence of censoring. A *generalized Wilcoxon test* (sometimes called the *Gehan test)* based on an approximate chi-square distribution has been developed for use in the presence of censored observations. Manual computations for this method can be tedious. (The reader is referred to Dawson-Saunders & Trapp (1990, p. 196) for an illustration of a worked example.) Results of this test are available in Output 21.1. The *generalized Wilcoxon* chi-square for Example 21.1 is 3.587 with a p-value of 0.0582 ❿, which is close to the results of the *log-rank test* for this example, but not significant.

Both the *log-rank* and the *generalized Wilcoxon tests* are non-parametric tests, and require no assumptions regarding the distribution of *event* times. When a greater *event* rate is seen early in the trial rather than toward the end of the trial, the *generalized Wilcoxon test* is the more appropriate test because it gives greater weight to the earlier differences.

▶ **21.4.5.** Survival and failure times often follow the exponential distribution. If such a model can be assumed, a more powerful alternative to the *log-rank test* is the *likelihood ratio test*, the results of which are also printed in the SAS output as –2Log(LR). Output 21.1 shows a likelihood ratio chi-square of 4.2589 with a p-value of 0.0390 ⓫.

This parametric test assumes that *event* probabilities are constant over time. That is, the chance that a patient becomes *event*-positive at time t given that he is *event*-negative up to time t does not depend on t. A plot of the negative log of the *event* times distribution that shows a linear trend through the origin is consistent with exponential *event* times. In SAS, the option PLOTS=(LS) in PROC LIFETEST can be specified to obtain such a plot.

▶ **21.4.6.** Life tables can be constructed to provide estimates of the *event* time distributions. Estimates commonly used for data sets similar to that for Example 21.1 are known as the Kaplan-Meier estimates. These are the default estimates given by SAS (although the output can be suppressed by using the ODS statement). A plot of the distribution function vs. time provides a good visual of the distributions. SAS will provide such a plot if you use the PLOTS=(S) option in PROC LIFETEST, as illustrated in Output 21.1 ⑫.

▶ **21.4.7.**   Additional summary statistics printed by SAS that might be useful are the estimated median and mean *event* times for each group. The median *event* times are shown in Output 21.1 as the 50% quartile, and, if possible to compute, they are accompanied by 95% confidence intervals. In Example 21.1, the median times until first recurrence are 35 and 15 weeks, respectively, for the gD2 and placebo vaccine groups ⑬, while the estimates of the means are 28.7 and 18.2 weeks, respectively ⑭. The estimates of the means will always be biased unless all patients become *event*-positive by study completion. As noted in the SAS output, these estimates are biased due to censored observations.

▶ **21.4.8.**   The *log-rank test* is presented here as a means for comparing two treatment groups. The same methods can be used with one treatment group to compare two strata. For example, a comparison of *event* times between males and females who are treated with the same test preparation can be made with the *log-rank test*.

▶ **21.4.9.**   The *log-rank test* can easily be extended to more than two groups. With g groups or strata, the hypothesis of equal *event*-time distributions can be tested with

$$\chi^2 = \sum_{i=1}^{g} \frac{(O_i - E_i)^2}{E_i}$$

which has an approximate chi-square distribution with g–1 degrees of freedom under H_0. It is easy to see that the techniques of the *log-rank test* can be used to compare *event* times among the levels of any categorical factor.

▶ **21.4.10.**   Covariates can be considered when comparing *event* times by using an extension of the *log-rank test*. For Example 21.1, the covariate X (number of episodes in past year) can be included in the *log-rank test* to obtain covariate-adjusted comparison of first-recurrence times between groups.

One method using SAS is to include the Vaccine Group effect in a TEST statement and the covariate X, in the STRATA statement. Because X is considered a continuous numeric variable, intervals of X need to be specified (for details, see the SAS Help and Documentation for PROC LIFETEST). Additionally, any variables included in the TEST statement must be numeric, so the Group effect VAC (with values GD2 and PBO) must first be converted from character to numeric values. Because results are dependent on the intervals chosen for X, this is not recommended unless the continuous covariate breaks into natural intervals.

SAS can also accommodate multiple covariates in the TEST statement in PROC LIFETEST. SAS will first determine the significance of each individual covariate's association with *event* time. Then, by including the most significant covariates, one at a time using a stepwise method, SAS determines the level of association of each covariate to *event* time adjusted for all other covariates already included. The STRATA statement is not used. Because of the nature of a stepwise method, there is no way to predict before conducting the analysis whether the Group effect in Example 21.1 would be adjusted for the covariate X when using this approach.

PROC PHREG in SAS is often more useful than PROC LIFETEST when comparing survival times in the presence of categorical cofactors or numeric covariates. This procedure is presented in Chapter 22.

The *Cox Proportional Hazards Model*

22.1 Introduction

Like the *log-rank test* discussed in the previous chapter, the *Cox proportional hazards model* (sometimes referred to as '*Cox regression*') is used to analyze event or 'survival' times. This is a modeling procedure that adjusts for censoring, may include numeric covariates, one or more of which may be time-dependent, and requires no assumption about the distribution of event times.

An example of where the Cox proportional hazards model might be useful in clinical trials is a comparison of time to death among treatment groups with adjustments for age, duration of disease, and family disease history.

Informally, the inverse of the time to event occurrence is called the 'hazard', given a suitable time unit. For example, if an event is expected to occur in 6 months, the hazard is 1/6 ('events per month'), assuming the unit of time is 'months'. Of chief concern when using the Cox proportional hazards model is the way in which the hazard changes over time. The hazard function is discussed in more detail later in this chapter (see Section 22.4.2).

The hazard of some events might be likely to increase with the passage of time, such as death due to certain types of cancer. Other types of events might become less frequent over longer periods of time. For example, reinfarction following coronary artery bypass can have the greatest risk in the weeks immediately following surgery, then risk might decrease as time passes. Still other types of events might be subject to fluctuating risks, both increasing and decreasing, over time.

Theoretically, survival analysis would be pretty easy if you could assume that the hazard remains constant over time. Recognizing the impracticalities of such an assumption, the *Cox proportional hazards model* adopts the more reasonable assumption that the *event* hazard rate does change over time, but that the ratio of *event* hazards between two individuals is constant. This is known as the 'proportional hazards' assumption, which requires that the ratio of hazards between any two values of a covariate not vary with time. If Age is a covariate used in the analysis, the proportional hazards assumption would require, for example, that the ratio of the hazard for 60-year-old patients to the hazard for 35-year-old patients be constant over time.

22.2 Synopsis

The *Cox proportional hazards model* is used to test the effect of a specified set of k covariates, X_1, X_2, ..., X_k on the *event* times. The X_i's can be numeric-valued covariates or numerically coded categorical responses that have some natural ordering. The X_i's can also be dummy variables that represent treatment groups in a comparative trial or levels of a nominal categorical factor as described for *logistic regression* (see Section 20.4.6).

The model for the hazard function of the *Cox proportional hazards* method has the form

$$h(t) = \lambda(t) \cdot e^{(\beta_1 X_1 + \beta_2 X_2 + \dots + \beta_k X_k)}$$

where h(t) represents the hazard function, the X_i's represent the covariates, the β_i's represent the parameter coefficients of the X_i's, and $\lambda(t)$ represents an unspecified initial hazard function. As with regression analysis, the magnitudes of the β_i's reflect the importance of the covariates in the model, and inference about these parameters is the focus here.

D. R. Cox, after whom the model is named, developed a method for estimating β_i (i=1,2,...,k) by b_i based on a 'maximum partial likelihood' approach, which is a modification of the maximum likelihood method mentioned in Chapter 20. Manual computations are impractical, and solutions generally require numerical techniques using high-speed computers. When using SAS, the PHREG procedure is recommended for fitting the *Cox proportional hazards model*.

For large samples, these estimates (b_i) have an approximate normal distribution. If s_b represents the standard error of the estimate b_i, then b_i/s_b has an approximate standard normal distribution under the null hypothesis that $\beta_i = 0$, and its square has the chi-square distribution with 1 degree of freedom. The test summary for each model parameter, β_i, can be summarized as follows:

null hypothesis: H_0: $\beta_i = 0$

alternative hypothesis: H_A: $\beta_i \neq 0$

test statistic: $$\chi^2_w = \left(\frac{b_i}{s_b}\right)^2$$

decision rule: reject H_0 if $\chi^2_w > \chi^2_1(\alpha)$

The magnitude of the effect of a covariate is often expressed as a hazard ratio, similar to the odds ratio discussed in Chapter 20. Because the hazard at any time, t, for a specified set of covariate values, $x_1, x_2, \ldots, x_k$, is given by

$$h(t) = \lambda(t) \cdot e^{(\beta_1 x_1 + \beta_2 x_2 + \ldots + \beta_k x_k)}$$

the ratio of hazards for a 1-unit increase in X_i (all other covariates held constant) is e^{β_i}. The estimated hazard ratio associated with the covariate X_i is found by simply exponentiating the parameter estimate, b_i.

Example 22.1, which follows, illustrates the *Cox proportional hazards model* with a simple example using one dichotomous group variable and one numeric covariate.

22.3 Examples

Example 22.1 -- HSV-2 Episodes with gD2 Vaccine (continued)
(See Example 21.1)

The data in Example 21.1 include a history of HSV-2 lesional episodes during the year prior to the study (X). Does the covariate X have any impact on the comparison of HSV-2 recurrence times between treatment groups?

Solution

Although covariates can be included in the TEST or STRATA statements when using PROC LIFETEST in SAS (Chapter 21), it is often easier to use PROC PHREG to model survival distributions that include one or more covariates. The SAS analysis below shows how to use PROC PHREG to fit the *Cox proportional hazards model* for this example.

SAS Analysis of Example 22.1

PROC PHREG requires all covariates included in the model to be numeric. The number of episodes in the prior 12 months (X) is a numeric variable. The vaccine group (VAC), however, must be converted. You can do this conversion with the new variable, TRT, which takes the value 1 for the gD2 vaccine group and 0 for the placebo group (see the SAS code for Example 21.1).

With PROC PHREG, the MODEL statement is used with the time variable and censoring indicator on the left side of the equal sign (=) and the covariates on the right side of the equal sign (=) ❶. Recall from Example 21.1 that the indicator variable CENS takes a value of 1 if the observation is censored, 0 if it is not censored. The left side of the MODEL equality is specified in the same format as the TIME statement in PROC LIFETEST for identifying censored values. You specify the vaccine group factor, TRT, and the HSV-2 lesion frequency during the prior year, X, as the two covariates. The TIES option is used in the event that more than one observation has tied *event* times. This is discussed further in Section 22.4.9.

The results are shown in Output 22.1. The estimate of the parameter associated with the covariate X is 0.176 ❷, which is significant (p = 0.0073) ❸ based on the *chi-square* value of 7.1896. This means that prior lesional frequency is an important consideration when analyzing the *event* times. The test for the group effect (TRT) is also significant (p = 0.0160) ❹ and indicates a difference in the distributions of *event* times between vaccine groups after adjusting for the covariate, X. The hazard ratio, 0.404 ❺, indicates that the covariate-adjusted 'hazard' of HSV-2 recurrence for the active (gD2) group is only about 40% of that for the placebo group.

The *log-rank test* using the same data set (ignoring the covariate, X) resulted in a significant finding with a p-value close to 0.05 (Example 21.1). The *Cox proportional hazards model* resulted in an even greater significance (p = 0.016) after adjusting for the important covariate, X.

SAS Code for Example 22.1

. . . (continued from Example 21.1)

```
PROC PHREG DATA = HSV;
   MODEL WKS*CENS(1) = TRT X / TIES = EXACT;        ❶
   TITLE1 'Cox Proportional Hazards Model';
   TITLE2 "Example 22.1: HSV-2 Episodes with gD2 Vaccine -
           cont'd." ;
RUN;
```

OUTPUT 22.1. SAS Output for Example 22.1

```
                  Cox Proportional Hazards Model
      Example 22.1: HSV-2 Episodes with gD2 Vaccine - cont'd.

                       The PHREG Procedure

                       Model Information

              Data Set               WORK.HSV
              Dependent Variable     WKS
              Censoring Variable     CENS
              Censoring Value(s)     1
              Ties Handling          EXACT

        Summary of the Number of Event and Censored Values

                                            Percent
           Total       Event    Censored    Censored

             48          31         17        35.42

                      Convergence Status
        Convergence criterion (GCONV=1E-8) satisfied.

                     Model Fit Statistics

                          Without          With
            Criterion     Covariates      Covariates

            -2 LOG L       183.628         172.792
            AIC            183.628         176.792
            SBC            183.628         179.660

        Testing Global Null Hypothesis: BETA=0

      Test                 Chi-Square      DF     Pr > ChiSq
      Likelihood Ratio       10.8364        2        0.0044
      Score        ❻         11.0159        2        0.0041
      Wald                   10.7236        2        0.0047

        Analysis of Maximum Likelihood Estimates

              Parameter  Standard                          Hazard
Variable  DF  Estimate    Error   Chi-Square  Pr > ChiSq   Ratio
TRT        1  -0.90578   0.37600    5.8033      0.0160 ❹   0.404 ❺
X          1   0.17627❷  0.06574    7.1896      0.0073 ❸   1.193
```

The next example illustrates the use of stratification in *Cox regression* and introduces the concept of time-dependent covariates.

Example 22.2 -- Hyalurise in Vitreous Hemorrhage

A new treatment, Hyalurise, is being tested to facilitate the clearance of vitreous hemorrhage, a condition that results in severe vision impairment. Patients were randomly assigned to receive a single injection of either Hyalurise (n =83) or saline (n = 60) in the affected eye and were followed for 1 year. Time, in weeks, to 'response' is shown in Table 22.1. ('Response' is defined as sufficient clearance of the hemorrhage to permit diagnosis of the underlying cause and appropriate intervention.)

The time for patients who discontinued or completed the trial before achieving 'response' is considered censored (†). Covariates include a measure of baseline hemorrhage density (Grade 3 or 4), study center (A, B, or C), and whether the patient developed certain infectious complications (ocular infection, inflammation, or herpetic lesion) during the study (based on 'Infect. Time' in Table 22.1). Does the time to response differ between the patients treated with Hyalurise and the control group treated with saline?

Solution

The response variable is time, in weeks, from randomization to 'response', some of whose values are censored. Because this analysis clearly calls for 'survival' methodology that incorporates covariates, you use PROC PHREG in SAS to fit a *Cox regression* model under the assumption of proportional hazards.

In addition to the treatment group effect, you want to include as covariates: baseline hemorrhage density, study center, and the occurrence of infectious complications. Notice that the last covariate is a bit unusual. The occurrence of complications can take the values 'yes' or 'no', which can be coded 1 and 0, respectively. However, these values can change during the study and depend on the time of the response. Clearly, the degree to which complications affect 'response' is only relevant if the complication develops before 'response' occurs. For this reason, this is called a 'time-dependent' covariate. Such time-dependent covariates can be included in the *Cox proportional hazards model*, as illustrated in the SAS analysis that follows.

SAS Analysis of Example 22.2

In the SAS program for Example 22.2, the variables are coded as follows:

RSPTIM	= time (weeks) from randomization to 'response'
TRT	= treatment group (0=saline, 1=Hyalurise)
DENS	= baseline hemorrhage density (3 or 4)
CENTER	= Study Center (A, B, or C)
INFTIM	= time (weeks) from randomization to onset of complication.

TABLE 22.1. Raw Data for Example 22.2

					Hyalurise Injection			
Center	Patient Number	Density	Infect. Time	Resp. Time	Patient Number	Density	Infect. Time	Resp. Time
A	101	3	.	32	132	4	18	46
	102	4	10	20	133	4	.	21
	105	4	52	24	134	3	.	14
	106	3	.	41	136	3	.	24 †
	108	4	.	32	139	3	.	19
	110	3	.	10 †	140	4	20	24
	112	4	.	32	141	3	12	31
	114	3	36	45	144	3	.	52 †
	116	3	.	6	146	4	.	40
	117	4	.	52 †	148	4	24	7
	119	3	.	13	150	4	.	16
	121	4	.	6	151	3	4	36
	123	3	28	44	153	3	.	28
	125	4	.	23	155	3	.	38 †
	126	3	.	30	156	3	.	9
	128	3	.	2	159	4	.	30
	130	4	.	26	160	4	.	6
B	202	3	.	4 †	220	4	.	25
	203	4	.	10	223	4	.	20
	206	3	.	11	224	3	24	9
	207	4	.	52 †	225	3	.	22
	208	3	.	12	226	3	.	23
	210	4	.	46	228	3	.	13
	212	3	.	10	230	4	.	8
	214	4	30	31	231	4	.	37
	215	4	.	4	233	3	10	24
	217	3	33	20	234	4	.	52 †
	219	3	.	2	237	3	.	27
C	301	3	.	10	324	4	.	22
	303	4	.	32	327	3	30	15
	304	4	20	14	329	3	.	20
	306	4	18	14	330	3	30	52 †
	309	3	.	7	332	3	.	10
	311	3	.	5	334	4	.	2 †
	312	3	.	9	337	3	.	16
	313	4	.	12	338	3	20	33
	315	3	.	10	340	3	.	12
	317	4	.	52 †	341	4	18	27
	318	3	.	10	342	4	.	2
	320	3	.	5	344	4	.	20 †
	321	3	16	34	346	3	.	3
	323	3	.	6				

† indicates censored observation

TABLE 22.1. Data Set for Example 22.2 (*continued*)

	--------------------------------- Saline Injection -------------------------------------							
Center	Patient Number	Density	Infect. Time	Resp. Time	Patient Number	Density	Infect. Time	Resp. Time
A	103	3	.	52 †	131	3	.	8
	104	4	.	4	135	3	.	52 †
	107	4	12	32	137	3	.	22 †
	109	3	20	25	138	3	.	35 †
	111	3	.	8	142	4	.	28
	113	4	38	52 †	143	4	34	52 †
	115	4	.	14 †	145	3	.	35
	118	4	28	9	147	3	.	4
	120	4	.	36	149	4	.	2 †
	122	4	.	42 †	152	3	.	12
	124	3	.	52 †	154	3	42	48
	127	3	.	16	157	3	.	11
	129	3	6	21	158	4	.	20
B	201	3	.	15 †	221	4	.	11
	204	4	9	10	222	4	40	52 †
	205	3	.	8	227	3	.	11
	209	3	.	20	229	4	.	7 †
	211	4	44	32	232	4	26	32
	213	3	.	42	235	4	.	20
	216	3	.	24 †	236	4	.	34
	218	3	.	16				
C	302	4	8	10 †	326	3	.	16
	305	3	.	24	328	4	22	33
	307	3	.	36	331	4	.	5
	308	3	.	52 †	333	3	15	16
	310	4	.	6	335	4	.	17
	314	3	.	21	336	4	.	16
	316	4	36	26	339	3	11	24
	319	4	12	27	343	4	.	6 †
	322	4	.	14	345	3	.	14
	325	4	12	45				

† indicates censored observation

In this example, the variable CENS is created to identify censored observations associated with a value of 0 ❼. Thus, the left side in the MODEL statement in PROC PHREG is 'RSPTIM*CENS(0) =' ❽.

The baseline hemorrhage density (DENS) is easily included in the MODEL statement as a dichotomous numeric covariate (Grade 4 indicates the most severe condition). Notice that Study Center is a nominal categorical factor that cannot be incorporated directly as a covariate because PROC PHREG can only use numeric valued covariates. You can create two new 0 and 1 dummy variables as described in Chapter 20. However, because differences among centers are not of direct interest, it is easier to include CENTER in a STRATA statement ❾. Essentially, this tells SAS to treat the centers as three distinct clusters and combine the results across centers. CENTER effects are not estimated, and use of CENTER in the STRATA statement does not require the proportional hazards assumption with respect to Study Center.

To include the possible effect of occurrence of complications in the analysis, you must create a new, time-dependent covariate (INFCTN) using a special feature in PROC PHREG that allows SAS DATA step type programming statements to be used in the procedure. This ensures that the covariate takes the correct values (0 or 1) at the appropriate time points. INFCTN is defined as 1 if a complication occurs prior to response, and 0, if a complication occurs after response or not at all **❿** .

In Output 22.2, you see the analysis of the maximum likelihood estimates of the model parameters, including p-values based on the *Wald chi-square tests*. The p-value for treatment effect (TRT), which controls for the covariates, is 0.0780**⓫**. The hazard ratio of 1.412**⓬** indicates that the 'hazard' of responding at any arbitrary time point is 41.2% higher with Hyalurise injection compared with saline. Neither the numeric covariate, baseline hemorrhage density (DENS), nor the time-dependent covariate (INFCTN) is significant. Notice that no tests are performed for the Study Center effect because Study Center is a categorical factor included in the STRATA statement.

SAS Code for Example 22.2

```
DATA VITCLEAR;
    INPUT PAT RSPTIM TRT CENTER $ DENS INFTIM @@;
    CENS   = (RSPTIM GE 0);                     ❼
    RSPTIM = ABS(RSPTIM);
    /* RSPTIM = time (wks) from randomization to response
               (RSPTIM is censored if negative)         */
    /* TRT    = 1 for Hyalurise, TRT = 0 for Saline      */
    /* CENTER = study center (A, B, or C)               */
    /* DENS   = 3, 4 for Grade 3 or 4, respectively      */
    /* INFTIM = time (wks) from randomization to onset of
                 infection or other complications        */
    DATALINES;
101   32 1 A 3  .   102   20 1 A 4 10   103 -52 0 A 3   .
104    4 0 A 4  .   105   24 1 A 4 52   106  41 1 A 3   .
107   32 0 A 4 12   108   32 1 A 4  .   109  25 0 A 3   .
110  -10 1 A 3  .   111    8 0 A 3  .   112  32 1 A 4   .
113  -52 0 A 4 38   114   45 1 A 3 36   115 -14 0 A 4   .
116    6 1 A 3  .   117  -52 1 A 4  .   118   9 0 A 4 28
119   13 1 A 3  .   120   36 0 A 4  .   121   6 1 A 4   .
122  -42 0 A 4  .   123   44 1 A 3 28   124 -52 0 A 3   .
125   23 1 A 4  .   126   30 1 A 3  .   127  16 0 A 3   .
128    2 1 A 3  .   129   21 0 A 3  6   130  26 1 A 4   .
131    8 0 A 3  .   132   46 1 A 4 18   133  21 1 A 4   .
```

SAS Code for Example 22.2 (*continued*)

```
134   14 1 A 3   .    135 -52 0 A 3   .    136 -24 1 A 3   .
137  -22 0 A 3   .    138 -35 0 A 3   .    139  19 1 A 3   .
140   24 1 A 4 20     141  31 1 A 3 12    142  28 0 A 4   .
143  -52 0 A 4 34     144 -52 1 A 3   .    145  35 0 A 3   .
146   40 1 A 4   .    147   4 0 A 3   .    148   7 1 A 4 24
149   -2 0 A 4   .    150  16 1 A 4   .    151  36 1 A 3   4
152   12 0 A 3   .    153  28 1 A 3   .    154  48 0 A 3 42
155  -38 1 A 3   .    156   9 1 A 3   .    157  11 0 A 3   .
158   20 0 A 4   .    159  30 1 A 4   .    160   6 1 A 4   .
201  -15 0 B 3   .    202  -4 1 B 3   .    203  10 1 B 4   .
204   10 0 B 4   .    205   8 0 B 3   .    206  11 1 B 3   .
207  -52 1 B 4   .    208  12 1 B 3   .    209  20 0 B 3   .
210   46 1 B 4   .    211  32 0 B 4 44    212  10 1 B 3   .
213   42 0 B 3   .    214  31 1 B 4 20    215   4 1 B 4   .
216  -24 0 B 3   .    217  20 1 B 3 33    218  16 0 B 3   .
219    2 1 B 3   .    220  25 1 B 4   .    221  11 0 B 4   .
222  -52 0 B 4   .    223  20 1 B 4   .    224   9 1 B 3   .
225   22 1 B 3   .    226  23 1 B 3   .    227  11 0 B 3   .
228   13 1 B 3   .    229  -7 0 B 4   .    230   8 1 B 4   .
231   37 1 B 4   .    232  32 0 B 4 26    233  24 1 B 3 10
234  -52 1 B 4   .    235  20 0 B 4   .    236  34 0 B 4   .
237   27 1 B 3   .    301  10 1 C 3   .    302 -10 0 C 4   8
303   32 1 C 4   .    304  14 1 C 4 20    305  24 0 C 3   .
306   14 1 C 4   .    307  36 0 C 3   .    308 -52 0 C 3   .
309    7 1 C 3   .    310   6 0 C 4   .    311   5 1 C 3   .
312    9 1 C 3   .    313  12 1 C 4   .    314  21 0 C 3   .
315   10 1 C 3   .    316  26 0 C 4 36    317 -52 1 C 4   .
318   10 1 C 3   .    319  27 0 C 4 12    320   5 1 C 3   .
321   34 1 C 3 16     322  14 0 C 4   .    323   6 1 C 3   .
324   22 1 C 4   .    325  45 0 C 4 12    326  16 0 C 3   .
327   15 1 C 3 30     328  33 0 C 4 22    329  20 1 C 3   .
330  -52 1 C 3 30     331   5 0 C 4   .    332  10 1 C 3   .
333   16 0 C 3   .    334  -2 1 C 4   .    335  17 0 C 4   .
336   16 0 C 4   .    337  16 1 C 3   .    338  33 1 C 3 20
339   24 0 C 3 11     340  12 1 C 3   .    341  27 1 C 4 18
342    2 1 C 4   .    343  -6 0 C 4   .    344 -20 1 C 4   .
345   14 0 C 3   .    346   3 1 C 3   .
;


PROC PHREG DATA = VITCLEAR;
   MODEL RSPTIM*CENS(0) = TRT DENS INFCTN / TIES = EXACT;     ❽
   IF INFTIM GT RSPTIM OR INFTIM = . THEN INFCTN = 0;         ❿
       ELSE INFCTN = 1;
   STRATA CENTER;                                             ❾
   TITLE1 'Cox Proportional Hazards Model';
   TITLE2 'Example 22.2: Hyalurise in Vitreous Hemorrhage' ;
RUN;
```

OUTPUT 22.2. SAS Output for Example 22.2

```
                    Cox Proportional Hazards Model
              Example 22.2: Hyalurise in Vitreous Hemorrhage

                         The PHREG Procedure

                         Model Information

             Data Set                 WORK.VITCLEAR
             Dependent Variable       RSPTIM
             Censoring Variable       CENS
             Censoring Value(s)       0
             Ties Handling            EXACT

        Summary of the Number of Event and Censored Values


                                                          Percent
   Stratum    CENTER     Total      Event     Censored    Censored

   1          A            60         45           15       25.00
   2          B            37         30            7       18.92
   3          C            46         39            7       15.22
   ------------------------------------------------------------------
   Total                  143        114           29       20.28

                         Convergence Status

           Convergence criterion (GCONV=1E-8) satisfied.

                       Model Fit Statistics

                           Without          With
              Criterion    Covariates       Covariates

              -2 LOG L       641.460          636.479
              AIC            641.460          642.479
              SBC            641.460          650.688

            Testing Global Null Hypothesis: BETA=0

          Test                Chi-Square      DF      Pr > ChiSq ⑬

          Likelihood Ratio       4.9809         3         0.1732
          Score                  4.9703         3         0.1740
          Wald                   4.9251         3         0.1774

            Analysis of Maximum Likelihood Estimates

                  Parameter   Standard                          Hazard
   Variable  DF   Estimate       Error  Chi-Square   Pr>ChiSq    Ratio

   TRT        1    0.34500     0.19577     3.1057     0.0780 ⑪  1.412 ⑫
   DENS       1   -0.23884     0.19598     1.4852     0.2230     0.788
   INFCTN     1    0.12835     0.27797     0.2132     0.6443     1.137
```

22.4 Details & Notes

▶ **22.4.1.** The *Cox proportional hazards model* is a 'semi-parametric' approach that does not require the assumption of any specific hazard function or distribution of survival times. In this sense, it takes the character of a non-parametric test. However, as in regression analysis, this method models the survival times as a function of the covariates with the goal of obtaining estimates of the model parameters (β_i's). Various types of functions can be used and different models can be specified for the distribution of the error variation. In this sense, the *Cox proportional hazards model* is parametric.

▶ **22.4.2.** The hazard is a function of time, t. Formally, the hazard represents the probability that the *event* of interest occurs at a specified time (t) given that it has not occurred prior to time (t).

If the hazard is constant over time, *event* times can be modeled with the exponential distribution. The natural log of the hazard function is

$$\ln h(t) = \lambda(t) + \beta_1 X_1 + \beta_2 X_2 + \ldots + \beta_k X_k$$

If the event times have an exponential distribution, $\lambda(t)$ is a constant, independent of t, such as α, and the model becomes

$$\ln h(t) = \alpha + \beta_1 X_1 + \beta_2 X_2 + \ldots + \beta_k X_k$$

which means the hazard is constant with respect to time and is a simple linear function of the covariates, X_i's, on the log-scale.

Section 21.4.5 describes how to test for exponential *event* times by checking whether a plot of the log of the survival probabilities is linear through the origin. This test is a direct result of the fact that the exponential distribution is associated with a constant hazard function (i.e., risk is independent of time).

In general, if a model for the hazard function can be assumed, then the survival distributions can be specified. In fact, the cumulative survival distribution is a function of the hazard function integrated over time. Therefore, the survival distribution can be described by the hazard function, and, conversely, the survival distribution uniquely defines a hazard function.

When the survival distribution is known or can be accurately assumed, a parametric analysis can be applied, often with greater efficiency than the non-parametric *log-rank test* or the 'semi-parametric' *Cox proportional hazards model*. The parametric approach with a known survival distribution can easily incorporate covariates into the analysis. In addition to exponential *event* times, widely used models include the log-normal, Weibull, gamma, and log-logistic distributions. The SAS procedure LIFEREG can be used to fit any of these parametric models with any number of covariates.

The main disadvantage of the parametric approach is that, in many cases, model assumptions might be incorrect and there might not be enough data to adequately test the assumptions or, perhaps, the actual hazard function is not well represented by any of those in common usage. Often, the results are highly dependent on the appropriate distributional assumptions.

▶ **22.4.3.** The strength of the *Cox proportional hazards model* is its ability to incorporate background factors as covariates. When many covariates are being considered, this method can be used in an exploratory fashion to build a model that includes significant covariates and excludes the covariates that have little apparent effect on the *event* times. This stepwise procedure is demonstrated in the SAS OnlineDoc for PROC PHREG.

▶ **22.4.4.** PROC PHREG prints the results of a global test that determines whether any of the covariates included in the model are significant after adjusting for all the other covariates. As shown in the output for Example 22.1 ❻, three different methods are used: "Likelihood Ratio", "Score" and "Wald". Each of these is a goodness-of-fit test with an approximate chi-square distribution with 2 degrees of freedom under the global null hypothesis of 'no covariate effects'. With the significant results of $p < 0.005$ for all three methods in the example, you conclude that fluctuations in *event* times are associated with either vaccine group (TRT) or prior lesional frequency (X) or both.

A poor fit is indicated by the global tests in Example 22.2, all of which show non-significant *chi-square tests* with p-values of approximately 0.17 ❽.

▶ **22.4.5.** A positive parameter estimate indicates that the hazard increases with increasing values of the covariate. A negative value indicates that the hazard decreases with increasing values of the covariate. In Example 22.1, the negative parameter estimate for TRT (–0.906) indicates that the hazard of HSV-2 recurrence decreases with active treatment (TRT=1) compared with a placebo (TRT=0). The hazard increases with larger prior lesional frequencies (X), as seen by the positive parameter estimate for X (0.176).

The term 'hazard' is often associated with the event of death or disease. However, in survival analysis, 'hazard' does not always connote a danger or an undesirable event. In Example 22.2, the event of interest is 'response,' which is a desirable result. Although it sounds awkward, an increasing 'hazard' in the desirable response with active treatment compared with saline injection is seen. Notice that the parameter estimate for TRT is positive, and the hazard ratio for the treatment effect is greater than 1 (1.412 ❿), just the opposite of Example 22.1.

▶ **22.4.6.** The model for the hazard function using *Cox proportional hazards* with only one covariate (k=1) is

$$h(t) = \lambda(t) \cdot e^{\beta X}$$

For two patients with different values of X, such as X_u and X_v, the ratio of hazards at time t is

$$\frac{h_u(t)}{h_v(t)} = \frac{\lambda(t) \cdot e^{\beta X_u}}{\lambda(t) \cdot e^{\beta X_v}} = e^{\beta(X_u - X_v)}$$

which is constant with respect to time, t. This is the proportional hazards assumption.

If X is a dummy variable with $X_u = 1$ (the active group) and $X_v = 0$ (the placebo group), $X_u - X_v = 1$ so that e^{β} represents the ratio of the hazard that's associated with the active treatment to the hazard that's associated with the placebo. This is the hazard ratio in the SAS printout for Example 22.1 ❺ and Example 22.2 ⓬.

> Note: In SAS releases prior to Version 7, the hazard ratio is labeled 'Risk Ratio' in SAS output.

In Example 22.1, the hazard ratio for TRT is $e^{-0.906} = 0.404$. This can be interpreted as the hazard at any time t for the active group is only 40.4% of the placebo group's hazard. The hazard ratio for X is 1.193. Because X is a numeric variable (rather than a numerically coded categorical variable), you interpret this as a 19.3% increase in the hazard of an HSV-2 recurrence for each additional prior lesion that was experienced.

▶ **22.4.7.** Example 22.2 illustrates the inclusion of a dichotomous time-dependent covariate. Continuous numeric covariates can also be time-dependent. For example, time to a certain response in a nutritional study might depend on a subject's protein intake, which might change during the course of the study. This type of continuous numeric time-dependent covariates can also be included in PROC PHREG. Details and an excellent discussion of time-dependent covariates using PROC PHREG can be found in *Survival Analysis Using the SAS System*, by Paul Allison (1995), which was written under the SAS Books By Users program.

▶ **22.4.8.** 'Non-proportional hazards' implies an increasing or decreasing hazard ratio over time. In PROC PHREG, this can be represented by a covariate-by-time 'interaction'. The proportional hazards assumption for any covariate can be checked by including the interaction of that covariate with time as a new time-dependent covariate in the MODEL statement in PROC PHREG. For example, to check the proportional hazards assumption for the covariate DENS in Example 22.2, you can include the time-dependent covariate, TDENS, by specifying the following SAS statement:

```
TDENS = DENS*RSPTIM;
```

after the MODEL statement. A significant test for the parameter that's associated with TDENS would indicate that the hazard changes over time.

This test is also illustrated in the SAS Help and Documentation for PROC PHREG, which recommends using the natural logarithm of the response times decreased by the average of the log response times to obtain greater stability. Use of this stabilizing transformation in Example 22.2 would require the statement

```
TDENS = DENS*(LOG(RSPTIM ) - 2.85);
```

in place of the preceding statement (2.85 is the mean of the ln(RSPTIM) over all observations).

A visual aid in determining conformance with the assumption of proportional hazards is a plot of the log(–log(S(t))) versus time, where S(t) is the estimated survival distribution. This can be done in SAS using the PLOTS=(LLS) option in the LIFETEST procedure. The graphs of these functions for each group should be parallel under the proportional hazards assumption. Lack of parallelism suggests deviations from the proportional hazards assumption.

When the proportional hazards assumption does not seem to hold for a specific covariate, the *Cox proportional hazards model* might still be used by performing the analysis within each of a series of sub-intervals of the range of the covariate's values, then combining the results. This is done in SAS by using the STRATA statement, which is illustrated in the SAS code for Example 22.2. If the covariate has continuous numeric values, the strata can be defined by numeric intervals in the STRATA statement (for details, see the SAS Help and Documentation for PROC PHREG).

22.4.9. An adjustment might be necessary when ties occur in *event* times. SAS has 4 adjustment options for handling ties: BRESLOW, EFRON, EXACT, and DISCRETE. BRESLOW is the default, although it might not be the best option to use. With small data sets or a small number of tied values, the EXACT option is usually preferable. Because of computational resources, the EXACT option is not efficient for larger data sets. The EFRON option provides a good approximation and is computationally faster when large amounts of data are being analyzed.

CHAPTER 23

Exercises

23.1 Introduction

The data set, TRIAL, in Chapter 3, is based on a contrived, simplified clinical study that measured three types of response variables for 100 patients. The exercises in this section provide an opportunity to practice applying some of the methods discussed in this book using this data set. Section 23.2 lists the exercises and requests an analysis that uses a specific method referenced in an earlier chapter. The SAS code for performing these exercises is shown in Appendix G. Section 23.3 provides a critique of the methods used and a discussion of their appropriateness, based on the assumptions the analyst is willing to make.

23.2 Exercises

Write a SAS program to perform the following analyses using the 'TRIAL' data set in Chapter 3. Analyses 1 to 11 use the continuous numeric response SCORE, Analyses 12 to 17 use the dichotomous response RESP, and Analyses 18 to 27 use the ordinal categorical response SEV.

▶ **23.2.1.** Using the SCORE response variable:

Analysis 1: Compare mean responses between treatment groups by using the *two-sample t-test* (Chapter 5).

Analysis 2: Apply the *Wilcoxon rank-sum test* to test for any shifts in the distribution between Treatment Groups A and B (Chapter 13).

Analysis 3: Using a *one-way ANOVA* model (Chapter 6), test for a difference in mean response between treatment groups.

Analysis 4:   Determine if there is an interaction between treatment group and study center by using the *two-way ANOVA* (Chapter 7).

Analysis 5:   Re-run the *two-way ANOVA* without the interaction effect to determine the significance of treatment group differences.

Analysis 6:   Compare treatment group responses by using *ANOVA* accounting for any effects due to Study Center and Sex. Include all interactions.

Analysis 7:   Check for a significant treatment group effect adjusted for Study Center and Sex by using a main effects *ANOVA* model.

Analysis 8:   Ignoring all group factors, determine if the response variable SCORE is linearly related to Age (Chapter 10). Plot the data.

Analysis 9:   Determine if the slope of the *linear regression* in Analysis 8 differs between treatment groups (Chapter 11).

Analysis 10:   Estimate the mean response for each treatment group using Age as a covariate. Assuming the answer to 9 is 'no', determine the p-value for comparing these adjusted means (Chapter 11). Plot the data by treatment group.

Analysis 11:   Compare treatment group means adjusted for Age and Study Center (Chapter 11). Assume there are no interactions.

▶ 23.2.2.   Using the RESP response variable:

Analysis 12:   Compare response rates between treatment groups by using the *chi-square test* (Chapter 16).

Analysis 13:   Compare response rates between treatment groups by using *Fisher's exact test* (Chapter 17).

Analysis 14:   Compare response rates between treatment groups controlling for Study Center by using the *Cochran-Mantel-Haenszel test* (Chapter 19).

Analysis 15:   Compare response rates between treatment groups by using *logistic regression* (Chapter 20).

Analysis 16:   Compare response rates between treatment groups adjusted for Age assuming a logistic model (Chapter 20).

Analysis 17:   Using a *logistic regression* model, test for a significant treatment group effect adjusted for Age, Sex, Study Center, and Treatment-by-Center interaction (Chapter 20).

▶ **23.2.3.** Using the SEV response variable:

Analysis 18: Test for general association between severity of response and treatment group by using the *chi-square test* (Chapter 16).

Analysis 19: Apply the generalized *Fisher's exact test* to determine if the distributions of response by severity differ between treatment groups (Chapter 17).

Analysis 20: Use the *chi-square test* to determine if the row mean scores differ between treatment groups (Chapter 16). Use 'table' scores for coding severity.

Analysis 21: Repeat Analysis 20 using modified ridit scores in place of 'table' scores.

Analysis 22: Test for a shift in the distribution of severity between treatment groups by using the *Wilcoxon rank-sum test* (Chapter 13).

Analysis 23: Test for a difference in mean severity scores between treatment groups controlling for Study Center (Chapter 19). Use 'table' scores.

Analysis 24: Repeat Analysis 23 using modified ridit scores in place of 'table' scores.

Analysis 25: Determine the significance of the treatment group effect by using a *logistic regression* model under the assumption of proportional odds (Chapter 20).

Analysis 26: Using a proportional odds model, compare response rates between treatment groups adjusted for Age (Chapter 20).

Analysis 27: Adjusting for Age, Sex, and Study Center, determine the significance of the treatment group effect by using the proportional odds model (Chapter 20).

23.3 Appropriateness of the Methods

SAS code for conducting the analyses in the previous section is given in Appendix G. Table 23.1 summarizes the p-values for the treatment group effect for each of these analyses. Although the exercises are assigned for practice in using SAS to perform commonly used statistical analyses, some of these methods would clearly be inappropriate to use in practice. Let's take a look at the results.

TABLE 23.1. Summary of Significance of Treatment Group Effects from Exercises

Analysis	Method	p-Value for Treatment Group effect
	Analyses Using the SCORE Variable	
1	Two-sample t-test	0.0422
2	Wilcoxon rank-sum test	0.0464
3	One-way ANOVA	0.0422
4	Two-way ANOVA with interaction	0.0702
5	Two-way ANOVA without interaction	0.0378
6	Three-way ANOVA with all interactions	0.1036
7	Three-way ANOVA main effects model	0.0493
8	Linear regression	--
9	ANCOVA / unequal slopes	0.5663
10	ANCOVA / equal slopes	0.0257
11	Stratified ANCOVA / equal slopes	0.0252
	Analyses Using the RESP Variable	
12	Chi-square test	0.4510
13	Fisher's exact test	0.4794
14	Cochran-Mantel-Haenszel test	0.4113
15	Logistic regression, TRT effect only	0.4523
16	Logistic regression, TRT and AGE effects	0.3576
17	Logistic regression, TRT, AGE, SEX, CENTER, TRTxCENTER effects	0.6984
	Analyses Using the SEV Variable	
18	Chi-square test	0.1216
19	Generalized Fisher's exact test	0.1277
20	Mantel-Haenszel, row mean scores differ / table scores	0.0514
21	Mantel-Haenszel, row mean scores differ / mod. ridit scores	0.0468
22	Wilcoxon rank-sum test	0.0472
23	CMH, row mean scores differ / table scores	0.0445
24	CMH, row mean scores differ / mod. ridit scores	0.0471
25	Proportional odds model, TRT effect only	0.0447
26	Proportional odds model, TRT and AGE effects	0.0244
27	Proportional odds model, TRT, AGE, SEX, CENTER	0.0313

The SCORE variable is considered a continuous numeric response. As such, you can apply a variety of *ANOVA*, *ANCOVA*, and non-parametric methods to test for equality of treatment groups.

▶ **23.3.1.**   The *two-sample t-test* and *one-way ANOVA* produce the same p-values (Analyses 1 and 3). This will always be the case when there are only two groups because the *ANOVA F-test* is functionally equivalent to the *t-test* in this situation. When using SAS, PROC TTEST would usually be preferable because it automatically provides a test for the assumption of equal variances and computes Satterthwaite's adjustment for the unequal variance case.

▶ **23.3.2.**   The p-values differ considerably for the *two-way ANOVA* with (Analysis 4) and without the interaction (Analysis 5). In an unbalanced design, the inclusion of an interaction term in the model, when, in fact, no interaction exists, can produce conservative main effects comparisons based on the SAS Type III sums of squares in the *ANOVA*. For this reason, many analysts prefer to use the interaction model only as a preliminary test, rather than as a final model.

▶ **23.3.3.**   Notice that inclusion of the Study Center effect using the two-way main effects model (Analysis 5) provides sufficient blocking effect to bring out a slightly more significant treatment effect than the one-way *ANOVA* (Analysis 3), even though it is not a significant effect. When a third main effect (Sex) is added (Analysis 7), the treatment comparison actually becomes less significant than either the one-way or two-way main effects models. Although such a scenario can occur for a number of reasons, in this case, it appears to be an inconsequential difference based on the sample size imbalance, which affects the SAS Type III sums of squares. The treatment effect can be masked, as in Analysis 6, when exploring interaction effects.

▶ **23.3.4.**   *ANCOVA* (Analysis 10) reveals that Age might be an important covariate, and the adjusted Treatment Group differences appear more significant than those unadjusted for Age. This comes at the expense of having to assume equal slopes between the two groups, an assumption that is supported by Analysis 9. As you've seen previously, the Treatment Group effect is masked when testing for the interaction (equal slope assumption) as in Analysis 9.

▶ **23.3.5.**   Addition of the Study Center effect to the *ANCOVA* (Analysis 11) does not appreciably alter the significance of the Treatment effect noted in Analysis 10. Overall, it is clear that the inclusion of the Age effect in the model removes more background noise than the inclusion of either Study Center or Sex.

▶ **23.3.6.**   Although the *t-test* and *ANOVA* methods assume a normal distribution of the response data, these methods are fairly robust against departures from this assumption, especially with larger sample sizes. A histogram of the data (Output 3.5) does not support the normality assumption in this case. However, treatment comparisons based on ranked data (Analysis 2) result in similar p-values with this size sample (N=100). Therefore, any of the following analyses: 1, 2, 3, 5, 7, 10, or 11, would be appropriate. The analyses intended to explore interactions (4, 6, and 9) would not be the best tests to use for treatment differences when interactions do not exist. In the presence of an interaction that involves Treatment Group, alternative approaches, such as subgroup analyses, might be more appropriate.

Notice that the treatment group comparisons adjusted for Age result in the greatest significance. This might be due to Age differences for this sample, or it might be a repeatable effect. In any case, to select appropriate statistical methods for pivotal studies prior to examination of the data, you must rely on trends found from previous studies. If a specific covariate (such as Age) was consistently found to be an important factor in Phase II studies, for example, the pre-specified statistical model to be used for the Phase III program should include that covariate. Usually, the simplest models that contain all factors known to have an important effect on the treatment comparisons should be used in pivotal studies.

The RESP variable is a dichotomous response. For this, you can apply multiple categorical methods to analyze differences between treatment groups.

▶   **23.3.7.**   Comparisons of response rates between treatment groups are not significant. Similar p-values for the treatment group comparisons, which range between 0.41 and 0.48, are found by using the *chi-square test* (Analysis 12), *Fisher's exact test* (Analysis 13), the *CMH test* stratified by Study Center (Analysis 14), and a *logistic regression* model with no covariates (Analysis 15) (a finding that might be expected in studies of moderate sample sizes, such as this one). With very small sample sizes or response rates close to 0 or 1, *Fisher's exact test* would be more appropriate than the other methods. Exact methods, useful in the case of small samples, are also available in *logistic regression* analysis.

▶   **23.3.8.**   The inclusion of Age as a covariate in the *logistic regression* model results in a smaller p-value for the treatment effect (Analysis 16). As shown in the *ANCOVA* (Analysis 10), Age appears to be an important factor when modeling treatment differences.

▶   **23.3.9.**   The inclusion of Study Center, Sex, and the Treatment-by-Center interaction in the *logistic regression* model results in even less significant treatment comparisons (Analysis 17), further supporting the recommendation to use parsimonious models. This can often be done by using *logistic regression* in a stepwise fashion to eliminate non-significant effects. Stepwise procedures are most often used in an exploratory role or in earlier phase studies.

The SEV variable is an ordinal categorical response with 4 levels. Here, you can apply a *rank test*, a *logistic regression* analysis using the proportional odds model, or a number of other categorical procedures.

▶ **23.3.10.** Both the *chi-square test* (Analysis 18) and the *generalized Fisher's exact test* (Analysis 19) are tests for general association. Notice that the p-values for treatment comparisons are much larger than those of the other tests (Analyses 20 to 27) for the SEV response variable. As explained in Chapter 16, these methods are testing a less-specific hypothesis.

▶ **23.3.11.** The *Mantel-Haenszel chi-square test* (Analysis 20) for 'row mean scores differ' is more appropriate for ordinal data than the test for 'general association'. The *Mantel-Haenszel chi-square* tests for equality of mean scores between treatment groups, when the scores are assigned to the categorical levels in integer increments ('table scores'). In this case, greater significance is found by using the modified ridit scores (Analysis 21) compared with the 'table scores' (Chapter 16).

This will not always be the case, as seen in Analyses 23 and 24. In these analyses, the *CMH test* controlling for Study Center is used for comparing mean scores between treatment groups. The p-value using the 'table scores' (Analysis 23) is slightly smaller than that based on the modified ridit scores (Analysis 24).

▶ **23.3.12.** The *Wilcoxon rank-sum test* (Analysis 22) is actually a special version of the *Kruskal-Wallis test*. Recall that the *Mantel-Haenszel chi-square* using modified ridit scores is identical to the *Kruskal-Wallis test* (Chapter 18). The difference in p-values (0.0472 in Analysis 22 vs. 0.0468 in Analysis 21) is due only to a correction factor.

▶ **23.3.13.** *Logistic regression* modeling, similar to the *ANCOVA* method, shows the most significant treatment comparison (Analysis 26) when adjusting only for Age. Interestingly, this p-value (0.0244) is slightly less than that obtained by using the *ANCOVA* method (Analysis 10), perhaps due to the deviation from normality of the SCORE variable.

23.4 Summary

When you can quantify degree of response, it is usually easier to discriminate between treatment groups because more powerful statistical methods are available. With only the knowledge of whether or not a patient responded, you see that treatment group differences are non-significant for all of the applicable methods (Analyses 12 to 17). When the response is categorized by severity, you obtain significant treatment group discrimination. Notably, when using a more precise response (continuous numeric representation of severity), the significance of treatment comparisons was not improved. This might be due, in part, to the non-normality of the SCORE results, but it also points out the power of categorical analyses when using ordinal response categories relative to *ANOVA* methods.

Comparison of these results points out the need to know how closely the underlying assumptions are satisfied before selecting an appropriate statistical method.

Appendix A

Probability Tables

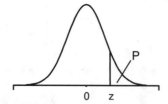

APPENDIX A.1. Probabilities of the Standard Normal Distribution

z	P	z	P	z	P	z	P	z	P	z	P
0.00	0.5000										
0.01	0.4960	0.51	0.3050	1.01	0.1562	1.51	0.0655	2.01	0.0222	2.51	0.0060
0.02	0.4920	0.52	0.3015	1.02	0.1539	1.52	0.0643	2.02	0.0217	2.52	0.0059
0.03	0.4880	0.53	0.2981	1.03	0.1515	1.53	0.0630	2.03	0.0212	2.53	0.0057
0.04	0.4840	0.54	0.2946	1.04	0.1492	1.54	0.0618	2.04	0.0207	2.54	0.0055
0.05	0.4801	0.55	0.2912	1.05	0.1469	1.55	0.0606	2.05	0.0202	2.55	0.0054
0.06	0.4761	0.56	0.2877	1.06	0.1446	1.56	0.0594	2.06	0.0197	2.56	0.0052
0.07	0.4721	0.57	0.2843	1.07	0.1423	1.57	0.0582	2.07	0.0192	2.57	0.0051
0.08	0.4681	0.58	0.2810	1.08	0.1401	1.58	0.0571	2.08	0.0188	2.58	0.0049
0.09	0.4641	0.59	0.2776	1.09	0.1379	1.59	0.0559	2.09	0.0183	2.59	0.0048
0.10	0.4602	0.60	0.2743	1.10	0.1357	1.60	0.0548	2.10	0.0179	2.60	0.0047
0.11	0.4562	0.61	0.2709	1.11	0.1335	1.61	0.0537	2.11	0.0174	2.61	0.0045
0.12	0.4522	0.62	0.2676	1.12	0.1314	1.62	0.0526	2.12	0.0170	2.62	0.0044
0.13	0.4483	0.63	0.2643	1.13	0.1292	1.63	0.0516	2.13	0.0166	2.63	0.0043
0.14	0.4443	0.64	0.2611	1.14	0.1271	1.64	0.0505	2.14	0.0162	2.64	0.0041
0.15	0.4404	0.65	0.2578	1.15	0.1251	1.65	0.0495	2.15	0.0158	2.65	0.0040
0.16	0.4364	0.66	0.2546	1.16	0.1230	1.66	0.0485	2.16	0.0154	2.66	0.0039
0.17	0.4325	0.67	0.2514	1.17	0.1210	1.67	0.0475	2.17	0.0150	2.67	0.0038
0.18	0.4286	0.68	0.2483	1.18	0.1190	1.68	0.0465	2.18	0.0146	2.68	0.0037
0.19	0.4247	0.69	0.2451	1.19	0.1170	1.69	0.0455	2.19	0.0143	2.69	0.0036
0.20	0.4207	0.70	0.2420	1.20	0.1151	1.70	0.0446	2.20	0.0139	2.70	0.0035
0.21	0.4168	0.71	0.2389	1.21	0.1131	1.71	0.0436	2.21	0.0136	2.71	0.0034
0.22	0.4129	0.72	0.2358	1.22	0.1112	1.72	0.0427	2.22	0.0132	2.72	0.0033
0.23	0.4090	0.73	0.2327	1.23	0.1093	1.73	0.0418	2.23	0.0129	2.73	0.0032
0.24	0.4052	0.74	0.2296	1.24	0.1075	1.74	0.0409	2.24	0.0125	2.74	0.0031
0.25	0.4013	0.75	0.2266	1.25	0.1056	1.75	0.0401	2.25	0.0122	2.75	0.0030
0.26	0.3974	0.76	0.2236	1.26	0.1038	1.76	0.0392	2.26	0.0119	2.76	0.0029
0.27	0.3936	0.77	0.2206	1.27	0.1020	1.77	0.0384	2.27	0.0116	2.77	0.0028
0.28	0.3897	0.78	0.2177	1.28	0.1003	1.78	0.0375	2.28	0.0113	2.78	0.0027
0.29	0.3859	0.79	0.2148	1.29	0.0985	1.79	0.0367	2.29	0.0110	2.79	0.0026
0.30	0.3821	0.80	0.2119	1.30	0.0968	1.80	0.0359	2.30	0.0107	2.80	0.0026
0.31	0.3783	0.81	0.2090	1.31	0.0951	1.81	0.0351	2.31	0.0104	2.81	0.0025
0.32	0.3745	0.82	0.2061	1.32	0.0934	1.82	0.0344	2.32	0.0102	2.82	0.0024
0.33	0.3707	0.83	0.2033	1.33	0.0918	1.83	0.0336	2.33	0.0099	2.83	0.0023
0.34	0.3669	0.84	0.2005	1.34	0.0901	1.84	0.0329	2.34	0.0096	2.84	0.0023
0.35	0.3632	0.85	0.1977	1.35	0.0885	1.85	0.0322	2.35	0.0094	2.85	0.0022
0.36	0.3594	0.86	0.1949	1.36	0.0869	1.86	0.0314	2.36	0.0091	2.86	0.0021
0.37	0.3557	0.87	0.1922	1.37	0.0853	1.87	0.0307	2.37	0.0089	2.87	0.0021
0.38	0.3520	0.88	0.1894	1.38	0.0838	1.88	0.0301	2.38	0.0087	2.88	0.0020
0.39	0.3483	0.89	0.1867	1.39	0.0823	1.89	0.0294	2.39	0.0084	2.89	0.0019
0.40	0.3446	0.90	0.1841	1.40	0.0808	1.90	0.0287	2.40	0.0082	2.90	0.0019
0.41	0.3409	0.91	0.1814	1.41	0.0793	1.91	0.0281	2.41	0.0080	2.91	0.0018
0.42	0.3372	0.92	0.1788	1.42	0.0778	1.92	0.0274	2.42	0.0078	2.92	0.0018
0.43	0.3336	0.93	0.1762	1.43	0.0764	1.93	0.0268	2.43	0.0075	2.93	0.0017
0.44	0.3300	0.94	0.1736	1.44	0.0749	1.94	0.0262	2.44	0.0073	2.94	0.0016
0.45	0.3264	0.95	0.1711	1.45	0.0735	1.95	0.0256	2.45	0.0071	2.95	0.0016
0.46	0.3228	0.96	0.1685	1.46	0.0721	1.96	0.0250	2.46	0.0069	2.96	0.0015
0.47	0.3192	0.97	0.1660	1.47	0.0708	1.97	0.0244	2.47	0.0068	2.97	0.0015
0.48	0.3156	0.98	0.1635	1.48	0.0694	1.98	0.0239	2.48	0.0066	2.98	0.0014
0.49	0.3121	0.99	0.1611	1.49	0.0681	1.99	0.0233	2.49	0.0064	2.99	0.0014
0.50	0.3085	1.00	0.1587	1.50	0.0668	2.00	0.0228	2.50	0.0062	3.00	0.0013

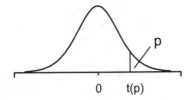

0   t(p)

APPENDIX A.2. Critical Values of the Student t-Distribution

df	t(0.100)	t(0.050)	t(0.025)	t(0.010)
1	3.078	6.314	12.706	31.821
2	1.886	2.920	4.303	6.965
3	1.638	2.353	3.182	4.541
4	1.533	2.132	2.776	3.747
5	1.476	2.015	2.571	3.365
6	1.440	1.943	2.447	3.143
7	1.415	1.895	2.365	2.998
8	1.397	1.860	2.306	2.896
9	1.383	1.833	2.262	2.821
10	1.372	1.812	2.228	2.764
11	1.363	1.796	2.201	2.718
12	1.356	1.782	2.179	2.681
13	1.350	1.771	2.160	2.650
14	1.345	1.761	2.145	2.624
15	1.341	1.753	2.131	2.602
16	1.337	1.746	2.120	2.583
17	1.333	1.740	2.110	2.567
18	1.330	1.734	2.101	2.552
19	1.328	1.729	2.093	2.539
20	1.325	1.725	2.086	2.528
21	1.323	1.721	2.080	2.518
22	1.321	1.717	2.074	2.508
23	1.319	1.714	2.069	2.500
24	1.318	1.711	2.064	2.492
25	1.316	1.708	2.060	2.485
26	1.315	1.706	2.056	2.479
27	1.314	1.703	2.052	2.473
28	1.313	1.701	2.048	2.467
29	1.311	1.699	2.045	2.462
30	1.310	1.697	2.042	2.457
31	1.309	1.696	2.040	2.453
32	1.309	1.694	2.037	2.449
33	1.308	1.692	2.035	2.445
34	1.307	1.691	2.032	2.441
35	1.306	1.690	2.030	2.438

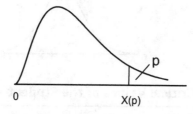

APPENDIX A.3. Critical Values of the Chi-Square Distribution

df	X(0.100)	X(0.050)	X(0.025)	X(0.010)
1	2.706	3.841	5.024	6.635
2	4.605	5.991	7.378	9.210
3	6.251	7.815	9.348	11.345
4	7.779	9.488	11.143	13.277
5	9.236	11.070	12.832	15.086
6	10.645	12.592	14.449	16.812
7	12.017	14.067	16.013	18.475
8	13.362	15.507	17.535	20.090
9	14.684	16.919	19.023	21.666
10	15.987	18.307	20.483	23.209
11	17.275	19.675	21.920	24.725
12	18.549	21.026	23.337	26.217
13	19.812	22.362	24.736	27.688
14	21.064	23.685	26.119	29.141
15	22.307	24.996	27.488	30.578
16	23.542	26.296	28.845	32.000
17	24.769	27.587	30.191	33.409
18	25.989	28.869	31.526	34.805
19	27.204	30.144	32.852	36.191
20	28.412	31.410	34.170	37.566
21	29.615	32.671	35.479	38.932
22	30.813	33.924	36.781	40.289
23	32.007	35.172	38.076	41.638
24	33.196	36.415	39.364	42.980
25	34.382	37.652	40.646	44.314
26	35.563	38.885	41.923	45.642
27	36.741	40.113	43.195	46.963
28	37.916	41.337	44.461	48.278
29	39.087	42.557	45.722	49.588
30	40.256	43.773	46.979	50.892
31	41.422	44.985	48.232	52.191
32	42.585	46.194	49.480	53.486
33	43.745	47.400	50.725	54.775
34	44.903	48.602	51.966	56.061
35	46.059	49.802	53.203	57.342

Common Distributions Used in Statistical Inference

B.1 Notation

$X \sim N(\mu, \sigma^2)$

    means that the random variable, X, is normally distributed with mean μ and variance σ^2.

$X \sim \chi^2_{\upsilon}$

    means that the random variable, X, has the chi-square distribution with υ degrees of freedom.

$X \sim F^{\upsilon_1}_{\upsilon_2}$

    means that the random variable, X, has the F-distribution with υ_1 upper and υ_2 lower degrees of freedom.

$X \sim t_{\upsilon}$

    means that the random variable, X, has the Student-t distribution with υ degrees of freedom.

$X \sim U_{[0-1]}$

    means that the random variable, X, has the Uniform distribution over the interval (0–1).

B.2   Properties

1. If $X \sim N(\mu, \sigma^2)$ and $Z = (X-\mu)/\sigma$, then $Z \sim N(0, 1)$.
    Z is called a standard normal random variable.

2. If $X_1 \sim N(\mu_1, \sigma^2_1)$ and $X_2 \sim N(\mu_2, \sigma^2_2)$, X_1 and X_2 are independent, and $Y = X_1 + X_2$, then $Y \sim N(\mu_1 + \mu_2, \sigma^2_1 + \sigma^2_2)$.

    More generally, for any constants, a_1, a_2, ..., a_k, if $X_i \sim N(\mu_i, \sigma^2_i)$ independently for $i = 1, 2, ..., k$, and $Y = a_1X_1 + a_2X_2 + ... + a_kX_k$, then

    $$Y \sim N\left(\sum_{i=1}^{k} a_i \mu_i, \sum_{i=1}^{k} a_i^2 \sigma_i^2 \right)$$

3. If $Z \sim N(0, 1)$, then $Z^2 \sim \chi^2_1$

4. If $Z_i \sim N(0, 1)$ independently for $i = 1, 2, ..., n$, and $Y = Z_1^2 + Z_2^2 + ... + Z_n^2$, then $Y \sim \chi^2_n$

5. If $X \sim \chi^2_m$ and $Y \sim \chi^2_n$ independently, and $W = X + Y$, then $W \sim \chi^2_{m+n}$

6. If $Z \sim N(0, 1)$ and $Y \sim \chi^2_\upsilon$ independently, and $T = Z/(Y/\upsilon)^{1/2}$, then $T \sim t_\upsilon$

7. If $X \sim \chi^2_m$ and $Y \sim \chi^2_n$, independently, and $F = (n/m)(X/Y)$, then $F \sim F^m_n$

8. If $X \sim U_{[0-1]}$, then $-2 \cdot \ln(X) \stackrel{.}{\sim} \chi^2_2$

B.3 Results

Let $X_i \sim N(\mu, \sigma^2)$ independently for $i = 1, 2, ..., n$, and let

$$\overline{X} = \frac{\sum_{i=1}^{n} X_i}{n}$$

represent the sample mean.

Then, Property 2 implies that

$$\overline{X} \sim N\left(\mu, \sigma^2/n\right) \tag{i}$$

Property 1 and Equation (i) imply that

$$Z = \frac{\sqrt{n}(\overline{X} - \mu)}{\sigma} \sim N(0,1) \tag{ii}$$

Property 3 and Equation (ii) imply that

$$Z^2 = \frac{n(\overline{X} - \mu)^2}{\sigma^2} \sim \chi_1^2 \tag{iii}$$

Also, Property 1 implies that

$$\frac{X_i - \mu}{\sigma} \sim N(0, 1) \tag{iv}$$

Property 4 and Equation (iv) imply that

$$\sum_{i=1}^{n} \frac{(X_i - \mu)^2}{\sigma^2} \sim \chi_n^2 \tag{v}$$

It can be shown that

$$\sum (X_i - \mu)^2 = \sum (X_i - \overline{X})^2 + n\,(\overline{X} - \mu)^2$$

and that the summations on the right side of the equal sign are independent, so that,

$$\frac{(n-1)\,s^2}{\sigma^2} = \frac{\sum (X_i - \mu)^2}{\sigma^2} - \frac{n\,(\overline{X} - \mu)^2}{\sigma^2} \qquad \text{(vi)}$$

where s^2 is the sample variance given by

$$s^2 = \frac{\sum (X_i - \overline{X})^2}{n-1}$$

Property 5 and Equations (iii), (v), and (vi) imply that

$$\frac{(n-1)\cdot s^2}{\sigma^2} \sim \chi^2_{n-1} \qquad \text{(vii)}$$

Property 6 and Equations (ii) and (vii) imply that

$$t = \frac{\left(\dfrac{(\overline{X} - \mu)}{\sigma/\sqrt{n}} \right)}{\left(\dfrac{s}{\sigma} \right)} = \frac{(\overline{X} - \mu)}{s/\sqrt{n}} \sim t_{n-1} \qquad \text{(viii)}$$

Property 7 and Equations (iii) and (vii) imply that

$$F = t^2 \sim F^{1}_{n-1} \qquad \text{(ix)}$$

With application to *ANOVA*, let MS_1 and MS_2 represent two independent, unbiased estimates of the error variance, σ^2, based on υ_1 and υ_2 degrees of freedom, respectively, then, by (vii),

$$\frac{\upsilon_1 MS_1}{\sigma^2} \sim \chi^2_{\upsilon_1} \quad \text{and} \quad \frac{\upsilon_2 MS_2}{\sigma^2} \sim \chi^2_{\upsilon_2} \qquad\qquad (x)$$

which, together with Property 7, imply that

$$\frac{MS_1}{MS_2} \sim F^{\upsilon_1}_{\upsilon_2} \qquad\qquad (xi)$$

With application to *meta-analysis*, let p_i represent the p-value for the treatment comparison for the ith of k studies. Under the null hypothesis of no treatment differences, $p_i \sim U_{(0-1)}$. By Property 8, $-2 \cdot \ln(p_i) \sim \chi^2_2$ and, together with Property 5,

$$W = -2 \cdot (\ln(p_1) + \ln(p_2) + \ldots + \ln(p_k)) \sim \chi^2_{2k} \qquad\qquad (xii)$$

B.4   Distributional Shapes

Figure B.1 illustrates the shapes of some common probability distributions. The value of the random variable is shown on the horizontal axis, and the probability is shown on the vertical axis. These shapes vary with changes in the distributional parameters, such as the variance or degrees of freedom. Notice the symmetry of the normal and the t-distributions and the skew associated with the chi-square and F-distributions.

FIGURE B.1. Distributional Shapes

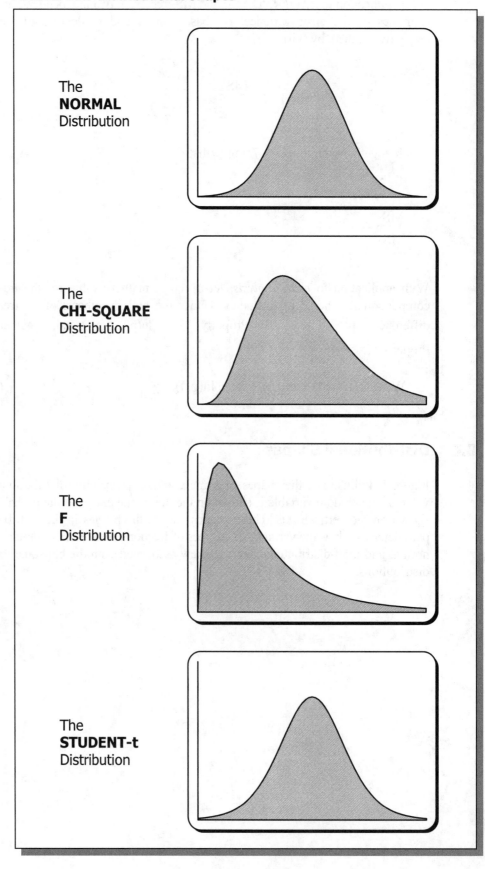

The **NORMAL** Distribution

The **CHI-SQUARE** Distribution

The **F** Distribution

The **STUDENT-t** Distribution

Basic ANOVA Concepts

C.1   Within- vs. Between-Group Variation

Suppose 12 recent college graduates are assigned to three groups: 4 subjects to an exercise group (I), 4 subjects to a drug treatment group (II), and 4 subjects to a control group (III). Ages, pulse rates, diastolic blood pressures, and triglyceride measurements are taken after 8 weeks in the study, with the following results:

	--- GROUP ---		

1. Age (years)

	I	II	III
The age measurements are the same for all 12 subjects. Clearly, there is no variation among the group means and, therefore, no difference among groups with respect to age.	22	22	22
	22	22	22
	22	22	22
	22	22	22

2. Pulse Rates (beats/min.)

	I	II	III
The pulse rate measurements are the same for all 4 subjects within each group, but the measurements vary across groups. Observation of these data without further analysis would likely lead to the conclusion of a difference in mean pulse rates among the three groups.	64	59	70
	64	59	70
	64	59	70
	64	59	70

3. Diastolic BP (mm Hg)

I	II	III
74	81	89
76	80	89
75	79	88
75	80	90

Diastolic blood pressure measurements show a variation both within and among groups. Within-group measurements vary by no more than 2 mm Hg, while the variation among the group means is as much as 14 mm. Because the among-group variation is large compared to the within-group variation, you would likely think that there is a difference among groups in mean diastolic blood pressure.

4. Triglycerides (mg/dl)

I	II	III
85	72	141
101	130	78
68	91	91
121	99	121

The triglyceride measurements show considerable variation both within and among groups. Because the variation within groups no longer allows our intuition to distinguish among groups, it is not clear whether a group effect exists.

For the triglyceride results, there might not be a real difference that can be attributed to the groups, but you need an analytic method to determine this. The ANOVA methods are used for exactly this purpose, i.e., to analyze the variability among groups relative to the variability within groups to determine if differences among groups are meaningful or significant.

The ANOVA methods seek to identify sources of variation for each measurement, and separate the total variability into components associated with each source. The total variability can generally be described as the sum of squared deviations of each measurement from the overall mean. This is comprised of a sum of squares due to suspected sources of variation (often called the 'model sum of squares') and a sum of squares (SS) due to error (SSE):

$$SS(Total) = SS(Model) + SS(Error)$$

The error variability includes such things as measurement error, normal variation due to repeated sampling, and variation among 'like' experimental units from other unknown factors. Such sources might be difficult to control even in a well-designed study. The sources that can be identified and controlled are included in the model SS.

An ANOVA is conducted using *F-tests* that are constructed from the ratio of between-group to within-group variance estimates. Assumptions, usually, entail independent samples from normally distributed populations with equal variances.

In the example given in the beginning of this Appendix, the three groups (I, II, III) represent levels of a factor named GROUP. A 'significant GROUP effect' indicates that there are significant differences in mean responses among the levels of the factor GROUP.

The *one-way ANOVA* has one main effect or grouping factor with two or more levels. In analyzing clinical trials, the main effect will often be a treatment effect. The levels of the factor Treatment might be 'low dose', 'middle dose', 'high dose', and 'placebo'. The *two-way ANOVA* has two main effects, usually a grouping or treatment factor and a blocking factor (such as Gender, Study Center, Diagnosis Group, etc.).

Statistical interactions among main effects can also be analyzed when two or more factors are used. An interaction occurs when differences among the levels of one factor change with different levels of another factor. A *two-way ANOVA* can have only one two-way interaction. A *three-way ANOVA* has three main effects (for example, A, B, and C), 3 two-way interactions (A-by-B, A-by-C, and B-by-C), and 1 three-way interaction (A-by-B-by-C). Multi-way ANOVA setups can have any number of factors, each at any number of levels. The *two-way ANOVA*, (Chapter 7) is one of the most commonly used analyses for multi-center clinical studies, usually with Treatment (or Dose group) and Study Center as the two main effects.

Other types of commonly used ANOVAs include the *repeated-measures ANOVA* (Chapter 8), *nested* or *random-effects ANOVA*, and an *ANOVA of mixed models*. *Analysis of Covariance* (Chapter 11) is a special type of ANOVA that includes adjustments of treatment effects for numeric covariates.

In most types of ANOVA used in clinical trials, the primary question the researcher wants to answer is whether there are any differences among the group population means based on the sample data. The null hypothesis to be tested is 'there is no Group effect' or, equivalently, 'the mean responses are the same for all groups'. The alternative hypothesis is that 'the Group effect is important' or, equivalently, 'the Group means differ for at least one pair of groups'.

The *one-way ANOVA* involves a straightforward comparison of the between-group variation to the within-group variation. An ANOVA that involves blocking factors or covariates seeks to refine treatment comparisons by factoring out extraneous variation due to *known* sources.

C.2   Noise Reduction by Blocking

The more extraneous variability or 'background noise' that you can account for, the more precise the Group comparisons become. Accounting for known blocking factors is one means of reducing background noise.

Suppose you collect body weight data (in pounds) for 31 patients randomized to two groups (as shown in Table C.1). You want to determine whether the groups, Treatment A or Treatment B, have different mean weights. Initially, you would use the *one-way ANOVA* methods shown in Chapter 6.

TABLE C.1. Body Weight Data for Two Treatment Groups

Treatment Group A		Treatment Group B	
Patient Number	Weight	Patient Number	Weight
10	110	11	121
12	101	13	116
14	124	15	144
17	120	16	125
18	111	19	115
21	117	20	118
22	120	23	127
24	131	30	205
31	185	33	193
35	181	34	196
37	173	36	189
40	190	38	180
42	181	39	193
44	202	41	210
45	175	43	189
		46	179

Mean weights are computed to be 148.1 and 162.5 for Treatment Groups A and B, respectively. *One-way ANOVA* (with k = 2 groups) produces an *F-test* statistic of 1.23 with 1 upper and 29 lower degrees of freedom, as shown in Table C.2. This results in a p-value of 0.277, leading to the conclusion that there's no significant difference in mean weights between the groups.

TABLE C.2. *One-Way ANOVA* Summary

Source	df	SS	MS	F
Treatment	1	1612.8	1612.8	F = 1.23
Error	29	38154.9	1315.7	
Total	30	39767.7		

F = 1.23 is not significant (p=0.277)

Now, suppose you know that patients with numbers less than 30 are females, and patients with numbers of 30 or above are males. It is clear from scanning the data that the males weigh more than the females. Because the error variance, σ^2, is a within-group (patient-to-patient) variability, the MSE of 1315.7 overestimates σ^2 because it includes a component due to variation between genders. The inflated estimate using this MSE leads to an F-value for treatment group differences that is smaller and less significant than if a more precise estimate of σ^2 were obtained. Removing the gender variation from the MSE might result in a more precise comparison of the groups.

After Gender is identified as a source of variation, you can include that factor in the ANOVA by computing a sum of squares, a mean square, and an F-value for this factor similar to the methods used for the Group effect in a *one-way ANOVA* (Chapter 6). In the *two-way ANOVA* (Chapter 7), you can test whether Gender is a significant factor, and remove its variation from the MSE to get a more precise test for the Treatment effect.

As seen in Table C.3, Gender is not only significant, but the estimate of error variance, MSE = 93.9, is substantially reduced from that of the *one-way ANOVA* (MSE = 1315.7). This leads to greater precision in testing for the Treatment group effect, which is now seen to be significant.

TABLE C.3 *Two-Way ANOVA* **Summary**

Source	df	SS	MS	F
Treatment	1	480.1	480.1	$F_t = 5.1$ *
Gender	1	35526.6	35526.6	$F_b = 378.5$ **
Error	28	2628.3	93.9	
Total	30	39767.7		

* Significant (p = 0.032)   ** Significant (p < 0.001)

The general setup of a two-way layout with g levels of the 'treatment' factor, Group, and b levels of the 'blocking' factor, Block, is shown in Table C.4. From each Group-by-Block combination or 'cell', you independently sample a number of observations, letting y_{ijk} represent the kth data value from Group i and Block j. The number of data values within Cell i-j is represented by n_{ij}.

TABLE C.4. Two-Way ANOVA Layout (Randomized Block Design)

Group	---------- Block ----------			
	1	2	...	b
1	n_{11}	n_{12}	...	n_{1b}
2	n_{21}	n_{22}	...	n_{2b}
...	...	...	...	...
g	n_{g1}	n_{g2}	...	n_{gb}

In the weight example discussed earlier, you have $g = 2$, $b = 2$, and n_{ij} as follows:

Treatment (Group)	Gender (Block)	
	Females	Males
A	$n_{11} = 8$	$n_{12} = 7$
B	$n_{21} = 7$	$n_{22} = 9$

If each cell in the two-way layout has the same number of observations ($n_{ij} = n$ for all i,j), you have a 'balanced' design. Computing formulas for balanced designs are straightforward and similar to those given for the one-way layout (Chapter 6). With imbalance, there are a number of different ways to compute the sums of squares. In SAS, there are four types of sums of squares computations available: Type I, Type II, Type III, and Type IV. The differences among these types are discussed in Appendix D. Analysis of clinical research data using an *ANOVA* often focuses on the Type III sums of squares from PROC GLM in SAS.

In the previous weight example, notice the p-value for Gender of <0.001, which means that there is a highly significant difference in mean weights between the males and the females. Furthermore, the p-value of 0.032 for Treatment tells you that a significant (<0.05) difference in mean weights *does* exist between the two treatment groups, A and B. This difference was masked by the large variability when the Gender factor was ignored.

The ANOVA results given in Table C.4 do not include the interaction between treatment group and gender as a source of variation. A statistical interaction between two effects suggests that differences in response means among the levels of one effect are not consistent across the levels of the other effect. A significant Treatment-by-Gender interaction in the weight example would indicate that the difference in mean weight between Treatment A and Treatment B depends on whether we're talking about males or females.

Different response patterns, which indicate interactions and no interactions, are shown in Chapter 7. Cell means from the weight example would depict a pattern as shown in Figure C.1, which suggests no interaction. The ANOVA that includes the interaction effect confirms this, as shown in Table C.5.

TABLE C.5 ANOVA Summary – Interaction Effect

Source	df	SS	MS	F
Treatment	1	476.8	476.8	$F_t = 4.9 *$
Gender	1	35475.8	35475.8	$F_b = 365.3 **$
Treatment-by-Gender	1	6.5	6.5	$F_{tg} = 0.07$
Error	28	2621.8	97.1	
Total	30	39767.7		

* Significant (p = 0.035)   ** Significant (p < 0.001)

**Figure C.1. Plot of Mean Weights Shows
No Treatment-by-Gender Interaction**

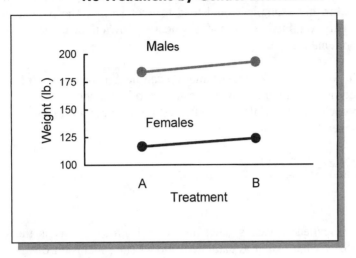

C.3 Least Squares Mean (LS-mean)

In the development of a new recumbent exercise bicycle, the designers needed to estimate the average height of potential users. They took the height of 100 members of a local health club chain and computed the mean height as

$$\overline{X} = \frac{\sum_{i=1}^{100} x_i}{100}$$

where x_i represents the height of the ith member. Is this a good estimate? Suppose it is known that the club selected has mostly male members, and that 90 of the 100 members selected were male. The sample mean above can then be represented as

$$\overline{X} = \frac{(90 \cdot \overline{X}_m) + (10 \cdot \overline{X}_f)}{100} = 0.9 \cdot \overline{X}_m + 0.1 \cdot \overline{X}_f$$

where $\overline{X}_m$ and $\overline{X}_f$ represent the mean heights of the males and females, respectively. This estimate is a good one if the population is composed of approximately 90% males, i.e., if 90% of the potential users of the new exercise equipment are male. However, if the sample that was taken is not in proportion to the true composition of the population, this simple average might be a poor estimate.

Suppose it is known that users of the recumbent cycle are, in general, equally distributed between males and females. Under such an assumption, the mean that was computed for this example would tend to overestimate the population mean because it is highly weighted by the males, who are known to be taller in the general population than females.

A mean height for males of 70 inches and a mean height for females of 62 inches would produce an overall mean height estimate of 69.2 inches when using the weighted approach just presented. A better estimate might be $(70 + 62)/2 = 66$ inches or, in general,

$$\overline{X} = \frac{(\overline{X}_m + \overline{X}_f)}{2} = 0.5 \cdot \overline{X}_m + 0.5 \cdot \overline{X}_f$$

This estimate is called a least squares mean or LS-mean. This is the estimate computed by SAS when using a 'saturated' model (i.e., inclusion of main effects and all possible interactions).

In clinical trials, the LS-mean is often used for estimating treatment effects when blocking by study center. A typical trial might involve a larger number of patients from one study center than from another. The LS-mean of the treatment effect would be equivalent to a combined average over study centers as if the same number of patients were studied within each center.

If the sample sizes from each study center are proportional to the population sizes, the usual arithmetic mean would be appropriate. When the population sizes are considered 'infinite', the LS-mean is used to give equal weighting to the effect sizes from each study center. Estimates based on the LS-mean can differ markedly from that of the usual arithmetic mean if either the cell means or the cell sample sizes within any dose group differ substantially among study centers. In such instances, the analyst must examine the assumptions of population sizes and sample representation to decide which estimate is more appropriate.

In Example 7.2 (Chapter 7), the means and LS-means of the number of items correctly remembered by patients in the 3 Dose groups in the memory study are shown in Table C.6.

TABLE C.6. Arithmetic and Least Squares Mean for Example 7.2

CENTER		Placebo	30 mg	60 mg
		------------ DOSE GROUP --------------		
Dr. Abel	Mean	5.67	8.38	10.11
	(N)	(12)	(8)	(9)
Dr. Best	Mean	6.82	6.40	12.11
	(N)	(11)	(10)	(9)
Combined	Mean	6.22	7.28	11.11
	LS-Mean	6.24	7.39	11.11

Notice that the two estimates are very close to each other. This might not be the case if, for example, there are 25 patients in one study center and only 5 patients in another. When such a degree of imbalance occurs in the sampling, it is important to consider the sampling assumptions before deciding which estimate of treatment effects is more appropriate.

SS Types I, II, III, and IV Methods for an Unbalanced Two-Way Layout

D.1   SS Types Computed by SAS

This section uses the randomized block design to illustrate the differences among the various ANOVA types of sums of squares (SS) computed by SAS: Type I, Type II, Type III, and Type IV.

Consider the unbalanced two-way layout that has two treatment groups (A and B) and 3 study centers (1, 2, and 3). Let μ_{ij} and n_{ij} represent the mean and sample size, respectively, for Treatment i, Center j. For this example, 8 patients receive Treatment A and 6 patients receive Treatment B. The patients are distributed among study centers as shown in Table D.1.

TABLE D.1. Sample Configuration for an Unbalanced Two-Way Layout

Center	---------- Treatment --------------	
	A	**B**
1	μ_{11} $n_{11} = 2$	μ_{21} $n_{21} = 1$
2	μ_{12} $n_{12} = 2$	μ_{22} $n_{22} = 3$
3	μ_{13} $n_{13} = 4$	μ_{23} $n_{23} = 2$
overall	μ_A $n_A = 8$	μ_B $n_B = 6$

Denote each treatment mean as a linear combination of the cell means for that treatment.

$$\mu_A = a_1\mu_{11} + a_2\mu_{12} + a_3\mu_{13}$$

and

$$\mu_B = b_1\mu_{21} + b_2\mu_{22} + b_3\mu_{23}$$

The goal is to test the hypothesis of equality of treatment means

$$H_0: \mu_A = \mu_B$$

The method used to perform this test depends on how you define the treatment means in terms of the cell means. Consider the following three cases:

Case (i): Let $a_j = n_{1j}/n_A$, $b_j = n_{2j}/n_B$ ($j = 1, 2, 3$)

The hypothesis of equal treatment means becomes

$$H_0: (2/8)\mu_{11} + (2/8)\mu_{12} + (4/8)\mu_{13} =$$
$$(1/6)\mu_{21} + (3/6)\mu_{22} + (2/6)\mu_{23}$$

The treatment means are the weighted averages of the cell means for that treatment, weighted by the cell sample sizes. This is the hypothesis tested by the SAS Type I sum of squares for Treatment if the Treatment factor is specified first in the MODEL statement.

Case (ii): Let $a_j = b_j = u_j/U$ ($j = 1, 2, 3$)
where
$$u_1 = n_{11}\, n_{21}\, (n_{12} + n_{22})\, (n_{13} + n_{23})$$
$$u_2 = n_{12}\, n_{22}\, (n_{11} + n_{21})\, (n_{13} + n_{23})$$
$$u_3 = n_{13}\, n_{23}\, (n_{11} + n_{21})\, (n_{12} + n_{22})$$
and
$$U = u_1 + u_2 + u_3$$

The hypothesis of equal treatment means becomes

$$H_0: (5/24)\mu_{11} + (9/24)\mu_{12} + (10/24)\mu_{13} =$$
$$(5/24)\mu_{21} + (9/24)\mu_{22} + (10/24)\mu_{23}$$

The treatment mean is the weighted average of the cell means, weighted by what seems to be a complex function of the cell sample sizes. This is the hypothesis tested by the SAS Type II sum of squares for Treatment.

The weights are actually inversely related to the variance of the estimates of the means for each center. This can be seen when the coefficients u_j/U (in Case ii) are rewritten in a more familiar form.

For Center j (j = 1, 2, or 3), let $w_j = \sigma^2 \cdot (1/n_{1j} + 1/n_{2j})$. Under the usual ANOVA assumptions of independent groups and variance homogeneity, this represents the variance of $\overline{X}_{1j} + \overline{X}_{2j}$. Letting $W = w_1 + w_2 + w_3$, the weights $(w_j)^{-1} / W^{-1}$ are proportional to the u_j/U shown in Case ii. Written this way, you see that each treatment mean is a weighted average of the center means for that treatment, where the weights are proportional to the inverse of the variances within the center.

> Case (iii):   Let $a_1 = a_2 = a_3 = b_1 = b_2 = b_3 (= 1/3)$

The hypothesis of equal treatment means becomes

$$H_0: (1/3)\mu_{11} + (1/3)\mu_{12} + (1/3)\mu_{13} =$$
$$(1/3)\mu_{21} + (1/3)\mu_{22} + (1/3)\mu_{23}$$

which does not depend on the sample sizes. This is the hypothesis tested by the SAS Type III and Type IV sums of squares for Treatment.

> Note: The SAS Type III and Type IV tests are identical in a two-way layout with no empty cells. If $n_{ij} = 0$ for at least one cell, the Type III and IV sums of squares for Treatment will differ if there are more than two levels of the Treatment factor. If there are empty cells, it is recommended that the Type IV tests be used (see Section D.3).

D.2   How to Determine the Hypotheses Tested

Note: This section assumes that the reader is familiar with vector notation.

You can express the mean response for cell i–j in terms of model parameters,

$$\mu_{ij} = \mu + \alpha_i + \beta_j + \gamma_{ij}$$

where μ represents the overall mean response, α_i represents the average additive effect of Treatment i, β_j is the average additive effect of Center j, and γ_{ij} is the average additive effect of the Treatment i-by-Center j combination (interaction). SAS uses vectors of the parameter coefficients and matrices to compute sums of squares, and it is also convenient to express hypotheses in terms of matrix algebra. With two treatment groups, the hypotheses tested by SAS are of the form

$$H_0: \mathbf{a'\beta} = 0$$

where $\underline{\boldsymbol{\beta}}$ is the vector of parameters and $\underline{\mathbf{a}}$ is a vector of parameter coefficients. In the example with 2 Treatments and 3 Centers, the parameter vector is

$$\underline{\boldsymbol{\beta}}' = (\mu \quad \alpha_1 \quad \alpha_2 \quad \beta_1 \quad \beta_2 \quad \beta_3 \quad \gamma_{11} \quad \gamma_{12} \quad \gamma_{13} \quad \gamma_{21} \quad \gamma_{22} \quad \gamma_{23})$$

Use the following SAS statements:

```
PROC GLM;
    CLASS TRT CENTER;
    MODEL Y = TRT CENTER TRT*CENTER / E1 E2 E3 E4;
```

to generate the ANOVA for the configuration in Table D.1, and print the form of the parameter coefficient vectors for each of the four types of sums of squares. The next section shows how these vectors can be used to convert the hypothesis from a parametric hypothesis ($\underline{\mathbf{a}}'\underline{\boldsymbol{\beta}} = 0$) to a hypothesis based on the cell means.

Type I Hypotheses

The output of the vector of parameter coefficients ($\underline{\mathbf{a}}$) for the Type I estimable functions for Treatment is shown in Output D.1.

L2 refers to any constant that is chosen by the user. Setting L2 = 12, the vector $\underline{\mathbf{a}}'$ is (0 12 –12 1 –3 2 3 3 6 –2 –6 –4), and the hypothesis becomes

$$\underline{\mathbf{a}}'\underline{\boldsymbol{\beta}} = \quad 0\mu + 12\alpha_1 - 12\alpha_2 + 1\beta_1 - 3\beta_2 + 2\beta_3 +$$
$$3\gamma_{11} + 3\gamma_{12} + 6\gamma_{13} - 2\gamma_{21} - 6\gamma_{22} - 4\gamma_{23} = 0$$

Algebraic manipulation of this equation yields

$$(3\mu + 3\alpha_1 + 3\beta_1 + 3\gamma_{11}) + (3\mu + 3\alpha_1 + 3\beta_2 + 3\gamma_{12}) +$$
$$(6\mu + 6\alpha_1 + 6\beta_3 + 6\gamma_{13}) = (2\mu + 2\alpha_2 + 2\beta_1 + 2\gamma_{21}) +$$
$$(6\mu + 6\alpha_2 + 6\beta_2 + 6\gamma_{22}) + (4\mu + 4\alpha_2 + 4\beta_3 + 4\gamma_{23})$$

which can be expressed in terms of the cell means as the SAS Type I hypothesis:

$$3\mu_{11} + 3\mu_{12} + 6\mu_{13} = 2\mu_{21} + 6\mu_{22} + 4\mu_{23}$$

or

$$(1/8)(2\mu_{11} + 2\mu_{12} + 4\mu_{13}) = (1/6)(\mu_{21} + 3\mu_{22} + 2\mu_{23})$$

OUTPUT D.1. Form of the SAS Type I Estimable Functions

```
          Type I Estimable Functions for: TRT

          Effect              Coefficients

          INTERCEPT           0

          TRT       A         L2
                    B         -L2

          CNTR      1         0.0833*L2
                    2         -0.25*L2
                    3         0.1667*L2

          TRT*CNTR  A 1       0.25*L2
                    A 2       0.25*L2
                    A 3       0.5*L2
                    B 1       -0.1667*L2
                    B 2       -0.5*L2
                    B 3       -0.3333*L2
```

The form of the Type I hypothesis for Treatment depends on the order in which the factors are listed in the MODEL statement. If Treatment is listed before Center, the Type I hypothesis is as given in the preceding example. If Center is listed before Treatment, the Type I hypothesis for Treatment is the same as the Type II hypothesis for Treatment. Types II, III, and IV do not depend on the order in which the factors are listed in the MODEL statement.

Type II Hypotheses

The output of the vector of parameter coefficients for the Type II estimable functions for Treatment is shown in Output D.2.

By substituting 24 for L2, the hypothesis becomes

$$\mathbf{a'\beta} = 0\mu + 24\alpha_1 - 24\alpha_2 + 0\beta_1 + 0\beta_2 + 0\beta_3 + \\ 5\gamma_{11} + 9\gamma_{12} + 10\gamma_{13} - 5\gamma_{21} - 9\gamma_{22} - 10\gamma_{23} = 0$$

Algebraic manipulation of this equation results in

$$(5\mu + 5\alpha_1 + 5\beta_1 + 5\gamma_{11}) + (9\mu + 9\alpha_1 + 9\beta_2 + 9\gamma_{12}) +$$
$$(10\mu + 10\alpha_1 + 10\beta_3 + 10\gamma_{13}) = (5\mu + 5\alpha_2 + 5\beta_1 + 5\gamma_{21}) +$$
$$(9\mu + 9\alpha_2 + 9\beta_2 + 9\gamma_{22}) + (10\mu + 10\alpha_2 + 10\beta_3 + 10\gamma_{23})$$

which is expressed in terms of the cell means as the SAS Type II hypothesis:

$$(1/24)(5\mu_{11} + 9\mu_{12} + 10\mu_{13}) = (1/24)(5\mu_{21} + 9\mu_{22} + 10\mu_{23})$$

OUTPUT D.2. Form of the SAS Type II Estimable Functions

```
          Type II Estimable Functions for: TRT

          Effect              Coefficients

          INTERCEPT           0

          TRT        A        L2
                     B        -L2

          CNTR       1        0
                     2        0
                     3        0

          TRT*CNTR   A 1      0.2083*L2
                     A 2      0.375*L2
                     A 3      0.4167*L2
                     B 1      -0.2083*L2
                     B 2      -0.375*L2
                     B 3      -0.4167*L2
```

Type III Hypotheses

The form of the Type III hypotheses for Treatment is a vector of parameter coefficients shown in Output D.3.

By using L2= 3 the hypothesis becomes

$$\mathbf{a'\beta} = 0\mu + 3\alpha_1 - 3\alpha_2 + 0\beta_1 - 0\beta_2 + 0\beta_3 +$$
$$1\gamma_{11} + 1\gamma_{12} + 1\gamma_{13} - 1\gamma_{21} - 1\gamma_{22} - 1\gamma_{23} = 0$$

Algebraic manipulation of this equation yields

$$(\mu + \alpha_1 + \beta_1 + \gamma_{11}) + (\mu + \alpha_1 + \beta_2 + \gamma_{12}) +$$
$$(\mu + \alpha_1 + \beta_3 + \gamma_{13}) = (\mu + \alpha_2 + \beta_1 + \gamma_{21}) +$$
$$(\mu + \alpha_2 + \beta_2 + \gamma_{22}) + (\mu + \alpha_2 + \beta_3 + \gamma_{23})$$

which can be re-expressed in terms of the cell means as the SAS Type III hypothesis:

$$(1/3)(\mu_{11} + \mu_{12} + \mu_{13}) = (1/3)(\mu_{21} + \mu_{22} + \mu_{23})$$

OUTPUT D.3. Form of the SAS Type III Estimable Functions

```
        Type III Estimable Functions for: TRT

        Effect              Coefficients

        INTERCEPT           0

        TRT       A         L2
                  B         -L2

        CNTR      1         0
                  2         0
                  3         0

        TRT*CNTR  A 1       0.3333*L2
                  A 2       0.3333*L2
                  A 3       0.3333*L2
                  B 1       -0.3333*L2
                  B 2       -0.3333*L2
                  B 3       -0.3333*L2
```

Type IV Hypotheses

As previously mentioned, the Type IV hypotheses for Treatment are identical to the Type III hypotheses when there are no empty cells.

D.3   Empty Cells

The SAS Type III and Type IV sums of squares (SS) for Treatment are identical when each cell in the two-way layout has at least one observation. If there is an empty cell ($n_{ij} = 0$ for some i-j combination), SS for Types III and IV will be the same if there are two treatment groups but different if there are more than two treatment groups (see next section). By printing the form of the Type IV parameter coefficient vector for Treatment when there is one empty cell, you see that the treatment means are unweighted averages of the cell means excluding the block that contains the empty cell.

For example, in the 2×3 example introduced in Section D.1, suppose that the $i = 2$, $j = 2$ cell has no observations ($n_{22} = 0$). The SAS Type IV sum of squares for Treatment tests the cell means hypothesis H_0: $(\mu_{11} + \mu_{13}) = (\mu_{21} + \mu_{23})$. Notice that Center 2 does not enter into the hypothesis at all because of its incomplete data.

When there are many empty cells, the *two-way ANOVA* can result in testing hypotheses that exclude many of the cell means. Such an analysis might not be beneficial due to the differences in the hypotheses actually tested versus those planned in the design phase of the study.

One method of circumventing these difficulties is to remove the Treatment-by-Center interaction effect as a source of variation if it can be assumed that no interaction exists, or if preliminary tests suggest that such an assumption is credible. The SAS Type I, II, III, and IV tests for the interaction effect are the same regardless of the empty cell pattern. This test for interaction, while not including all cells, can provide an indication of whether an interaction is present. If this test is not significant, the analysis might be re-run using just the main effects Treatment and Center. With no interaction in the MODEL statement, the SAS Types II, III, and IV sums of squares are identical, and each Type tests the hypothesis of equality of treatment means when the treatment means are represented by an unweighted average of the cell means for that treatment.

Sometimes, creative ways can be found to combine blocks to eliminate empty cells while retaining the advantages of blocking and ease of interpretation. For example, suppose a study that includes 10 study centers is conducted using 2 treatment groups and targets 5 patients per cell. At the end of the study, perhaps a number of empty cells exist due to attrition of patients or protocol violations leading to exclusion of data. It might be possible to combine centers by specialty, region, or some other common factor. By combining centers from the same geographic regions, the analyst can ignore Center and use Geographic Region (e.g., North, South, West, Midwest) as a new blocking factor. This technique can help eliminate the problem of empty cells by combining blocks that are alike.

If a preliminary test for interaction is significant, you might proceed immediately to treatment comparisons *within* each level of the blocking factor (e.g., Center or Geographic Region) using a *two-sample t-test* (Chapter 5) or a *one-way ANOVA* (Chapter 6). This can often be helpful in revealing subgroups of study centers (or regions) that have similar response patterns within each subgroup. In general, caution must be used in the analysis and interpretation of results when there are empty cells.

D.4 More Than Two Treatment Groups

The preceding examples apply to the often-used case of two treatment groups. When there are g (g > 2) treatment groups, the hypothesis of 'no Treatment effect' is tested by SAS using simultaneous statements of the form

$$H_0: \underline{a_2}' \underline{\beta} = \underline{a_3}' \underline{\beta} = ... = \underline{a_g}' \underline{\beta} = 0$$

By requesting the form for the parameter coefficient vectors using the E1, E2, E3, or E4 options in the MODEL statement in PROC GLM, values denoted by L2, L3, ..., Lg appear in the SAS output. The analyst may select g-1 sets of values for L2 through Lg to obtain the actual coefficients that determine the simultaneous statements that comprise the hypothesis. One set of selections for the (L2,L3,...,Lg) values is ((1,0,...,0), (0,1,...,0), ..., (0,0,...,1)).

For example, suppose g = 3 in the layout shown in Table D.2.

TABLE D.2. Sample Configuration for Two-Way Layout with >2 Treatments

Center	---------------------- Treatment ----------------------		
	A	B	C
1	μ_{11} $n_{11} = 3$	μ_{21} $n_{21} = 5$	μ_{31} $n_{31} = 4$
2	μ_{12} $n_{12} = 1$	μ_{22} $n_{22} = 2$	μ_{32} $n_{32} = 3$
3	μ_{13} $n_{13} = 3$	μ_{23} $n_{23} = 4$	μ_{33} $n_{33} = 2$
4	μ_{14} $n_{14} = 4$	μ_{24} $n_{24} = 1$	μ_{34} $n_{34} = 2$
5	μ_{15} $n_{15} = 3$	μ_{25} $n_{25} = 3$	μ_{35} $n_{35} = 2$
overall	μ_A $n_A = 14$	μ_B $n_B = 15$	μ_C $n_C = 13$

The parameter coefficient vectors for the Type III hypotheses for Treatment generated by SAS are shown in Output D.4.

OUTPUT D.4. Form of the Type III Estimable Functions in SAS for >2 Treatment Groups

```
           Type III Estimable Functions for: TRT
           Effect              Coefficients

           INTERCEPT           0

           TRT        A        L2
                      B        L3
                      C        -L2-L3

           CNTR       1        0
                      2        0
                      3        0
                      4        0
                      5        0

           TRT*CNTR   A 1      0.2*L2
                      A 2      0.2*L2
                      A 3      0.2*L2
                      A 4      0.2*L2
                      A 5      0.2*L2
                      B 1      0.2*L3
                      B 2      0.2*L3
                      B 3      0.2*L3
                      B 4      0.2*L3
                      B 5      0.2*L3
                      C 1      -0.2*L2-0.2*L3
                      C 2      -0.2*L2-0.2*L3
                      C 3      -0.2*L2-0.2*L3
                      C 4      -0.2*L2-0.2*L3
                      C 5      -0.2*L2-0.2*L3
```

This printout can be used to state the hypotheses in terms of cell means using a similar procedure as shown in Section D.2. Using the selection set $((1,0), (0,1))$ for the $(L2,L3)$ values results in the vectors $\underline{a}_2$ and $\underline{a}_3$ as follows:

$$H_0: \underline{a}_2' \underline{\beta} = 0 \implies$$

$$H_0: (1/5)\mu_{11} + (1/5)\mu_{12} + (1/5)\mu_{13} + (1/5)\mu_{14} + (1/5)\mu_{15} =$$
$$(1/5)\mu_{31} + (1/5)\mu_{32} + (1/5)\mu_{33} + (1/5)\mu_{34} + (1/5)\mu_{35}$$

$$H_0: \underline{a}_3' \underline{\beta} = 0 \implies$$

$$H_0: (1/5)\mu_{21} + (1/5)\mu_{22} + (1/5)\mu_{23} + (1/5)\mu_{24} + (1/5)\mu_{25} =$$
$$(1/5)\mu_{31} + (1/5)\mu_{32} + (1/5)\mu_{33} + (1/5)\mu_{34} + (1/5)\mu_{35}$$

Taken together, the hypothesis tested by the Type III sum of squares for Treatment is the equality of treatment means, H_0: $\mu_A = \mu_B = \mu_C$, when each treatment mean is the unweighted average of the cell means for that treatment.

When there are no empty cells, the Type IV hypothesis for Treatment is the same as the Type III. However, suppose a number of empty cells exist, for example, cells 1-1, 2-4, and 3-5 (that is, $n_{11} = n_{24} = n_{35} = 0$), as shown in Table D.3.

TABLE D.3. Sample Layout with Empty Cells

Center	Treatment		
	A	**B**	**C**
1	0	5	4
2	1	2	3
3	3	4	2
4	4	0	2
5	3	3	0

The SAS Type IV sum of squares simultaneously tests the equality of pairs of treatment means when each treatment mean is an unweighted average of the cell means for that treatment, excluding any cell in a block that has one or more empty cells. The hypothesis is framed in terms of statements about the cell means as

$$H_0: \mu_{12} + \mu_{13} + \mu_{14} = \mu_{32} + \mu_{33} + \mu_{34}$$

and

$$\mu_{21} + \mu_{22} + \mu_{23} = \mu_{31} + \mu_{32} + \mu_{33}$$

The Type III hypothesis for the same configuration defines a treatment mean in terms of its cell means plus extraneous effects from other treatments, making interpretation very difficult. Therefore, the Type IV results seem to be more useful in the empty cell case with more than two treatment groups. As previously discussed, if the interaction is omitted as a source of variation from the ANOVA, the Types II, III, and IV results are the same, each testing for pure Treatment effects that are free of block effects and are not a function of the cell sizes.

D.5   Summary

Knowing the sampling plan and the reasons for design imbalance help the analyst determine the most appropriate SAS SS type to use when performing analysis of variance. The first step in the analysis is to request a printout from SAS of the form of the estimable functions by using the option E1 E2 E3 E4 in the MODEL statement in PROC GLM. It is then possible to specify the hypotheses tested by each SS type. Selection of the most appropriate type can be made by most closely matching the hypothesis that is actually tested with the intended hypothesis. The Type III sum of squares, which ignores the cell sample sizes, is often used in the analysis of clinical study data under the assumption of 'infinite' or very large population sizes within each Block level.

The Type I tests weight the cell means in proportion to the amount of information they contribute, i.e., the cell sample sizes. The Type II tests also weight the amount of information contributed to the treatment means, but they do this by block and cell rather than just individual cells. The Type II tests for Treatment are appealing because they will always be free of block effects, regardless of the degree of imbalance. This can be seen in the example shown under "Type II Hypotheses", where the coefficients of the block effects (β_1, β_2, β_3) are 0. The same is true of the Type III methods, which are also simple to interpret and do not depend on the sample sizes in each cell. As mentioned in Chapter 6, the Type III tests are generally the choice of clinical data analysts and should be used when the LS-means are used for estimation (LS-means are discussed in Appendix C). However, Type I or II tests are preferable if it is known that the sample sizes are proportional to the population sizes. In each analysis, the assumptions should be reviewed before automatically selecting one of the SAS Types of sum of squares.

Multiple Comparison Methods

E.1   Multiple Comparisons of Means

The Treatment effect is of primary concern in comparative clinical trials. Many of the statistical methods described in this book are illustrated with examples comparing two treatment groups. When there are more than two treatment groups, say K (K > 2), an 'omnibus' approach, such as *analysis of variance,* can be applied to test the overall null hypothesis of 'no difference among the treatment groups'. If rejected, the next step is to determine which pairs of groups differ, resulting in as many as $K \cdot (K-1)/2$ possible pairwise comparisons.

First, consider the situation in which it is appropriate to compare mean responses among groups, such as *ANOVA*. This is one of the most common situations involving pairwise treatment comparisons. A number of approaches to multiple comparisons are shown using the following example.

⫽ **Example E.1**

Consider a parallel study that includes a placebo group, a reference group, and 3 different dose levels of an experimental treatment. The response, Y, is measured for each patient in each of the 5 groups shown in Table E.1.

TABLE E.1. Raw Data for Example E.1

Treatment Group				
A Lo-Dose	B Mid-Dose	C Hi-Dose	D Reference	E Placebo
21	27	25	23	14
13	28	19	18	17
25	31	22	22	21
18	24	24	19	20
17	20	34	24	13
23		26	14	23
	19			
16	18	29	20	27
12	24	28	29	12
	27	32		16
	29			

Treatment group summaries are shown in Table E.2, with a pooled standard deviation of 4.671 (see Chapter 6 for calculating formula).

TABLE E.2. Summary Statistics by Treatment Group for Example E.1

	A	B	C	D	E
Mean	18.125	24.700	26.556	21.125	18.111
SD	4.612	4.473	4.746	4.486	5.011
N	8	10	9	8	9

With 5 treatment groups, there are $(5) \cdot (4) / 2 = 10$ possible pairwise comparisons. You can proceed by conducting a series of 10 *two-sample t-tests* (Chapter 5) to obtain the 'raw' (unadjusted) p-values for these comparisons. With the assumption of homogeneous variability across groups, the estimate of the standard deviation pooled over the 5 groups (4.671) is used in the calculation of the *t-tests,* as demonstrated in Chapter 5. Alternatively, you could use the *one-way ANOVA*, as shown next.

In SAS, pairwise *t-tests* can be performed as part of the *ANOVA* by using PROC GLM and specifying the PDIFF option in the LSMEANS statement as shown in the SAS code and output that follow. You can omit the ADJUST=T option ❶, which requests pairwise *t-tests*, because that is the default.

SAS Code for Example E.1

```
DATA MC;
    INPUT TRT $ Y @@;
    DATALINES;
A 21   A 13   A 25   A 18   A 17   A 23   A 16   A 12   B 27   B 28
B 31   B 24   B 20   B 19   B 18   B 24   B 27   B 29   C 25   C 19
C 22   C 24   C 34   C 26   C 29   C 28   C 32   D 23   D 18   D 22
D 19   D 24   D 14   D 20   D 29   E 14   E 17   E 21   E 20   E 13
E 23   E 27   E 12   E 16
;
PROC GLM DATA = MC;
    CLASS TRT;
    MODEL Y = TRT / SS3;
        LSMEANS TRT / PDIFF ADJUST=T;               ❶
    TITLE1 'EXAMPLE E.1: Multiple Comparisons';
    TITLE2 'All-Pairwise Comparisons of Means';
RUN;
```

OUTPUT E.1. SAS Output with Pairwise t-Tests for Example E.1

```
                    EXAMPLE E.1: Multiple Comparisons
                    All-Pairwise Comparisons of Means

                          The GLM Procedure
                        Class Level Information

                 Class          Levels    Values
                 TRT               5       A B C D E
                   Number of observations    44

Dependent Variable: Y
                          Sum of
Source            DF      Squares      Mean Square    F Value    Pr > F

Model              4    521.470707     130.367677      5.97      0.0008
Error             39    850.961111      21.819516
Corrected Total   43   1372.431818

              R-Square     Coeff Var      Root MSE       Y Mean

              0.379961     21.34268       4.671136      21.88636

Source            DF    Type III SS    Mean Square    F Value    Pr > F

TRT                4    521.4707071    130.3676768      5.97      0.0008

                        Least Squares Means
                                            LSMEAN
                  TRT        Y LSMEAN        Number
                               ❷
                  A         18.1250000          1
                  B         24.7000000          2
                  C         26.5555556          3
                  D         21.1250000          4
                  E         18.1111111          5
```

OUTPUT E.1. (*continued*)

```
                  Least Squares Means for effect TRT
                  Pr > |t| for H0: LSMean(i)=LSMean(j)

                        Dependent Variable: Y

    i/j        1          2          3          4          5
    1                  0.0051     0.0006     0.2066     0.9951
    2       0.0051                0.3926     0.1147     0.0039
    3       0.0006     0.3926                0.0216     0.0004     ❷
    4       0.2066     0.1147     0.0216                0.1919
    5       0.9951     0.0039     0.0004     0.1919


    NOTE: To ensure overall protection level, only probabilities
    associated with pre-planned comparisons should be used.
```

The p-values associated with the 10 pairwise comparisons are summarized in Table E.3 based on the results shown in Output E.1.❷ (Note: The LS-means are the same as the arithmetic means for the *one-way ANOVA*). The values that are flagged with an asterisk (*) indicate a value less than 0.05, the nominal significance level of each test. Because the 'raw' p-values are not adjusted for multiple testing, the overall 'experiment-wise' error rate is not controlled. To maintain an overall significance level at the 0.05 level, you can use one of the methods described in the sections that follow Table E.3.

TABLE E.3. p-Values from t-Tests for Pairwise Treatment Group Comparisons in Example E.1

Comparison	|Mean Difference|	'Raw' p-value
C vs. E	8.444	0.0004*
A vs. C	8.431	0.0006*
B vs. E	6.589	0.0039*
A vs. B	6.575	0.0051*
C vs. D	5.431	0.0216*
B vs. D	3.575	0.1147
D vs. E	3.014	0.1919
A vs. D	3.000	0.2066
B vs. C	1.856	0.3926
A vs. E	0.014	0.9951

The Tukey-Kramer Method

Tukey developed a test statistic for simultaneous comparisons of means, which is related to the maximum mean difference over all pairwise comparisons. This statistic has the so-called 'studentized range' distribution when sample sizes are the same for all groups. Probabilities associated with this distribution can be found by using numerical techniques and are tabulated in many statistical texts.

The *Tukey-Kramer* method is based on an approximation to the studentized range distribution when sample sizes differ among groups, as is usually the case in clinical trials. The SAS function PROBMC with the "RANGE" distribution can be used to obtain the adjusted p-values for all pairwise comparisons associated with the *Tukey-Kramer* approach.

Let T_{ij} represent the two-sample t-statistic for comparing the means of Groups i and j.

$$T_{ij} = \frac{\overline{x}_i - \overline{x}_j}{s \cdot \sqrt{\dfrac{1}{n_i} + \dfrac{1}{n_j}}}$$

where s is the square root of the ANOVA mean square error (MSE). The *Tukey-Kramer* p-value can be found by using a SAS statement in the form

$$P_{ij} = 1 - \text{PROBMC}(\text{"RANGE"}, \text{ABS}(\text{SQRT}(2){*}T_{ij}), .\,, df, K)$$

where *df* is the number of ANOVA error degrees of freedom, and *K* is the number of treatment groups.

For example, to compute the *Tukey-Kramer* adjusted p-value for comparing Groups A (Lo-Dose) and B (Mid-Dose) in Example E.1, find

$$T_{AB} = (18.125 - 24.700) \,/\, 4.671((1/8) + (1/10))^{\frac{1}{2}} = -2.9675$$

then use SAS to obtain the adjusted p-value P_{AB},

```
P_AB = 1 - PROBMC("RANGE", SQRT(2)*2.9675, . , 39, 5);
```

for which SAS returns a value of 0.0386.

These probabilities can also be obtained directly by using PROC GLM for all comparisons. Simply specify the ADJUST=TUKEY option in the LSMEANS statement, as follows.

```
LSMEANS TRT / PDIFF ADJUST=TUKEY;
```

The results from this statement are shown in Output E.2.

OUTPUT E.2. Tukey-Kramer Results for Example E.1

```
                 EXAMPLE E.1: Multiple Comparisons
                 All-Pairwise Comparisons of Means

                       The GLM Procedure
                      Least Squares Means
           Adjustment for Multiple Comparisons: Tukey-Kramer

                                            LSMEAN
                  TRT          Y LSMEAN     Number

                   A          18.1250000       1
                   B          24.7000000       2
                   C          26.5555556       3
                   D          21.1250000       4
                   E          18.1111111       5


              Least Squares Means for effect TRT
              Pr > |t| for H0: LSMean(i)=LSMean(j)

                     Dependent Variable: Y

        i/j        1         2         3         4         5

         1                0.0386    0.0054    0.7021    1.0000
         2      0.0386              0.9080    0.4980    0.0300
         3      0.0054    0.9080              0.1389    0.0039
         4      0.7021    0.4980    0.1389              0.6759
         5      1.0000    0.0300    0.0039    0.6759
```

Dunnett's Test

Although the *Tukey-Kramer* method has wide appeal for all pairwise comparisons, *Dunnett's test* is the preferred method if the goal is to maintain the overall significance level when performing multiple tests to compare a set of treatment means with a control group. With K groups, you now have only K–1 comparisons.

Similar to the *Tukey-Kramer* p-values, the adjusted p-values based on a two-sided *Dunnett's test* can be obtained by using the SAS function PROBMC with the distribution "DUNNETT2", as shown below.

Let T_i represent the two-sample t-statistic (Chapter 5) for comparing the mean of Group i with the control Group mean.

$$T_i = \frac{\overline{x}_i - \overline{x}_0}{s \cdot \sqrt{\dfrac{1}{n_i} + \dfrac{1}{n_0}}}$$

where s is the square root of the ANOVA mean square error (MSE) and the subscript 0 refers to the control group. The *Dunnett* p-value can be found by using a SAS statement of the form

$$P_i = 1 - PROBMC(\text{``DUNNETT2''}, ABS(T_i), \ . \ , df, K\text{--}1, L_1, L_2, \ldots, L_{K-1})$$

where *df* is the number of ANOVA error degrees of freedom, *K* is the number of treatment groups (including the control group), and the L_i's are distributional parameters used to adjust for unequal sample sizes, defined as

$$L_i = \sqrt{\frac{n_i}{n_i + n_0}}$$

For example, to compute *Dunnett's* adjusted p-value for comparing Group B (Middle-Dose) with Group E (Placebo) in Example E.1, find

$$T_B = (24.700 - 18.111) \ / \ 4.671((1/10) + (1/9))^{\frac{1}{2}} = 3.0701$$

and

$$L_1 = (8/(8+9))^{\frac{1}{2}} \ = 0.6860$$

$$L_2 = (10/(10+9))^{\frac{1}{2}} = 0.7255$$

$$L_3 = (9/(9+9))^{\frac{1}{2}} \ = 0.7071$$

$$L_4 = (8/(8+9))^{\frac{1}{2}} \ = 0.6860$$

then, evaluate

```
P_B=1-PROBMC("DUNNETT2",3.0701, . ,39,4,0.6860,0.7255,0.7071,0.6860);
```

to obtain the adjusted p-value, P_B, for which SAS returns a value of 0.0138.

These probabilities can be easily obtained for all comparisons by using PROC GLM. You must use the CONTROL option to identify Group E as the control group, and specify the ADJUST=DUNNETT option in the LSMEANS statement, as follows:

```
LSMEANS TRT / PDIFF=CONTROL('E') ADJUST=DUNNETT;
```

The results from this statement are shown in Output E.3.

OUTPUT E.3. Dunnett's Results for Example E.1

```
                    EXAMPLE E.1: Multiple Comparisons
                Treatment Comparisons vs. Control Group (TRT=E)

                            The GLM Procedure
                           Least Squares Means
                  Adjustment for Multiple Comparisons: Dunnett

                                            H0:LSMean=
                                             Control
               TRT          Y LSMEAN         Pr > |t|

                A          18.1250000         1.0000
                B          24.7000000         0.0138
                C          26.5555556         0.0017
                D          21.1250000         0.4901
                E          18.1111111
```

p-Value Adjustment Methods

Both the *Tukey-Kramer* and *Dunnett* methods rely on numerical integration to evaluate complex probability distributions and require the assumption of normality. They are robust statistical methods that have good power and enjoy widespread usage in statistical programs, including SAS. Let's look at the *Bonferroni*, the *Sidak*, the step-down *Bonferroni* (Holm), and the step-up *Bonferroni* (Hochberg) methods, which are useful in multiple comparisons. These methods attempt to control the overall significance level by adjusting p-values without requiring the evaluation of complex distributions. They can be used in making pairwise comparisons of means but also have a much wider application. Although versatile and very easy to compute, these methods are generally very conservative and might fail to detect important differences.

The adjusted p-values for the 10 pairwise comparisons of Example E.1 are shown in Table E.4 based on the methods listed in the preceding paragraph, in addition to the results previously obtained by using the *Tukey-Kramer* and *Dunnett* methods.

TABLE E.4. Adjusted p-Values for Example E.1

(i) Comparison	t-Test ('Raw') p_{RAW}	Tukey-Kramer p_{TUK}	Dunnett p_{DUN}	Bonferroni p_{BON}	Sidak p_{SID}	Step-Down Bonferroni p_{STPDWN}	Step-Up Bonferroni p_{STPUP}
(1) C v. E	0.0004*	0.0039*	0.0017*	0.004*	0.004*	0.004*	0.004*
(2) A v. C	0.0006*	0.0054*		0.006*	0.006*	0.005*	0.005*
(3) B v. E	0.0039*	0.0300*	0.0138*	0.039*	0.038*	0.031*	0.031*
(4) A v. B	0.0051*	0.0386*		0.051	0.050*	0.036*	0.036*
(5) C v. D	0.0216*	0.1389		0.216	0.196	0.130	0.130
(6) B v. D	0.1147	0.4980		1.000	0.704	0.574	0.574
(7) D v. E	0.1919	0.6759	0.4901	1.000	0.881	0.768	0.620
(8) A v. D	0.2066	0.7021		1.000	0.901	0.768	0.620
(9) B v. C	0.3926	0.9080		1.000	0.993	0.785	0.785
(10) A v. E	0.9951	1.0000	1.0000	1.000	1.000	0.995	0.995

The adjusted p-values using the *Bonferroni* and *Sidak* methods, are found from the raw p-values by using the formulas,

$$p_{BON} = m \cdot p_{RAW}$$

and

$$p_{SID} = 1 - (1 - p_{RAW})^m$$

where m is the number of comparisons and p_{RAW} is the raw (unadjusted) p-value. Values greater than 1.0 are truncated to 1.0. For example, adjusted p-values for Comparison (5) in Table E.4 are

$$p_{BON} = 10(0.0216) = 0.216 \quad \text{and} \quad p_{SID} = 1 - (1 - 0.0216)^{10} = 0.1962$$

The *Bonferroni* step-down method adjusts the raw p-values in a stepwise fashion starting with the smallest. Comparison (1) is adjusted as $p_{STPDWN}(1) = m \cdot p_{RAW}(1)$ or $10(0.0004) = 0.004$. The next smallest raw p-value, Comparison (2), is adjusted as $p_{STPDWN}(2) = (m-1)p_{RAW}(2) = 9(0.0006) = 0.0054$. Comparison (3) is adjusted as $p_{STPDWN}(3) = (m-2)p_{RAW} = 8(0.0039) = 0.0312$, and so on.

Any adjusted p-value calculated to be greater than 1 is set to 1.0. Also, all comparisons that follow the first non-significant comparison must be non-significant, and an adjusted p-value is set equal to its predecessor if its calculated value is less. Therefore for Comparison (8), the adjusted p-value is calculated to be $3(0.2066) = 0.6198$, which is less than the preceding adjusted p-value (0.7676), so the Comparison 8 p-value is set to 0.7676. The *Bonferroni* step-down method is sometimes referred to as Holm's method.

The *Bonferroni* step-up-method adjusts the raw p-values in a stepwise fashion, but it starts with the largest value. For Comparison (10) in Table E.4., you compute $p_{STPUP}(10) = 1 \cdot p_{RAW}(10) = 0.9951$. The next largest value, Comparison (9), is adjusted as $p_{STPUP}(9) = 2 \cdot p_{RAW}(9) = 2(0.3926) = 0.7852$. Comparison (8) is adjusted as $p_{STPUP}(8) = 3 \cdot p_{RAW}(8) = 3(0.2066) = 0.6198$, and so on. Each adjusted p-value must be no greater than its predecessor. Those values that are greater are set equal to the preceding adjusted p-value. The *Bonferroni* step-up method is also known as Hochberg's method.

Adjusted p-values using the *Bonferroni, Sidak,* and *Bonferroni* stepwise methods can be found by using PROC MULTTEST in SAS as shown below with the MC data set of Example E.1. The BONFERRONI, SIDAK, HOLM, and HOC options are specified in the PROC MULTTEST statement, and the results are written to the data set NEWMC ❸. The treatment group (TRT) is specified as the grouping variable in a CLASS statement ❹, and the MEAN option in the TEST statement ❺ identifies the response variable (Y) for which comparisons of means are to be performed. One CONTRAST statement is used for each pairwise comparison.

You see very similar results between the *Bonferroni* step-down and step-up methods for Example E.1 (stpbon_p and hoc_p, respectively, in Output E.4). However, the step-up method is actually more powerful and, in many cases, will find more significant comparisons, but it must be used with caution because the step-up method assumes that the raw p-values are mutually independent. Notice also that the *Bonferroni* step-down and step-up methods produce results that are very comparable to the *Tukey-Kramer* method for Example E.1.

Although the *Bonferroni* and *Sidak* methods are very easy to use, they are not recommended for the primary analysis in confirmatory or pivotal clinical trials because of their overly conservative nature.

SAS Code for Example E.1 (*continued*)

```
PROC MULTTEST BONFERRONI SIDAK HOLM HOC
     NOPRINT OUT=NEWMC DATA=MC;              ❸
     CLASS TRT;                              ❹
     TEST MEAN(Y);                           ❺
         CONTRAST 'A v B' -1  1  0  0  0;
         CONTRAST 'A v C' -1  0  1  0  0;
         CONTRAST 'A v D' -1  0  0  1  0;
         CONTRAST 'A v E' -1  0  0  0  1;
         CONTRAST 'B v C'  0 -1  1  0  0;
         CONTRAST 'B v D'  0 -1  0  1  0;
         CONTRAST 'B v E'  0 -1  0  0  1;
         CONTRAST 'C v D'  0  0 -1  1  0;
         CONTRAST 'C v E'  0  0 -1  0  1;
         CONTRAST 'D v E'  0  0  0 -1  1;
RUN;


PROC PRINT DATA=NEWMC;
    TITLE1 'EXAMPLE E.1: Multiple Comparisons';
    TITLE2 'p-Value Adjustment Procedures';
RUN;
```

OUTPUT E.4. p-Values for Pairwise Treatment Comparisons

```
                         EXAMPLE E.1: Multiple Comparisons
                             p-Value Adjustment Procedures

                    c
                    o                                        s
                    n                                        t
            _       t       _                                p
        t   _       r       v       _           b       b       s       h
        e   v       a       l       _   v   r   o       o       i       o
    O   s   a       s       u   s   v   a   w   n       n       d       c
    b   t   r       t       e   e   l   _   _   _       _       _       _
    s   _   _       _       _   _   _   p   p   p       p       p

    1 MEAN  Y   A v B   289.300   97.491  39  0.00511  0.05109  0.03577  0.04993  0.03577
    2 MEAN  Y   A v C   370.944   99.870  39  0.00064  0.00637  0.00573  0.00635  0.00573
    3 MEAN  Y   A v D   132.000  102.765  39  0.20655  1.00000  0.76780  0.90110  0.61965
    4 MEAN  Y   A v E    -0.611   99.870  39  0.99515  1.00000  0.99515  1.00000  0.99515
    5 MEAN  Y   B v C    81.644   94.435  39  0.39257  1.00000  0.78513  0.99316  0.78513
    6 MEAN  Y   B v D  -157.300   97.491  39  0.11470  1.00000  0.57352  0.70428  0.57352
    7 MEAN  Y   B v E  -289.911   94.435  39  0.00389  0.03887  0.03109  0.03820  0.03109
    8 MEAN  Y   C v D  -238.944   99.870  39  0.02165  0.21645  0.12987  0.19654  0.12987
    9 MEAN  Y   C v E  -371.556   96.888  39  0.00045  0.00447  0.00447  0.00446  0.00447
   10 MEAN  Y   D v E  -132.611   99.870  39  0.19195  1.00000  0.76780  0.88132  0.61965
```

The *Dunnett's* p-values are not directly comparable to the other p-values in Table E.4 because they are testing different hypotheses. The *Dunnett* p-values are included to show how the values change when the alternative hypothesis is changed from "at least one pair of means differs" to "at least one treatment mean differs from the control mean". Adjusted p-values can be found for the latter hypothesis by using the *Bonferroni* and *Sidak* methods in the same way that is described for the all-pairwise comparisons method. For example, when restricting attention only to the treatment versus control comparisons, the *Sidak* adjusted p-value for the B v. E comparison would be $1-(1-0.0039)^4 = 0.0155$.

'Closed' Testing

Multiple testing of individual null hypotheses that control for the overall significance level can be performed by using a principle called 'closure'. This concept is discussed in depth with good examples in Chi (1998) and Bauer (1991). Here, the concept is introduced for the case of K=3 (3 groups) and m=3 pairwise comparisons.

Under the principle of closure, each of the 3 pairwise comparisons can be conducted at the full α (0.05) level with no p-value adjustments, but only if the omnibus hypothesis (i.e., 'all groups equal') is first rejected at the α level. This method has great utility in the analysis of clinical trials data because many studies include 3 treatment groups. Pairwise comparisons of the mean responses among the 3 groups can be performed with *t-tests* for example, each at the 0.05 level of significance following a significant *F-test* when *analysis of variance* is used. If the Treatment effect is not significant based on the *ANOVA F-test*, each pairwise comparison must be declared non-significant under closed testing in order to maintain the experiment-wise error rate at 0.05.

E.2   Multiple Comparisons of Binomial Proportions

Because the p-value adjustment methods discussed in the previous section are based only on the raw p-values and not the underlying distribution of response data, you can use these same methods for a wide range of applications, including those with non-normal data (e.g., categorical responses and time-to-event data). When responses are binomial, you can use a set of raw p-values from a series of *chi-square tests*, *Fisher's exact tests*, *Cochran-Mantel-Haenszel tests*, and many other methods to adjust for multiple comparisons of group proportions, such as response rates among treatments. In fact, PROC MULTTEST in SAS can be executed from an input list of raw p-values, as shown next.

The comparison identification must be in the variable named TEST, and the raw (input) p-values must be values of the variable named RAW_P. The output shows the same adjusted p-values as previously obtained. Notice that in this program, no TEST or CLASS statements are used with PROC MULTTEST. Also, these adjusted p-values are not as accurate as those shown in Output E.4 because the raw p-values are entered using only 4-decimal place accuracy.

```
DATA ADJST;
    INPUT TEST RAW_P @@;
    DATALINES;
1 0.0004  2 0.0006  3 0.0039  4 0.0051  5 0.0216
6 0.1147  7 0.1919  8 0.2066  9 0.3926 10 0.9951
;

PROC MULTTEST BONFERRONI SIDAK HOLM HOC PDATA = ADJST;
    TITLE 'DATA SET ADJST';
RUN;
```

OUTPUT E.5. p-Value Adjustments Using PROC MULTTEST for Example E.1

```
                         DATA SET ADJST

                     The Multtest Procedure

                           p-Values
```

Test	Raw	Bonferroni	Stepdown Bonferroni	Sidak	Hochberg
1	0.0004	0.0040	0.0040	0.0040	0.0040
2	0.0006	0.0060	0.0054	0.0060	0.0054
3	0.0039	0.0390	0.0312	0.0383	0.0312
4	0.0051	0.0510	0.0357	0.0498	0.0357
5	0.0216	0.2160	0.1296	0.1962	0.1296
6	0.1147	1.0000	0.5735	0.7043	0.5735
7	0.1919	1.0000	0.7676	0.8812	0.6198
8	0.2066	1.0000	0.7676	0.9012	0.6198
9	0.3926	1.0000	0.7852	0.9932	0.7852
10	0.9951	1.0000	0.9951	1.0000	0.9951

Resampling Methods

'Resampling' is another method that can be used for performing multiple comparisons with binomial data. This method uses the same randomization principle on which *Fisher's Exact test* (Chapter 17) is based and requires the use of a computer program. In SAS, you can use PROC MULTTEST to perform 'permutation' resampling, as shown in Example E.2. In essence, the algorithm randomly selects, with replacement, a sample of all possible permutations of outcomes assuming the null hypothesis is true. The adjusted p-value is the proportion of those samples that have outcomes more extreme than the observed outcome.

◢ Example E.2

Suppose a binomial response ('response' or 'non-response') is measured on a new sample of 168 patients randomized to the 5-group parallel study given in Example E.1, with summary results as follows.

TABLE E.5. Response Rates for Example E.2

	A	B	C	D	E
	Lo-Dose	**Mid-Dose**	**Hi-Dose**	**Reference**	**Placebo**
N	33	31	34	35	35
Responders	9	14	23	10	5
Non-Responders	24	17	11	25	30
Response Rate	27.3%	45.2%	67.6%	28.6%	14.3%

Use PROC MULTTEST to perform permutation resampling and compare the results with other p-value adjustment methods.

SAS Code for Example E.2

```
DATA RR;
    INPUT TRT $ RESP COUNT @@;
    /* RESP=0 is "non-response", RESP=1 is "response" */
    DATALINES;
A 0 24   A 1  9
B 0 17   B 1 14
C 0 11   C 1 23
D 0 25   D 1 10
E 0 30   E 1  5
;
```

```
ODS SELECT
    Multtest.pValues;
PROC MULTTEST ORDER = DATA PERMUTATION
    NSAMPLE=20000 SEED=28375 DATA = RR;          ❷
    CLASS TRT;
    TEST FISHER(RESP);                            ❶
    FREQ COUNT;
        CONTRAST 'A vs B' -1  1  0  0  0;
        CONTRAST 'A vs C' -1  0  1  0  0;
        CONTRAST 'A vs D' -1  0  0  1  0;
        CONTRAST 'A vs E' -1  0  0  0  1;
        CONTRAST 'B vs C'  0 -1  1  0  0;
        CONTRAST 'B vs D'  0 -1  0  1  0;
        CONTRAST 'B vs E'  0 -1  0  0  1;
        CONTRAST 'C vs D'  0  0 -1  1  0;
        CONTRAST 'C vs E'  0  0 -1  0  1;
        CONTRAST 'D vs E'  0  0  0 -1  1;
    TITLE1 'EXAMPLE E.2: Multiple Comparisons of Proportions';
    TITLE2 'Permutation Resampling Method';
RUN;
/* (prespecify the seed value so results can be duplicated) */;
```

OUTPUT E.6. Resampling Method Using PROC MULTTEST for Example E.2

```
            EXAMPLE E.2: Multiple Comparisons of Proportions
                      Permutation Resampling Method

                      The Multtest Procedure

                          p-Values


        Variable    Contrast        Raw      Permutation
                                     ❶
        RESP        A vs B        0.1932        0.5530
        RESP        A vs C        0.0014        0.0080
        RESP        A vs D        1.0000        1.0000
        RESP        A vs E        0.2365        0.7095
        RESP        B vs C        0.0831        0.3666
        RESP        B vs D        0.2038        0.6039
        RESP        B vs E        0.0072        0.0397
        RESP        C vs D        0.0017        0.0093
        RESP        C vs E       <.0001        <.0001
        RESP        D vs E        0.2436        0.7095
```

The 'raw' p-values are the values that result from unadjusted pairwise comparisons using two-tailed *Fisher's exact tests* (Chapter 17). The values are found directly by using PROC MULTTEST with the FISHER option in the TEST statement ❶, which eliminates the need to run PROC FREQ. A resampling size of 20,000 is requested, and a random seeding value is provided ❷. If no value is specified for SEED, SAS randomly selects a value, which results in slightly different adjusted p-values each time the program is run.

For comparison, compute adjusted p-values by using the *Bonferroni*, *Sidak*, step-down *Bonferroni* and step-up *Bonferroni* methods from the raw p-values based on *Fisher's exact test* (Output E.6).

```
DATA BINP;
    INPUT TEST RAW_P @@;
    DATALINES;
1 0.1932  2 0.0014  3 1.0000  4 0.2365  5 0.0831
6 0.2038  7 0.0072  8 0.0017  9 0.0001 10 0.2436
;

PROC MULTTEST BONFERRONI SIDAK HOLM HOC PDATA = BINP;
RUN;
```

The p-values from the SAS output are reproduced in Table E.6, which compares the adjusted p-values for the permutation resampling method with the methods previously described. Notice that permutation resampling results in 4 significant comparisons ($p < 0.05$), while each of the other methods find only 3 that are significant. Resampling techniques are preferred, when possible, because they generally have greater power than the other methods previously discussed.

In the past, application of resampling methods has been limited by the huge computing resources required, but they are gaining in use with the increasing power of desktop computing. One disadvantage of resampling is that the adjusted p-values will differ slightly with each implementation. When using PROC MULTTEST, results can be duplicated by specifying the same value for SEED each time you run the program.

TABLE E.6. Adjusted p-Values for Example E.2

Comparison	Fisher's ('Raw')	Permutation Resampling	Bonferroni	Sidak	Stepdown Bonferroni	Stepup Bonferroni
C v. E	0.0001*	0.0001*	0.001*	0.001*	0.001*	0.001*
A v. C	0.0014*	0.0080*	0.014*	0.014*	0.013*	0.013*
C v. D	0.0017*	0.0093*	0.017*	0.0170*	0.014*	0.014*
B v. E	0.0072*	0.0397*	0.072	0.070	0.050	0.050
B v. C	0.0831	0.3666	0.831	0.580	0.499	0.487
A v. B	0.1932	0.5530	1.000	0.883	0.966	0.487
B v. D	0.2038	0.6039	1.000	0.898	0.966	0.487
A v. E	0.2365	0.7095	1.000	0.933	0.966	0.487
D v. E	0.2436	0.7095	1.000	0.939	0.966	0.487
A v. D	1.0000	1.0000	1.000	1.000	1.000	1.000

The adjusted p-values found by PROC MULTTEST are based on the entire set of CONTRAST statements used. To compare each treatment group with the control, use the same SAS statements as shown in the SAS Code for Example 4.2, and replace the ten CONTRAST statements with the following set of four statements:

```
CONTRAST 'A vs E' -1  0  0  0  1;
CONTRAST 'B vs E'  0 -1  0  0  1;
CONTRAST 'C vs E'  0  0 -1  0  1;
CONTRAST 'D vs E'  0  0  0 -1  1;
```

E.3　Summary

This introduction to multiple comparisons illustrates just some of the many methods available for conducting multiple comparisons for hypothesis testing. Many of the same methods can be used when addressing the multiplicity problem caused by simultaneous analysis of multiple response variables, such as that which occurs with multiple primary endpoints or study objectives. Adjustments based on methods discussed here can also be implemented for simultaneous confidence intervals.

The *Tukey-Kramer* and *Dunnett's* methods presented in this section using *one-way ANOVA* (Chapter 6) are widely used when response data have a normal distribution. These methods can also be used with more complex models, such as *two-way ANOVA* (Chapter 7), *repeated measures ANOVA* (Chapter 8), and *analysis of covariance* (Chapter 11), although these methods can be somewhat more conservative with these models.

You have also seen how to adjust the raw pairwise p-values to maintain a pre-specified, overall α-level without requiring *ANOVA* assumptions. The p-value adjustment methods discussed here can be used for pairwise treatment comparisons when response data do not follow the normal distribution. This approach can be applied to most of the methods discussed in this book that involve comparisons of more than two treatment groups.

In addition, resampling techniques and simulation methods are gaining greater attention with the increasing power of low-cost computing.

The field of multiple comparisons is a broad and rapidly evolving field. Entire books have been written and professional conferences are held, about this one subject. Standard tests of the past, such as *Duncan's* test, have been replaced by more powerful methods. 'Stepwise' methods can be used with the *Tukey, Dunnett,* and *Sidak* methods, re-sampling methods, and tests under the closure principle. Improvement in power often results by implementing stepwise versions of the methods discussed in this chapter.

Note: For a more detailed discussion of multiple comparisons with SAS examples, refer to the excellent book, *"Multiple Comparisons and Multiple Tests Using the SAS System,"* by Westfall, Tobias, Rom, and Wolfinger, which was written under the SAS Books By Users program.

Data Transformations

F.1   Introduction

Many statistical tests, including the *two-sample t-test* (Chapter 5) and *ANOVA* (Chapters 6, 7, and 8) are performed under the assumption of normally distributed data with variance homogeneity among groups. Although such tests are known to be robust against mild deviations to these assumptions, especially with larger sample sizes, clinical data are often encountered that appear to have skewed distributions or larger variability within certain groups. The underlying distribution in such tests might actually be non-normal, or there might be a small proportion of the data called 'outliers' that occur outside the range of usual expectation under the normality assumption, for known or unknown reasons.

Data transformations can often be used effectively in normalizing the data and/or stabilizing the variability. The logarithmic, square root, arcsine, and rank transformations are among the most frequently used data transformations in applied statistics. The square root and arcsine transformations are infrequently used in clinical statistics, however. Converting the observations to their ranks before analysis is one of the most common methods of transforming the data (see Chapters 12, 13, and 14). The logarithmic ('log') transformation is also frequently used, and its application is discussed in the next section.

Log transformations are commonly used in analyzing many types of clinical research data. One example is in vaccine and immunogenicity studies in which antibody titer values are measured. These values (x_i's) are usually modeled with the log-normal distribution, and results are summarized in terms of the geometric mean titer and the geometric mean ratio (or 'n-fold increase'). Another common application of the log-transformation is in the analysis of area-under-the-curve (AUC) data based on blood levels from bioavailability and pharmacokinetic studies.

F.2   The Log Transformation

▶ The Log-Normal Distribution

If the logarithm of a response, Y, denoted as log(Y), has a normal distribution, the random variable Y is said to come from a 'log-normal' distribution. The log-normal distribution looks like a normal distribution (see Chapter 1 or Figure B.1 in Appendix B) with its left tail compressed and its right tail stretched out due to a small number of very large values. (This is also called a 'skewed' distribution). It is appropriate to perform the log transformation on clinical data prior to analysis if the data come from a log-normal distribution. More generally, the log transformation is often used to 'improve' the normality of data sets that have any type of skewed distribution as described above.

▶ What Is a Logarithm?

A logarithm has an associated base, b. The base b logarithm of X is expressed as $\log_b X$. A logarithm is the inverse function of exponentiation. That is, if $Y = \log_b X$, then $X = b^Y$. When not specified, b is usually 10. Most often, b is selected to be ("Euler's constant") e. In fact, this selection is so common, the base e logarithm has a special name, the 'natural logarithm', which is abbreviated as 'ln'. Thus, $\ln(X) = \log_e(X)$, which implies $X = e^Y$ (also denoted, $X = \exp(Y)$). Only the natural logs are referred to in the discussion that follows.

▶ Analyzing Data Using the Log Transformation

Following transformation, analyses are carried out using an ANOVA on the transformed data, and summary statistics are computed in the usual way. These statistics can be expressed in terms of the original data by using the relationships discussed next.

Observe the response measures x_1, x_2, ..., x_n. Apply the log transformation as $y_i = \ln(x_i)$, and conduct analyses as usual on the y_i's. Let $\bar{Y}$ and s_Y denote the mean and standard deviation of the y_i's, and let L_Y and U_Y represent the lower and upper limits of the $100(1-\alpha)\%$ confidence interval, found by

$$\bar{Y} \pm t_{\alpha/2} \cdot s_{\bar{y}}$$

that is,

$$L_Y = \bar{Y} - t_{\alpha/2} \cdot s_{\bar{y}} \quad \text{and} \quad L_U = \bar{Y} + t_{\alpha/2} \cdot s_{\bar{y}}$$

A $100(1-\alpha)\%$ confidence interval based on the original data (x_i's) is found by exponentiating L_Y and U_Y.

$$(e^{\overset{L}{Y}} - e^{\overset{U}{Y}})$$

Because

$$\overline{Y} = \frac{\sum y_i}{n} = \sum \frac{\ln(x_i)}{n} = \ln\left(\Pi x_i\right)^{\frac{1}{n}}$$

you see that $\exp(\overline{Y})$ is simply the geometric mean of the x_i's (denoted by $\overline{X}^g$). This represents the 'geometric mean titer' or GMT used in immunogenicity studies. You can make inferences on this GMT by noting that the standard error of $\exp(\overline{Y})$ may be approximated with a second-order Taylor series expansion as

$$SE(e^{\overline{y}}) = \frac{e^{\overline{y}} \cdot s_y}{\sqrt{n}}$$

Finally, let Δ represent the difference between two treatment means, say, A and B,

$$\Delta = \overline{Y}_A - \overline{Y}_B$$

This difference is easily converted to the "geometric mean ratio" by exponentiating

$$e^{\Delta} = e^{\overline{Y}_A - \overline{Y}_B} = \frac{\overline{X}_A^g}{\overline{X}_B^g}$$

Notice that the transformation does not substantively change the hypothesis that's being tested. The hypothesis of no treatment difference is equivalent to the hypothesis that the ratio of treatment means is 1.

Similarly, changes from a baseline value, expressed as $\Delta = \overline{Y} - \overline{Y}_0$, can be converted to a percent change in geometric means as $100 \cdot (e^{\Delta} - 1)\%$.

SAS Code for Exercises in Chapter 23

SAS Code for Exercises (see Chapter 23)

```
LIBNAME EXAMP 'c:\bookfiles\examples\sas';
OPTIONS NODATE NONUMBER;



*=========================================================*
|   STATISTICAL ANALYSES for Response Variable = "SCORE"|
|       (continuous numeric response variable)          |
*=========================================================* ;

/* ANALYSIS #1: Two-Sample t-Test */
PROC TTEST DATA = EXAMP.TRIAL;
    CLASS TRT;
    VAR SCORE;
    TITLE 'ANALYSIS #1: Two-Sample t-Test';
RUN;



/* ANALYSIS #2: Wilcoxon Rank-Sum Test */
PROC NPAR1WAY WILCOXON DATA = EXAMP.TRIAL;
    CLASS TRT;
    VAR SCORE;
    TITLE 'ANALYSIS #2: Wilcoxon Rank-Sum Test';
RUN;



/* ANALYSIS #3: One-Way ANOVA */
PROC GLM DATA = EXAMP.TRIAL;
    CLASS TRT;
    MODEL SCORE = TRT;
        MEANS TRT;
    TITLE 'ANALYSIS #3: One-Way ANOVA';
RUN;
```

```
/* ANALYSIS #4: Two-Way ANOVA with Interaction */
PROC GLM DATA = EXAMP.TRIAL;
    CLASS TRT CENTER;
    MODEL SCORE = TRT CENTER TRT*CENTER;
        LSMEANS TRT / STDERR PDIFF;
    TITLE 'ANALYSIS #4: Two-Way ANOVA With Interaction';
RUN;


/* ANALYSIS #5: Two-Way ANOVA without Interaction */
PROC GLM DATA = EXAMP.TRIAL;
    CLASS TRT CENTER;
        MODEL SCORE = TRT CENTER;
    TITLE 'ANALYSIS #5: Two-Way ANOVA Omitting Interaction';
RUN;


/* ANALYSIS #6: Three-Way ANOVA, with All Interactions */
PROC GLM DATA = EXAMP.TRIAL;
    CLASS TRT CENTER SEX;
    MODEL SCORE = TRT | CENTER | SEX;
        LSMEANS TRT / STDERR PDIFF;
    TITLE 'ANALYSIS #6: Three-Way ANOVA - all Interactions';
RUN;


/* ANALYSIS #7: Three-Way Main Effects ANOVA */
PROC GLM DATA = EXAMP.TRIAL;
    CLASS TRT CENTER SEX;
        MODEL SCORE = TRT CENTER SEX;
    TITLE 'ANALYSIS #7: Three-Way Main Effects ANOVA';
RUN;


/* ANALYSIS #8: Regression of Score on Age */
PROC GLM DATA = EXAMP.TRIAL;
    MODEL SCORE = AGE / SOLUTION;
    TITLE 'Linear Regression of Score on Age';
RUN;

PROC PLOT DATA = EXAMP.TRIAL;
    PLOT SCORE*AGE;
RUN;


/* ANALYSIS #9: Analysis of Covariance - Test for Equal Slopes */
PROC GLM DATA = EXAMP.TRIAL;
    CLASS TRT;
    MODEL SCORE = TRT AGE TRT*AGE;
    /* use interaction to check for equal slopes */
    TITLE1 'ANALYSIS #9: ANCOVA Using Age as Covariate,';
    TITLE2 'Test for Equal Slopes';
RUN;
```

```
/* ANALYSIS #10: Analysis of Covariance - Assuming Equal Slopes */
PROC GLM DATA = EXAMP.TRIAL;
    CLASS TRT;
    MODEL SCORE = TRT AGE / SOLUTION;
        LSMEANS TRT / STDERR PDIFF;
    TITLE 'ANALYSIS #10: ANCOVA Using Age as Covariate';
RUN;


PROC PLOT DATA = EXAMP.TRIAL;
    PLOT SCORE*AGE=TRT;
RUN;



/* ANALYSIS #11: Stratified ANCOVA */
PROC GLM DATA = EXAMP.TRIAL;
    CLASS TRT CENTER;
    MODEL SCORE = TRT CENTER AGE / SOLUTION;
    TITLE1 'ANALYSIS #11: ANCOVA -- using Age as covariate,';
    TITLE2 'Stratified by Center';
RUN;



*=========================================================*
|    STATISTICAL ANALYSES for Response Variable = "RESP" |
|              (dichotomous response variable)           |
*=========================================================*   ;

PROC FORMAT;
    VALUE RSPFMT 0 = 'NO ' 1 = 'YES';
RUN;



/* ANALYSES #12 and #13: Chi-Square and Fishers Exact Test
                      -- Dichotomous Response */
PROC FREQ DATA = EXAMP.TRIAL;
    TABLES TRT*RESP / CHISQ NOCOL NOPCT;
    FORMAT RESP RSPFMT.;
    TITLE1 'ANALYSIS #12:  Chi-Square Test';
    TITLE2 'ANALYSIS #13:  Fishers Exact Test';
RUN;



/* ANALYSIS #14: Stratified CMH Test for Response Rate Analysis */
PROC FREQ DATA = EXAMP.TRIAL;
    TABLES CENTER*TRT*RESP / CMH NOCOL NOPCT;
    FORMAT RESP RSPFMT.;
    TITLE 'ANALYSIS #14: CMH Test Controlling for Center';
RUN;
```

```
/* ANALYSIS #15: Logistic Regression - Dichotomous Response */
PROC LOGISTIC DATA = EXAMP.TRIAL;
    CLASS TRT / PARAM = REF;
    MODEL RESP = TRT;
    TITLE1 'ANALYSIS #15: Logistic Regression Analysis for';
    TITLE2 'Treatment Group Differences Using Dichotomized
Response';
RUN;



/* ANALYSIS #16: Logistic Regression - Dichotomous Response,
                 Adjusted for Age  */
PROC LOGISTIC DATA = EXAMP.TRIAL;
    CLASS TRT / PARAM = REF;
    MODEL RESP = TRT AGE;
    TITLE1 'ANALYSIS #16: Logistic Regression Analysis for';
    TITLE2 'Treatment Group Differences Using Dichotomized
Response';
    TITLE3 'Adjusted for Age';
RUN;



/* ANALYSIS #17: Logistic Regression - Dichotomous Response,
                 Adjusted for Age, Sex, Center  */
PROC LOGISTIC DATA = EXAMP.TRIAL;
    CLASS TRT SEX CENTER / PARAM = REF;
    MODEL RESP = TRT AGE SEX CENTER TRT*CENTER;
    TITLE1 'ANALYSIS #17: Logistic Regression Analysis for';
    TITLE2 'Treatment Group Differences Using Dichotomized
Response';
    TITLE3 'Adjusted for Age, Sex, Center & Interactions';
RUN;



*=======================================================*
|    STATISTICAL ANALYSES for Response Variable = "SEV"  |
|          (ordinal categorical response variable)       |
*=======================================================*   ;

\* Obtain Severity Distributions based on the Response = "SEV" *\

PROC FORMAT;
  VALUE SEV1FMT  0 = '0 = None'      1 = '1 = Mild'
                 2 = '2 = Mod '      3 = '3 = Sev '      ;

  VALUE SEV2FMT  0 = '0 = None    '  1 = '1.036 = Mild'
                 2 = '2.185 = Mod '  3 = '3 = Sev     ' ;

  VALUE SEV3FMT  0 = 'None'          1 = 'Mild'
                 2 = 'Mod.'          3 = 'Sev.'         ;
RUN;



/* ANALYSES #18 and #19: Chi-Square / Fishers Exact Test --
                         Multinomial Response */
PROC FREQ DATA = EXAMP.TRIAL;
    TABLES TRT*SEV / CHISQ EXACT NOCOL NOPCT;
    FORMAT SEV SEV1FMT.;
```

```
      TITLE1 'ANALYSIS #18: Chi-Square Test';
      TITLE2 'ANALYSIS #19: Generalized Fishers Exact Test';
RUN;



/* ANALYSIS #20: CMH Test for Comparing Severity Distributions -
                 Using Table Scores */
PROC FREQ DATA = EXAMP.TRIAL;
    TABLES TRT*SEV / CMH NOCOL NOPCT;
    FORMAT SEV SEV1FMT.;
    TITLE1 'ANALYSIS #20: Mantel-Haenszel Test on Severity';
    TITLE2 '(Using Table Scores)';
RUN;



/* ANALYSIS #21: CMH Test for Comparing Severity Distributions
                 - Using Modified Ridit Scores */
PROC FREQ DATA = EXAMP.TRIAL;
    TABLES TRT*SEV / CMH SCORES = MODRIDIT NOCOL NOPCT;
    FORMAT SEV SEV2FMT.;
    TITLE1 'ANALYSIS #21: Mantel-Haenszel Test on Severity';
    TITLE2 '(Using Modified Ridit Scores)';
RUN;



/* ANALYSES #22: Wilcoxon Rank-Sum Test on Response = "SEV" */
PROC NPAR1WAY WILCOXON DATA = EXAMP.TRIAL;
    CLASS TRT;
    VAR SEV;
    TITLE 'ANALYSIS #22: Wilcoxon Rank-Sum Test on "SEV"
Response';
RUN;



/* ANALYSIS #23: Stratified CMH Test for Comparing Severity
                 Distributions - Using Table Scores */
PROC FREQ DATA = EXAMP.TRIAL;
    TABLES CENTER*TRT*SEV / CMH NOCOL NOPCT;
    FORMAT SEV SEV3FMT.;
    TITLE1 'ANALYSIS #23: CMH Test on Severity Distributions';
    TITLE2 '(Using Table Scores), Controlling for Center';
RUN;



/* ANALYSIS #24: Stratified CMH Test for Comparing Severity
                 Distributions - Using Modified Ridit Scores */
PROC FREQ DATA = EXAMP.TRIAL;
    TABLES CENTER*TRT*SEV / CMH SCORES = MODRIDIT NOCOL NOPCT;
    FORMAT SEV SEV3FMT.;
    TITLE1 'ANALYSIS #24: CMH Test on Severity Distributions';
    TITLE2 '(Using Modified Ridit Scores), Controlling for
Center';
RUN;
```

```
/* ANALYSIS #25: Logistic Regression: Proportional Odds Model */
PROC LOGISTIC DATA = EXAMP.TRIAL;
    CLASS TRT / PARAM = REF;
    MODEL SEV = TRT;
    TITLE1 'ANALYSIS #25: Proportional Odds Model for Treatment';
    TITLE2 'Differences Using Ordinal Response Categories';
RUN;



/* ANALYSIS #26: Logistic Regression: Proportional Odds Model,
                 Adjusted for Age */
PROC LOGISTIC DATA = EXAMP.TRIAL;
    CLASS TRT / PARAM = REF;
    MODEL SEV = TRT AGE;
    TITLE1 'ANALYSIS #26: Proportional Odds Model for Treatment';
    TITLE2 'Differences Using Ordinal Response Categories';
    TITLE3 'Adjusted for Age';
RUN;



/* ANALYSIS #27: Logistic Regression: Proportional Odds Model,
                 Adjusted for Age, Sex, Center */
PROC LOGISTIC DATA = EXAMP.TRIAL;
    CLASS TRT SEX CENTER;
    MODEL SEV = TRT AGE SEX CENTER;
    TITLE1 'ANALYSIS #27: Proportional Odds Model for Treatment';
    TITLE2 'Group Differences Using Ordinal Response Categories';
    TITLE3 'Adjusted for Age, Sex & Center';
RUN;
```

REFERENCES
and Additional Reading

Allison, P.D. (1995). *Survival Analysis Using the SAS System: A Practical Guide*. Cary, NC: SAS Institute Inc.

Allison, P.D. (1999). *Logistic Regression Using the SAS System: Theory and Application*. Cary, NC: SAS Institute Inc.

Altman, D.G. (1991). *Practical Statistics for Medical Research*. New York: Chapman & Hall.

Anderson, S., Auquier, A., Hauck, W.W., Oakes, D., Vandaele, W., and Weisberg, H.I. (1980). *Statistical Methods for Comparative Studies*. New York: John Wiley & Sons.

Armitage, P. and Berry, G. (1987). *Statistical Methods in Medical Research. 2d ed.* Palo Alto, CA: Blackwell Scientific Publications.

Bancroft, T.A. (1968). *Topics in Intermediate Statistical Methods, Volume One*. Ames, IA: The Iowa University Press.

Bauer, P. (1991). Multiple Testing in Clinical Trials. *Statistics in Medicine* 10: 871-890.

Cantor, A. (1997). *Extending SAS Survival Analysis Techniques for Medical Research*. Cary, NC: SAS Institute Inc.

Chi, G.Y.H. (1998). Multiple Testings: Multiple Comparisons and Multiple Endpoints. *Drug Information Journal* 32: 1347S-1362S.

Cochran, W.G. and Cox, G.M. (1957). *Experimental Designs. 2d ed.* New York: John Wiley & Sons.

Conover, W.J. and Iman, R.L. (1981). Rank Transformations as a Bridge between Parametric and Nonparametric Statistics. *The American Statistician* 35: 124-129.

Cox, D.R. and Oakes, D. (1984). *Analysis of Survival Data.* New York: Chapman & Hall.

D'Agostino, R.B., Massaro, J., Kwan, H., and Cabral, H. (1993). "Strategies for Dealing with Multiple Treatment Comparisons in Confirmatory Clinical Trials." *Drug Information Journal* 27: 625-641.

Dawson-Saunders, B. and Trapp, R.G. (1990). *Basic and Clinical Biostatistics.* San Mateo, CA: Appleton & Lange.

Delwiche, L.D. and Slaughter, S.J. (1998). *The Little SAS Book: A Primer. 2d ed.* Cary, NC: SAS Institute Inc.

DeMets, D.L. and Lan, K.K.G. (1994). "Interim Analysis: The Alpha Spending Function Approach." *Statistics in Medicine* 13: 1341-1352.

Elashoff, J.D. and Reedy, T.J. (1984). "Two-Stage Clinical Trial Stopping Rules." *Biometrics* 40: 791-795.

Elliott, R.J. (2000). *Learning SAS in the Computer Lab. 2d Ed.* Pacific Grove, CA: Brooks/Cole.

Fleiss, J.L. (1981). *Statistical Methods for Rates and Proportions. 2d ed.* New York: John Wiley & Sons.

Freund, R.J. and Littell, R.C. (1991). *SAS System for Regression. 2d ed.* Cary, NC: SAS Institute Inc.

Geller, N.L. and Pocock, S.J. (1987). "The Consultant's Forum: Interim Analyses in Randomized Clinical Trials: Ramifications and Guidelines for Practitioners." *Biometrics* 43: 213-223.

Gillings, D. and Koch, G. (1991). "The Application of the Principle of Intention-to-Treat to the Analysis of Clinical Trials." *Drug Information Journal* 25: 411-424.

Hand, D.J. and Taylor, C.C. (1987). *Multivariate Analysis of Variance and Repeated-Measures: A Practical Approach to Behavioural Scientists.* New York: Chapman & Hall.

Hatcher, L. and Stepanski, E.J. (1994). *A Step-by-Step Approach to Using the SAS System for Univariate and Multivariate Statistics.* Cary, NC: SAS Institute Inc.

Hollander, M. and Wolfe, D.A. (1973). *Nonparametric Statistical Methods*. New York: John Wiley & Sons.

Hosmer, D.W. and Lemeshow, S. (1989). *Applied Logistic Regression*. New York: John Wiley & Sons.

Johnson, M.F. (1990). "Issues in Planning Interim Analyses." *Drug Information Journal* 24: 361-370.

Jones, B. and Kenward, M.G. (1989). *Design and Analysis of Crossover Trials*. New York: Chapman & Hall.

Kalbfleisch, J.D. and Prentice, R.L. (1980). *The Statistical Analysis of Failure Time Data.* New York: John Wiley & Sons.

Koch, G.G. and Gansky, S.A. (1996). "Statistical Considerations for Multiplicity in Confirmatory Protocols." *Drug Information Journal* 30: 523-534.

Lachin, J.M. (1981). "Introduction to Sample Size Determination and Power Analysis for Clinical Trials." *Controlled Clinical Trials* 2: 93-113.

Lachin, J.M. (2000). "Statistical Considerations in the Intent-to-Treat Principle." *Controlled Clinical Trials* 21: 167-189.

Lan, K.K.G., and DeMets, D.L. (1983). "Discrete Sequential Boundaries for Clinical Trials." *Biometrika* 70: 659-663.

Lee, J. (1981). "Covariance Adjustment of Rates Based on the Multiple Logistic Regression Model." *Journal of Chronic Diseases* 34: 415-426.

Lehman, E.L. (1988). *Theory of Point Estimation*. New York: John Wiley & Sons.

Littell, R.C., Freund, R.J. and Spector, P.C. (1991). *SAS System for Linear Models. 3rd ed*. Cary, NC: SAS Institute Inc.

Littell, R.C., Milliken, G.A., Stroup, W.W., and Wolfinger, R.D. (1996). *SAS System for Mixed Models*. Cary, NC: SAS Institute Inc.

Mendenhall, W. (1975). *Introduction to Probability and Statistics. 4th ed*. North Scituate, MA: Duxbury Press.

Munro, B.H. and Page, E.B. (1993). *Statistical Methods for Health Care Research. 2d ed.* Philadelphia: JB Lippincott Co.

O'Brien, P.C. and Fleming, T.R. (1979). "A Multiple Testing Procedure for Clinical Trials." *Biometrics* 35: 549-556.

PMA Biostatistics and Medical Ad Hoc Committee on Interim Analysis. (1993). "Interim Analysis in the Pharmaceutical Industry." *Controlled Clinical Trials* 14: 160-173.

Pocock, S.J. (1977). Group Sequential Methods in the Design and Analysis of Clinical Trials." *Biometrika* 64, 191-199.

Pocock, S.J., Geller, N.L., and Tsiatis, A.A. (1987). "The Analysis of Multiple Endpoints in Clinical Trials." *Biometrics* 43: 487-498.

Reboussin, D.M., DeMets, D.L., Kim, K.M., and Lan, K.K.G. (2000). "Computations for Group Sequential Boundaries Using the Lan-DeMets Spending Function Method. *Controlled Clinical Trials* 21:190-207.

Sankoh, A.J. (1999). "Interim Analyses: An Update of an FDA Reviewer's Experience and Perspective." *Drug Information Journal* 33: 165-176.

SAS OnlineDoc, Version 8. 1999. CD-ROM. SAS Institute Inc., Cary, NC.

SAS Institute Inc. (1996). *SAS/STAT Software: Changes and Enhancements through Release 6.11.* Cary, NC: SAS Institute Inc.

SAS Institute Inc. (1998). *SAS/STAT User's Guide, Version 6, 4th ed. 2 Vols.* Cary, NC: SAS Institute Inc.

Stokes, M.E., Davis, C.S., and Koch, G.G. (2000). *Categorical Data Analysis Using the SAS System. 2d ed.* Cary, NC: SAS Institute Inc.

Tibshirani, R. (1982). "A Plain Man's Guide to the Proportional Hazards Model." *Clinical and Investigative Medicine* 5: 63-68.

Walker, G.A. (1999). *Considerations in the Development of Statistical Analysis Plans for Clinical Studies.* San Diego, CA: Collins-Wellesley Publishing.

Westfall, P.H., Tobias, R.D., Rom, D., Wolfinger, R.D., and Hochberg, Y. (1999). *Multiple Comparisons and Multiple Tests Using the SAS System*. Cary, NC: SAS Institute Inc.

Winer, B.J. (1971). *Statistical Principles in Experimental Designs, 2d ed.* New York: McGraw-Hill.

Zeger, S.L., Liang, K.Y., and Albert, P.S. (1988). "Models for Longitudinal Data: A Generalized Estimating Equation Approach." *Biometrics* 44: 1049-1060.

Index

Call your local SAS office to order these books from Books by Users Press

www.sas.com/pubs

www.sas.com/pubs

*Welcome * Bienvenue * Willkommen * Yohkoso * Bienvenido*

SAS Publishing Is Easy to Reach

Visit our Web page located at www.sas.com/pubs

You will find product and service details, including

- **companion Web sites**
- **sample chapters**
- **tables of contents**
- **author biographies**
- **book reviews**

Learn about

- **regional user-group conferences**
- **trade-show sites and dates**
- **authoring opportunities**
- **e-books**

Explore all the services that SAS Publishing has to offer!

Your Listserv Subscription Automatically Brings the News to You

Do you want to be among the first to learn about the latest books and services available from SAS Publishing? Subscribe to our listserv **newdocnews-l** and, once each month, you will automatically receive a description of the newest books and which environments or operating systems and SAS® release(s) each book addresses.

To subscribe,

1. Send an e-mail message to **listserv@vm.sas.com**.

2. Leave the "Subject" line blank.

3. Use the following text for your message:

> **subscribe NEWDOCNEWS-L** *your-first-name your-last-name*

> For example: subscribe NEWDOCNEWS-L John Doe

You're Invited to Publish with SAS Institute's Books by Users Press

If you enjoy writing about SAS software and how to use it, the Books by Users program at SAS Institute offers a variety of publishing options. We are actively recruiting authors to publish books and sample code.

If you find the idea of writing a book by yourself a little intimidating, consider writing with a co-author. Keep in mind that you will receive complete editorial and publishing support, access to our users, technical advice and assistance, and competitive royalties. Please ask us for an author packet at **sasbbu@sas.com** or call 919-531-7447. See the Books by Users Web page at **www.sas.com/bbu** for complete information.

Book Discount Offered at SAS Public Training Courses!

When you attend one of our SAS Public Training Courses at any of our regional Training Centers in the U.S., you will receive a 20% discount on book orders that you place during the course. Take advantage of this offer at the next course you attend!

SAS Institute Inc.
SAS Campus Drive
Cary, NC 27513-2414
Fax 919-677-4444

E-mail: sasbook@sas.com
Web page: www.sas.com/pubs
To order books, call SAS Publishing Sales at 800-727-3228*
For other SAS business, call 919-677-8000*

* Note: Customers outside the U.S. should contact their local SAS office.

The Power to Know.™

SAS Publishing